D0349259

Preventing Nuclear Theft: Guidelines for Industry and Government

edited by
Robert B. Leachman
Phillip Althoff

The Praeger Special Studies program—utilizing the most modern and efficient book production techniques and a selective worldwide distribution network—makes available to the academic, government, and business communities significant, timely research in U.S. and international economic, social, and political development.

Preventing Nuclear Theft: Guidelines for Industry and Government

Praeger Publishers   New York   Washington   London

PRAEGER PUBLISHERS
111 Fourth Avenue, New York, N.Y. 10003, U.S.A.
5, Cromwell Place, London S.W.7, England

Published in the United States of America in 1972
by Praeger Publishers, Inc.

All rights reserved

© 1972 by Kansas State University

Library of Congress Catalog Card Number: 72-76452

Printed in the United States of America

HD9698
A22
P74

For Lenore and Candace,
whose names deserve to be mentioned in this book

917871

Rare

FOREWORD
Glenn T. Seaborg

The subject of safeguards should be one of vital interest throughout the world. On a global level, the renunciation and control of further nuclear weapons proliferation constitute major elements of an essential strategy for achieving a lasting international peace. To achieve this goal requires the marshaling of dedicated expertise committed to the development of feasible systems of nuclear materials controls. Such controls must not deprive the nations of an energy-hungry world of their opportunity to use nuclear energy for the benefit of their peoples. In turn, those nations must commit the necessary resources and management to attain controls compatible with and verifiable by the supranational bodies they have designated to oversee these international safeguards.

Among the most vital resources for achieving these goals are those to be found at the universities. Scholarship, research, training, and testing comprise some of the human endeavors that, properly organized, will create the systems and tactics needed for this peace strategy. These endeavors of course must proceed with adequate insight into the practicalities of industrial and commerical methods and structures. They also should relate to the realities of international, legal, political, and economic forces.

The concepts of nuclear materials safeguards integrate the workings of commercial plants, national regulatory bodies, and supranational systems. Throughout such a relationship there is an essential requirement for an interchange of ideas and competent personnel. These personnel must of necessity contribute and grow through periods of service in several or all of these areas. Here too lies a stimulus that the universities are uniquely able to promote, for their products are knowledge and trained minds.

The symposium that generated these pages has made an invaluable contribution to the knowledge of nuclear safeguards. It has illuminated the interplay of technology, government, and social forces that must take place if we are to secure a just and lasting peace in this otherwise perilous nuclear age.

Robert B. Leachman
Phillip Althoff

With appropriate levels of knowledge and technology, an explosive device of much greater destructive potential than from ordinary explosive materials can be constructed from only about ten kilograms of enriched uranium of plutonium. However, by 1980 many tens of thousands of kilograms of plutonium alone will be processed each year in the facilities preparing fuel for the nuclear-powered generating plants required to meet the world's demand for electricity.

Clearly, quantities of the fissile materials, ^{235}U and ^{239}Pu, necessary for the construction of an explosive device cannot be allowed to go astray. Thus, the crucial question is: How is the nuclear industry—in both the public and the private spheres—to operate with a lower level of loss, including and especially loss through theft, than that commonly encountered by other industries? One must assume that the normal operating losses experienced by nonnuclear industries, either inside or outside the plant, would be intolerably large for the nuclear industry. The yearly normal operating losses of the nonnuclear industry, if experienced by the nuclear industry, could provide fissile material for the construction of many clandestine nuclear explosive devices.

Although the general public seems to have expressed little or no concern about the possible diversion of nuclear materials, responsible officials in international agencies, national governments, and the nuclear industry as well as individuals in national laboratories, consulting firms, and the academic community have been making substantial headway in providing the means for a solution to the safeguards problem. For example, largely under the terms of the Non-Proliferation Treaty, statutory arrangements allowing for precedent-setting methods of control through inspection have been enacted. Nevertheless, many of the means thus far adopted or under discussion in order to solve the safeguards problem remain in the initial stages of development.

As of now the problems associated with safeguards as well as the means necessary for their satisfactory solution seem complex. This is the case primarily because the vast system of safeguards, parts of which are in existence and parts of which are not yet even in the idea stage, entail a multitude of specific details, especially as regards human judgments, the execution of which could well be of vital importance to the future survival of significant portions of the human species.

In order to provide a forum for the careful consideration of the different interpretations of the difficulties associated with the present and future of the safeguards system, a Symposium of Implementing Nuclear Safeguards was sponsored by the Diversion Safeguards Program on the campus of Kansas State University, October 25-27, 1971. The symposium was attended by over 100 experts on the safeguards problem. These included representatives from international agencies, national governments, the nuclear industry, national laboratories, consulting firms, and the academic community. (A complete list of symposium participants and their professional affiliations is presented in the Appendix.)

The present volume includes the papers presented as well as summaries of the discussions held at the symposium. Many of the papers and summaries presented here indicate the existing state of thinking on the overall safeguards problem; others are ventures into areas relevant to the safeguards problem that have received relatively little attention in public forums. In general, the symposium concentrated on those elements of the safeguards problem and its solution that were deemed by its organizers and participants to be of developing importance. This volume reflects that concentration. As such, it supplements and to some extent expands upon the various works already in print relevant to the safeguards problem.

April 1972

Since its inception in June 1970, the Diversions Safeguards Program at Kansas State University has been funded by the Research Applied to National Needs (formerly Interdisciplinary Research Relevant to Problems of Our Society) office of the National Science Foundation. The Symposium on Implementing Nuclear Safeguards was made possible by generous financial assistance from this National Science Foundation office.

Many of our colleagues at Kansas State University contributed significantly both to the details of the symposium and in preparing these proceedings for publication. Noteworthy among them are Rebecca Farrell, Patricia Lewis, F. A. Costanzi, Clifford Rudy, Dean Zollman, and Alexander Cornella.

CONTENTS

PART VI: OPTIMIZING INSPECTIONS

LIST OF TABLES

LIST OF FIGURES

LIST OF ILLUSTRATIONS

ROBERT B. LEACHMAN is Professor of Physics, Director of the Nuclear Science Laboratories, and Director of the Diversion Safeguards Program at Kansas State University. He received his Ph.D. from Iowa State University, was a staff member at the Los Alamos Scientific Laboratory from 1950-67, heading the Cyclotron Group at Los Alamos from 1956-67, and taught at Iowa State University and the University of New Mexico before coming to Kansas State in 1967. Mr. Leachman was a Guggenheim Fellow at the Nobel Institute of Physics in Stockholm in 1955-56 and a Fulbright Fellow at the Niels Bohr Institute in Copenhagen in 1962-63. He has published numerous articles in such journals as the Physical Review, the Journal of Nuclear Engineering, Nuclear Physics, the Transactions of the American Nuclear Society, and Scientific American, contributed to numerous proceedings in the fields of nuclear physics and atomic energy, and prepared a world survey of fission physics for the 1958 Geneva Conference on the Peaceful Uses of Atomic Energy.

PHILLIP ALTHOFF is Assistant Professor of Political Science at Kansas State University. He received his Ph.D. from the University of Iowa and taught at Western Michigan University, the University of Western Ontario, and Cornell College before coming to Kansas State in 1970. Mr. Althoff was a Woodrow Wilson Fellow in 1963-64 and a National Defense Education Act Fellow from 1963-66. He has published several articles in such journals as the Midwest Journal of Political Science, the Proceedings of the Michigan Academy of Science, Arts, and Letters, and the International Journal, and is co-author of An Introduction to Political Sociology.

RUDOLF AVENHAUS, Wissenschaftlicher Mitarbeiter, Institut für Angewandte Reaktorphysik, Kernforschungszentrum

J. R. BEYSTER, President, J. R. B. Associates, Incorporated

GERARD BILLY, Contrôleur des Matières Nucléaires de Base, Commissariat à l'Energie Atomique

DAVID BRADY, Assistant Professor of Political Science, Kansas State University

RICHARD BUTLER, Member, Australian Mission to the United Nations

S. CHATTERJEE, Graduate Student in Industrial Engineering, Kansas State University

F. A. COSTANZI, Research Associate in Physics, Kansas State University

GENERAL DELMAR L. CROWSON, Director of the Office of Safeguards and Materials Management, U.S. Atomic Energy Commission

D. B. HALL, Division Leader, Assay and Accountability Division Los Alamos Scientific Laboratory

DAVID J. HAYMON, Assistant to the Manager, Operations, Nuclear Fuel Division, Westinghouse Electric Corporation

W. A. HIGINBOTHAM, Technical Support Organization, Brookhaven National Laboratory

CRAIG HOSMER, Member, U.S. House of Representatives, Member, Joint Committee on Atomic Energy

ENRICO JACCHIA, Director of the Safeguards Department, Commission of the European Communities

JON H. JENNEKENS, Scientific Advisor, Safeguards, Canadian Atomic Energy Control Branch

RALPH J. JONES, Manager, Nuclear Fuel Control, Nuclear Fuel Service, Incorporated

L. A. KULL, J. R. B. Associates, Incorporated

JAMES E. LOVETT, Manager, Nuclear Materials Control, Nuclear Material and Equipment Corporation

RALPH F. LUMB, President, Nuclear Surveillance and Auditing Corporation

JOERG H. MENZEL, Member, Nuclear Assay Research Group, Los Alamos Scientific Laboratory

FRANK MORGAN, Head of the Chemistry Division, Atomic Weapons Research Establishment, United Kingdom Atomic Energy Authority

K. R. OSBORN, Vice-President, Allied Chemical Corporation

J. D. PETTINELLI, Ph.D. Candidate in Psychology, Kansas State University

LEON RAPPOPORT, Associate Professor of Psychology, Kansas State University

NORMAN C. RASMUSSEN, Professor of Nuclear Engineering, Massachusetts Institute of Technology

G. M. REYNOLDS, J. R. B. Associates, Incorporated

INSPECTOR GENERAL RUDOLF ROMETSCH, Head of the Department of Safeguards and Inspection, International Atomic Energy Agency

LAWRENCE SCHEINMAN, Associate Professor of Political Science, University of Michigan

A. E. SCHUBERT, Vice President, General Electric Company, and Chairman, Nuclear Materials Safeguards Committee, Atomic Industrial Forum

THEODORE B. TAYLOR, President, International Research and Technology Corporation

F. A. TILLMAN, Professor and Head of the Department of Industrial Engineering, Kansas State University

C. D. W. THORNTON, Director of the Division of Nuclear Materials Safeguards, U.S. Atomic Energy Commission

DEAN ZOLLMAN, Assistant Professor of Physics, Kansas State University

SAFEGUARDS OVERVIEW

1

KEYNOTE
REMARKS

Craig Hosmer

With the discovery of nuclear processes over three decades ago there came as a twin the need for precautions to keep the special materials and knowledge involved out of the wrong hands. At that time "the wrong hands" was defined by the Manhattan District as "anybody else's." However, this simplicity was not to be for long.

Over the years, holding the ever-expanding applications of atomic energy inside peaceful channels has become a matter of world-wide concern. Almost a hundred countries have signed the nuclear Non-Proliferation Treaty (NPT) and numerous other precautions have been instituted to guard against misuse of the atom. So many, in fact, that in the overall effort to prevent the perversion of nuclear science some confusion exists as to who is policing whom, which agencies are guarding what, and by whose authority.

The confusion results because the overall antiproliferation problem is several-sided and complex. Possible proliferators might be desperately imperiled countries or even some evil conspiracy of ruthless or irrational individuals. Many separate endeavors are required to meet such challenges. The need to protect society and its members from nuclear proliferation spans the entire spectrum of human interest. And in the countereffort to contain nuclear dangers there are a large number of possible controls that can be imposed selectively, separately, or simultaneously at international regional, national, or industrial levels.

ANTIPROLIFERATION:
A MANY-SIDED EFFORT

Despite the focus of attention on nuclear safeguards envisioned at the international level by the NPT, this category of restraints constitutes a response to but one of the several facets of the anti-proliferation problems. Similarly, on a national level the disappearance of special fissionable material from peaceful channels at some par-ticular point in the nuclear fuel cycle may constitute but one of several non-proliferation concerns. Therefore, in order to pinpoint specific deficiencies in the total structure being erected to prevent the multi-plication of nuclear weapons states and to inhibit the proliferation of like dangers, we must first examine the individual building blocks from which it has been fashioned.

The guidelines of the NPT and the International Atomic Energy Agency (IAEA) for the structure and content of safeguards agreements fully recognize this basic multiplicity of the antiproliferation challenge and the wisdom of the division of effort in meeting it. These documents begin by acknowledging the large technical and political gulf between weapons states and non-weapons states. They impose IAEA safeguards and mandatory inspections upon the latter but make these burdens discretionary with the former.

As it has worked out, the United States and the United Kingdom have voluntarily submitted to some inspections but the Soviet Union has not. The other nuclear weapons states, France and mainland China, refuse even to sign the NPT but insist that their nuclear hearts are pure and that their atomic arsenals are pacific.

Meanwhile, non-nuclear weapons states must comply fully with IAEA requirements in order (1) to obtain special nuclear materials for strictly peaceful purposes and (2) to be spared the embarrassment of being reported to the United Nations should they carelessly lose them.

This separate but unequal treatment of nations based on nuclear club membership stems from the obvious fact that the two categories of countries necessarily function with different effectiveness in dif-ferent antiproliferation roles.

For instance, Articles I and II of the NPT prohibit the transfer between nuclear states and non-nuclear states of "nuclear weapons or other nuclear explosive devices." These articles also ban the

"manufacture, or assistance with the manufacture, or other acquisition
whatsoever" of these troublesome items. Yet the safeguards provisions
of Article III are cast exclusively in terms of monitoring diversions
from peaceful channels of "source or special fissionable material."
Article III does not even mention safeguard monitoring of A-bombs or
H-bombs as such.

International safeguards thus focus almost exclusively upon that
one facet of the total antiproliferation problem having to do with
accounting for fissionable isotopes legitimately in the possession of
non-nuclear weapons states. This of course is a form of atomic bomb
birth control. It can be quite helpful in preventing the spread of nuclear
weapons. It is a logical responsibility to be assigned to non-nuclear
countries. But no matter who does it, materials accounting is by no
means the only antiproliferation precaution that must be taken: it is
but one of many.

WEAPONS PHYSICAL SECURITY

Very special efforts are required to insure that existing nuclear
weapon stockpiles are maintained physically secure in the hands of
their rightful owners. Yet the NPT contains not a word about procedures to enforce the bans in Articles I and II upon trafficking in nuclear
weapons, and properly so. Implementation of this distinct facet of the
antiproliferation effort is correctly remanded to the conspicuous self-
interest of nuclear club members. It is backstopped by their respective
civilian and military police organizations and networks of spies,
counterspies, and informers.

This is not to say, however, that pressure for top-notch performance should not constantly be kept upon these organizations. Speaking
as one who has been active in the military, has worked in the weapons
labs, has ridden storage site perimeters, and over a decade ago took
part in a review of nuclear weapons storage, handling, and shipping
safety and security practices that resulted in a series of major re-
forms, I will state flatly that, no matter how well a physical security
job is being done, it can always be done better and ought to be done
better. Frankly, I think members of the nuclear cartel ought to keep
under constant review their procedures to prevent the theft or misuse
of their bombs. They also ought to pass around tips to each other on
improving such procedures whenever that can be done with a net gain
for the common security.

WEAPONS DESIGN SECURITY

It is interesting to note that the related subject of security of
nuclear weapons design data, which to the uninitiated might seem to
be highly important in preventing nuclear spread, is actually of little
or no concern from strictly a non-proliferation standpoint. Nuclear
weapons designs are only an incidental facet of the general antiproliferation effort. This is because the laws of physics from which
nuclear weapons are designed have become so universally understood
that any effort now to suppress the data would be absurd. This cat
has been out of the bag for a long, long time.

A potential proliferator enterprising enough to lay hands on
illicit supplies of fissionable material is certain to be smart enough
to know how to weaponize them. Refined and sophisticated designs
are unnecessary. Whether such a proliferator be one country seeking
to overpower another or a criminal organization bent on cruder forms
of nuclear blackmail, it does not need to become an instant super-
power: it requires only primitive explosive devices.

Insofar as nuclear powers are concerned, their weapon designs
are top security items not primarily due to proliferation fears but
simply because compromising them will reveal to a rival the characteristics and vulnerabilities of one's own arsenal.

EVOLUTION, EXPANSION, AND
FORMALIZATION OF CONTROLS

If at this point a theme begins to emerge in these rather sim-
plistic remarks, it is that preventing the proliferation of nuclear
weapons requires the integrated efforts of several separate national
forces and multinational institutions. It is the same theme that runs
through the U.S. Atomic Energy Act of 1954 and the U.S. Atoms-for-
Peace program announced in 1956 which established the legitimacy
of peaceful uses of atomic energy and encouraged their application
on a global scale.

The many bilateral and multilateral agreements for cooperation
that followed these historic landmarks frequently required practical
judgments as to the identity of critical weapons proliferation danger
points and the best means of dealing with them. As antiproliferation
efforts have expanded and become formalized, with only minor changes
these earlier judgments gradually have been incorporated into treaties,
international law, and various regional and national statutes.

Now, both formally and as a practical matter, the physical security of nuclear weapons is recognized as a national responsibility of the nuclear weapons states. So also is fissionable material in the hands of the weapons states, except to the extent that they themselves submit it to international safeguards. In clear contrast, safeguards against diversion of fissionable material from peaceful channels are made both international and national responsibilities of the signatory non-nuclear weapons states.

The IAEA safeguards system thereupon functions to engage the non-weapons nuclear community in a parallel effort with the nuclear weapons powers aimed at deterring illicit diversions of fissionable material by means of an established capability to detect and report diversions should they occur. These international safeguards depend heavily upon the functioning of regional or national safeguards systems, which in turn rely upon strict materials accounting and other security measures at the individual plant level. Great resources and manpower are devoted to these efforts and their improvement.

International safeguards have become the glamor segment of the overall antiproliferation effort. Safeguards people, their systems and analyses, methodologies, black boxes, game theories, nondestructive test paraphernalia, and so on fascinate experts and laymen alike. But it must not be forgotten that other antiproliferation efforts also must receive attention and support if the fight to permanently freeze the nuclear club at five is to succeed.

The threat to the peace and security of the world from more nuclear weapons in more hands is about the same whether the hands are those of countries, criminals, or madmen and whether the explosives are stolen ready-made atomic bombs or home-made MUF-bombs fashioned from overdue oralloy and purloined plutonium.

DO ZERO-SUM GAMES EQUAL
DIVERSION DETERRENCE?

So it is not solely to the wise and effective implementation of institutionalized safeguards that I urge attention. Beyond these there are broader areas of proliferation concern and wider opportunities for proliferation suppression. In this regard, I note with considerable interest the Part IV, "Thefts, Criminology, and Jurisdictions." It will move into areas that may seriously challenge the assumption that even high probabilities of diversion detection will function as a deterrent.

Deterrence is based on the rationale that one will refrain from an act when the probability of detection is high and the penalty for performing it is more painful than the denial suffered by not performing it. When the penalty is death and the chance of getting caught is great, deterrence is strong. Under other circumstances, it may weaken.

Right now the penalties for getting caught stealing fissionable material differ radically in various jurisdictions around the world, but in general they do not equate to the awesome crime against humanity of putting an atomic device in the way of being used as a weapon of mass destruction. Nor, with any certainty, can the chance of getting caught in that act be universally estimated as large. Throughout most of the world national safeguards systems are still rudimentary. The potentiality for diversion remains low not primarily because the systems are working well but because the major flow of materials into them is yet to come.

Moreover, there is considerable suspicion in my mind that, even if current IAEA recommendations and proposals are followed to the letter, deterrence still may not be the ultimate in safeguards. The systems analysis and game theory studies being relied upon to solve the problems of detecting and deterring diversions may be much over-idealized and far too removed from reality to be reliable. The problem is that the studies assume a zero-sum game according to which the advantage to a diverter escaping with nuclear material is exactly equal to the advantage to the safeguards of preventing this diversion. This may be a very dangerous assumption in the real world populated by very fallible people, some of whom are very certain to be just no good.

ANTIPROLIFERATION AND PUBLIC OPINION

In any event, the world political community probably should be doing a lot more than it now is under IAEA leadership to foster a climate of public opinion exceedingly hostile to the idea of nuclear spread. Trafficking in the ingredients of mass destruction is equatable to the heinous war crime of genocide, and its penalty should be fixed accordingly. An international norm boosting the intensity of disapprobation accorded anyone who might participate in nuclear black marketing certainly would do no harm and might provide additional insurance against a day when incentives to divert may be on the rise.

COORDINATION WITH NATIONAL
POLICE SYSTEMS

Deterrence also can be made more certain by boosting the illicit diverter's risk of getting caught and thereby both incurring punishment and losing the profits of his crime.

If, under our safeguards systems of international public opinion, when a diversion is discovered, the alarm sounds, whistles blow, sirens scream, the United Nations is notified, and it all strikes fear and terror in the hearts of the general public, that is one thing. Quite another and far better thing is if it scares the criminal because he knows that the jig is up.

Every increase in the likelihood of a quick and positive identification and apprehension of a nuclear criminal plays a key role in fortifying the deterrent equation. So also does every increase in the degree of certainty with which the stolen item can be recovered.

Yet neither apprehension nor recovery are functions of the current nuclear safeguards structure. These are the responsibility of independent and relatively uncoordinated national and even local police systems. Undoubtedly the IAEA and other nuclear authorities can do far more than they do now to prepare these police authorities to move rapidly and effectively in nuclear cases.

This is a facet of the overall antiproliferation problem that is relatively neglected. It is not a glamorous facet as are systems analyzing the five components of MUF to estimate the confidence level with which a material balance can be closed in some hypothetical nuclear fuel factory. But effective international police coordination will be of the utmost importance when and if the world ever faces a real criminal threat of nuclear blackmail, and we ought to be promoting it.

Inspector General Rometsch reiterated during the Fourth UN International Conference on the Peaceful Uses of Nuclear Energy at Geneva in 1971 that the IAEA policy is only to render advice to national police authorities when requested. However, my feeling is that both IAEA and the police authorities ought to do more than wait for each other's ideas to get on with the serious business of improving and

sharing the capabilities of over one hundred national police systems
to cope with possible nuclear crimes.

The IAEA could serve a particularly useful function by setting
guidelines for police training, indoctrination, and equipment for this
specialized work. The principal nuclear nations of the world could
actively assist other countries in developing a worldwide network of
nuclear competent police systems. When the need for such systems
comes, it will be a sudden and critical one. It will then be too late
to start putting things in shape. Therefore, the more concern in
advance to this subject, the better.

REWARDS AND BOUNTIES

The practice of rewards for information leading to the arrest
and conviction of offenders and the return of specific stolen goods
has always been an historic companion of efficient police work.
Informants are the backbone of any security apparatus. Today there
are no particular assurances by the IAEA or any of the major nations
that persons cooperating with the authorities on nuclear cases will
even get a pleasant "thank you" for their troubles. Establishment of
standing nuclear theft rewards and a "no questions asked" bounty
system for return of materials unaccounted for should be put on the
agenda at Vienna and elsewhere.

PROLIFERATION PROFILES

Along similar lines, IAEA and national authorities should be
encouraged to arm themselves with psychological and other data
useful in forestalling nuclear thefts. The airlines have developed
fairly comprehensive profiles for potential highjackers. Potential
proliferators also could be profiled. Is such a man more likely to
be a three-time loser in the criminal courts or an underpaid, under-
promoted worker in a reprocessing facility with a large debt and a
nagging wife, or some other type? Which persons in which positions
for how long deserve special observation? These questions also are
facets of antiproliferation to which attention must be given if the total
effort is to succeed.

RELAXATION OF ACCOUNTING FOR
LOW ENRICHMENT U-235

If more attention is to be devoted to some matters, it is likely that less can be paid to others. It seems unwarranted for the safeguards systems to spend a lot of time and effort accounting for low enrichment U-235. This material is little more useful from a diversionary standpoint than source material. Notice of shipments and receipts are about all that is required with regard to source material and all that seems reasonably necessary for U-235 enriched 5 percent or less. This product is totally different from plutonium and U-233 which are explosively fissionable as soon as a critical mass is accumulated.

DECLASSIFICATION OF
DIFFUSION TECHNOLOGY

For this same reason, a relaxation of the zealous classification of diffusion enrichment technology has long seemed warranted. Anyone wishing to make an atomic bomb by enriching U-235 in a diffusion plant could hardly be secretive about it. At Geneva IV, Wataru Hiraizumi, President of the Japanese Atomic Energy Commission, recommended diffusion declassification and advised the owners of these secrets to get themselves some good patents, start licensing them, and stop worrying about proliferation via the diffusion route, because it is not in the cards.

So long as we make sure that no high enrichment cascades are built into these plants, I agree. We can better spend our safeguards time and money checking alternate enrichment processes that can be carried out in secrecy because they do not require large physical installations. We can safely take our eyes off the diffusion plants and concentrate on the ultracentrifuge, the Becker Nozzle, laser and thermal diffusion techniques, and possibly whatever unique enrichment process the South Africans claim to have invented.

"BOMBS FOR ALL"

Since one unusual thought breeds another, I am now emboldened to mention the fantastic proposal that we contain the dangers from nuclear weapons not by limiting their ownership but by deliberately and rapidly accelerating proliferation on a worldwide basis.

This is the "bombs for all" idea that proliferation is inevitable, that efforts to slow it down only unevenly delay the deadly day of reckoning, and that mutual deterrence should work as well for ordinary powers as it has for the superpowers for over a quarter of a century. Therefore, every non-nuclear country is to be given four atomic bombs and made a nuclear power. It then can deter its enemies and in turn be deterred by them. The bombs are rigged with permissive action links that keep them from being turned against the supplier members of the nuclear club.

The catch in this proposal is that any country that uses its bombs does not get any more. That will leave it a very, very lowly non-nuclear weapons state in a hostile world of nuclear powers. Such a possibility, it is argued, blanks out the proliferation problem and permanently guarantees a super-safeguarded worldwide nuclear truce. That, of course, is a fallacy and the idea of "bombs for all" as the answer to proliferation is an absurdity or an obscenity, depending on one's own preference for adjectives.

THE INCREASING NEED FOR TIGHT PHYSICAL SECURITY

Almost everyone but Theodore B. Taylor has neglected one very promising means to effectuate society's containment of nuclear dangers. His ideas for enhanced physical security of the devices and materials concerned make a lot of sense and should receive serious attention. Taylor points out that the emphasis in nuclear material safeguards has been and continues to be concerned primarily with detection of losses after they have occurred. Physical security measures to prevent thefts in the first place are accorded only a secondary role.

The intrinsic value of special nuclear materials is high. At $10,000 per kilogram, the value of plutonium by weight is about ten times that of gold. Yet the physical security levels provided for plutonium are considerably lower than those generally obtaining for the protection of bank vaults or large shipments of money and other valuables. And here is another pertinent statistic: during the last decade successful million dollar robberies have averaged one a year and robberies or thefts of $100,000 and over have occurred at a rate of around five per year.

Within about two years, plutonium recycle will commence on a large scale and the flow of this product through the civilian power reactor fuel cycle will increase rapidly. The quantity, price, and value of plutonium for illicit use could easily rise to a point where deterrence of theft becomes much too weak a reed to rely upon. Taylor believes this will happen and contends that improved physical security is absolutely essential to reduce the vulnerability of these materials to large-scale theft not only during shipment, which already is recognized as a serious hazard, but also during storage and handling. He points out that stolen special nuclear materials could supply an illegal national or international market, be incorporated into crude but highly destructive nuclear explosives for use by domestic or foreign extremist organizations, or sold to countries that want to make nuclear explosives but that do not have direct access to special nuclear materials.

Recently, the U.S. Atomic Energy Commission (AEC) somewhat tightened up its 10 CFR Part 73 physical security regulations, but they still fall short of constituting major barriers to special nuclear materials thefts or robberies by highly motivated professional criminals. Regardless of monetary costs, Taylor recommends that the U.S. government vigorously press for action by appropriate foreign governments and the International Atomic Energy Agency to set up dependable special nuclear materials (SNM) physical security systems on a worldwide basis. These should be designed to lock up SNM at least as tight as conventional valuables, and possibly tighter.

CONCLUSION

In conclusion let me say that this is a very distinguished audience of noted experts gathered together from many parts of the world. As this symposium begins, I am proud and pleased to have been given this opportunity to focus its attention upon the sea of problems associated with keeping vital atomic ingredients in the right hands and securely out of mischief. My remarks have only skimmed the surface of that sea. During these few days here on the campus of Kansas State University, you will probe its depths for answers which may contribute significantly to the peace of the planet and the safety of its citizens.

I wish you well. All of civilization wishes you Godspeed.

Referring to the matter of enhancing purposeful proliferation, Theodore Taylor (International Research and Technology) emphasized that in times like these he was very concerned about the idea of built-in security. Specifically, the idea that a situation in which any nation possesses nuclear weapons and can use them to attack another nation if that nation does something it does not like perpetuates a balance of deterrence. However, situations can be visualized in which a nation possessing nuclear weapons might indirectly threaten a small nation through an intermediary and thus not be required to reveal its identity. Thus, a situation in which a small nation experiences an internal revolution backed by a nuclear power might cause that nation to use perhaps a small number of nuclear explosives in order to force the nuclear power to stop interfering in its internal affairs.

Craig Hosmer (U. S. House of Representatives, Joint Committee on Atomic Energy) replied that the problem was even more complicated than Taylor suggested. Referring to President John F. Kennedy's agreement with the United Kingdom and France allowing them to utilize the Polaris, Hosmer pointed out that a nation being attacked could identify the attacking nation by the characteristic flight pattern of the Polaris. Thus, given Kennedy's agreement, the identity of attackers became a problem associated with proliferation.

John Stumpf (Atomic Industrial Forum) stated that Hosmer had pointed out that a nation attempting to acquire clandestine nuclear weapons for the purpose of attack or defense would need only primitive explosive devices, but Stumpf emphasized that few nations have the aircraft necessary to deliver such devices. Hosmer replied that delivery might not be necessary. For example, he mentioned a scenario developed by Taylor in which "dedicated disarmers," dissatisfied with progress toward disarmament, might divert fissile materials, clandestinely construct explosive devices throughout the world, and then threaten to set them off if their disarmament demands are not met.

At this point, Taylor stated for purposes of discussion that at the present time, given the required amounts of special nuclear material—either highly enriched uranium or plutonium—any nation in the world not only could make a few nuclear devices but also could deliver them simply by smuggling them into the target country or by acquiring the special nuclear materials in the target country and constructing the nuclear devices clandestinely in that country. Hosmer commented that he felt that delivery through smuggling or clandestine

14

construction would hardly be worth the gain since, if attempted delivery through such methods were discovered, the most decisive kind of counteraction would be taken. Hosmer also emphasized that it is always possible to get into the "maximum conceivable accident, not credible but conceivable, syndrome." The upshot of this is that, if an attempt is made to cover every imaginable bet, the task is impossible. The point then is to limit consideration to the truly credible.

C. D. W. Thornton (Director, Division of Nuclear Materials Safeguards, AEC) stated that he was interested in Hosmer's observation that perhaps declassification of gaseous diffusion technology is not particularly dangerous provided that there are some guarantees against installation of very high enrichment cascades. He pointed out that, given the considerable flexibility in new types of enrichment facilities, an escalation in capacity far beyond what is presently the case can be postulated. He then asked whether this meant that no enrichment facility is a hazard even though the number of stages required to take material to 3 percent is almost the sufficient number of diffusion stages required to take the material to weapon level. He noted that other enrichment plants can be simply rearranged to do so. Hosmer replied that there are a limited number of diffusion plants that can satisfy all the enrichment requirements of the civilian nuclear power program pending the period when the breeders take over and that these are under control. As a result of this control, it is possible to insure that enrichment facilities are not arranged so that material can be taken to weapon level. He added that, if gaseous diffusion technology is allowed to spread under control, the possibility of secret enrichment by other methods might possibly be less. Thornton responded that dispersal of technology under control is thus analogous to the dispersal of weapons under control.

Lawrence Scheinman (University of Michigan) raised the question of whether deterrence theory is not perhaps more a figment of our imagination than a reality and thus whether we ought not to devote more attention to demonstrating the ineffectiveness of deterrence theory. Hosmer answered that he felt Scheinman was correct and that we are dangerously deceiving ourselves if we believe that deterrence theory can be accepted as an answer to all problems.

Frank Morgan (United Kingdom Atomic Energy Authority) requested Hosmer to comment on the proposition that society addresses itself to a threat as it sees it at that particular time. Specifically, since things are not static but dynamic, care must be taken in assessing future threats because the scenario is constantly changing. The problem is not to legislate for every conceivable situation, whether soundly

based or not, but to make balanced judgments of what action should be
taken in context of the NPT; each signatory should seek to foster the
cooperation of police forces in order to insure that nuclear materials
do not cross international boundaries. Hosmer replied that he felt
the observation correct but perhaps incomplete. He emphasized that
an ongoing safeguards system must exist because fissile material can
be diverted at any time and that it is totally unrealistic to believe
that a diversion situation will never occur.

Marc Kramer (University of Michigan) asked Hosmer if there
is any assurance that no nuclear materials have been stolen or if our
system is good enough to have determined that as well as whether we
might have to hold back the growth of the nuclear power industry
because we have not solved some of the safeguards problems. Hosmer
replied that, since we live in a very complex economic society that
depends not only upon power but upon an ever increasing amount of
it, it would be impossible to slow the growth of the nuclear power
industry. Hosmer also said that, although the material unaccounted
for (MUF) problem is relatively complex, the fact that apparently
MUF has not been weaponized or put to use in other manners thus
far indicates a high degree of reluctance to employ fissile material
in an illicit manner; this presently seems to be one of the best
assurances that such materials are not utilized for illegal purposes.

SOME HISTORICAL DATA

The successful conclusion of the Non-Proliferation Treaty (NPT) was the culmination of ten years of effort in the United Nations and in the Conference of the Eighteen-Nation Committee on Disarmament.

When the Treaty was commended for the widest possible adherence by the UN General Assembly in the summer of 1968, international safeguards gained new importance. International safeguards in connection with NPT will be the focus of this chapter. However, a very brief historical review to show the origin of international safeguards seems appropriate.

An early attempt at the end of the 1940s to confine all nuclear activities to an "International Atomic Energy Commission" failed to reach international acceptance.

In 1954 President Eisenhower delivered the Atoms for Peace Message. It led to the conclusion of cooperation agreements between the United States and many nations all over the world. These agreements provided the legal basis for the supply of nuclear material and equipment and contained a safeguards clause. According to the latter, either the United States directly or a recognized international body had the right to control that the supplies were not used to further any military purpose. Preparations for such an international body, the International Atomic Energy Agency (IAEA), were successfully completed in 1956 and led to the establishment of the IAEA in 1957.

Article II of the IAEA Statute defines its objectives as follows:

The Agency shall seek to accelerate and enlarge the contribution of atomic energy to peace, health and prosperity
throughout the world. It shall ensure, so far as it is able,
that assistance provided by it or at its request or under
its supervision or control is not used in such a way as to
further any military purpose.

The IAEA Statute further defines the safeguards functions by
saying that safeguards shall apply as follows: (1) to Agency sponsored
Projects (Project Agreements); (2) to any bilateral or multilateral
arrangements, at the request of the parties (Transfer Agreements);
and (3) to any of a State's activity in the field of atomic energy, at the
request of that State (Unilateral Submission Agreements) Between
1960 and late 1971 forty-six safeguards agreements of all three types
were concluded between thirty-two states and IAEA. Their implementation covers some 200 nuclear facilities.

Of course, the practical implementation of all these safeguards
agreements during the past ten years also implied the establishment
and periodic revision of what is known as the Agency's Safeguards
System. For that purpose, the international democratic process of
relying on expert groups, advisory panels, and committees was used.
Expert groups and advisory panels are appointed by the Director
General of the IAEA applying the criterion of widest possible geo-
graphical distribution. Committees are established by the IAEA
Board of Governors and are open to all Member States (now 102).
They formulate the final recommendation for approval by the Board.
The IAEA's Safeguards System—before NPT and referred to in the
Treaty—is laid down in a guideline for implementation in INFCIRC/
66/Rev.2 dated September 1968.

ADAPTATION OF THE IAEA SAFEGUARDS
SYSTEM IN CONNECTION WITH NPT

Within the IAEA's Secretariat it was recognized at an early
stage that considerable preparation was needed to enable the Safeguards Department to cope with the new task not only with a view to
adapting the organization to a rapidly expanding workload but mainly
to develop further and systematically detailed safeguards techniques.

This was, for instance, stated at the opening of a Panel of
Experts on Safeguards Techniques invited to Vienna in August 1967.

To formulate technical approaches to various aspects of safeguards, five more such panels were held during the years 1968 and 1969. In addition, in 1968 the Director General appointed a group of eight experts as consultants to study and report on the impact of NPT on the IAEA's safeguards work. In fact, these consultants reformulated some basic concepts. At the same time, within the Safeguards Department a new division was established devoted to safeguards development work. In 1970 an IAEA Symposium on Safeguards Techniques was held in Karlsruhe, and experts from several Member States were at IAEA headquarters to participate in four different working groups.

Three weeks after the NPT came into force on March 5, 1970, the IAEA Board of Governors decided to establish a Committee (on which any Member State could be represented) that, inter alia, was given the task to "advise the Board as a matter of urgency on the Agency's responsibilities in relation to safeguards in connection with the Treaty, and in particular on the content of the agreements which will be required in connection with the Treaty."

Within nine months (June 1970 to March 1971) the Committee, with the participation of delegations from some fifty Member States, completed the required work including the additional task of developing and recommending a financing scheme for the IAEA's safeguards activities.

The Committee worked out recommendations for a complete agreement text consisting of 116 articles and including definitions of the most important technical notions. This material represents the IAEA safeguards system which must be used as a basis for negotiating and concluding agreements between States party to the NPT and the IAEA. It was published in May 1971 as document INFCIRC/ 153.

Before settling down to the constructive work of actually drafting, the Committee held an extensive general debate. Through it, ground was laid for important policy decisions and the working rules were defined. Basis for the latter was the consensus that all delegations should be able to participate in all deliberations. Policy decisions were not taken by vote but on a consensus basis. In almost all cases it was possible to achieve consensus. The three exceptions were liability and arbitration (to which two delegations declared to reserve their position) and financing (the adopted solution was clearly opposed by one delegation).

Of the problem areas requiring policy decisions and brought out during the general debate, I would like to mention four.

Most fundamental was the fear that safeguards might be misused for aims foreign to that generally accepted: to avoid further proliferation of nuclear weapons. It would be an unwanted side effect if any influencing, directing, or limiting of peaceful nuclear activities in non-nuclear weapon states occurred through international safeguards activity. This fear will remain for some time a real political problem despite many written formulations guarding against it. The Agency's Statute and Safeguards System both contain the phraseology "that safeguards should be designed to avoid hampering the economic or technological development." It is repeated in the NPT, which also includes a separate article (Article IV) dealing specifically with the same question. Protective clauses are also explicitly and implicitly incorporated in INFCIRC/153.

I am confident that this particular problem will diminish as a result of continuous display of integrity and objectivity in the IAEA's safeguards work. It will finally disappear when negotiations foreseen in Article VI of NPT on the cessation of the nuclear arms race prove successful.

A second point of concern in the Committee was to find the right balance between acceptability and effectiveness of safeguards.

Many delegations were critical of the lack of detailed definition of the safeguards work by the guidelines in INFCIRC/66. In fact a number of governments of highly developed countries had made declarations to that point at the signing of NPT: they would ratify only after further and more detailed definition of the safeguards system and its constraints were formulated. One should note that INFCIRC/153 shows a great step forward in this direction.

Optimization of cost and effectiveness of safeguards was another major concern. It was connected with the additional task of the Committee to find an appropriate formula for financing the IAEA's safeguards work.

Cost projections by various authors showing up to a hundredfold cost increase within 10 years caused concern to all Member States but particularly to developing countries. They feared to be burdened beyond their means.

Careful systems studies by the IAEA Secretariat, confirmed by independent studies in Member States, brought the cost projections into the right perspective. Also, a financing scheme was devised to relieve the burden on developing countries in case the ratio between safeguards costs and costs for promoting activities of the IAEA grew beyond the 1971 value.

Finally, the interface between international safeguards and any domestic or regional system of accountancy for and control of nuclear material had to be better defined. This is at the same time a matter of sovereignity and a question of divided responsibility. It became clear that, for instance, physical protection of nuclear material cannot be the responsibility of an international safeguards authority: it must remain the task of sovereign States.

The objective of international safeguards, as spelled out in Article 28 of INFCIRC/153, is the "timely detection of diversion of significant quantities of nuclear material from peaceful nuclear activities to the manufacture of nuclear weapons or of other nuclear explosive devices or for purposes unknown, and deterrence of such diversion by the risk of early detection."

SUMMARY OF THE COMMITTEE RESULTS

As mentioned above, the results of the Safeguards Committee's work are laid down in INFCIRC/153. This document may be character-ized as a "model" for agreements to be concluded between the IAEA and States Party to the Non-Proliferation Treaty. By highlighting it, I now seek to explain the essentials of a widely accepted international safeguards system.

The Non-Proliferation Treaty determines the point of departure in three ways:

1. The safeguards agreements to be negotiated and concluded between the States Party to the Treaty and the International Atomic Energy Agency should be based on the Statute of the latter.

2. The safeguards functions should be defined according to the Agency's safeguards system for the exclusive purpose of verification of the fulfillment of a State's obligation assumed under the Treaty "with a view to preventing diversion of nuclear energy from peaceful uses to nuclear weapons or other nuclear explosive devices."

3. The principle would be applied of safeguarding effectively the flow of source and special fissionable material by use of instru-ments and other techniques at certain strategic points.

Having defined the objective of international safeguards above, it was further necessary to determine the technical conclusions to be drawn from safeguards verification activities. None of the existing safeguards systems had provided for this. The most suitable basis for such a provision was found in the notion of material unaccounted for (MUF). The amount of MUF in respect of a given area and over a specific period should be stated as a result of the IAEA's verification activities giving also the limits of accuracy.

What are the means to reach this conclusion? Systematic analysis by the Secretariat and an expert working group that met in 1970 led to the following formulation: "material accountancy should be adopted as the safeguards measure of fundamental importance, with containment and surveillance as important complementary measures."

This formulation has been incorporated as one of the principal articles in the proposed text for a safeguards agreement in connection with NPT. It is also discussed in IAEA paper A/CONF.49/P/770 at the Fourth United Nations International Conference on the Peaceful Uses of Atomic Energy in 1971.

The guidelines (INFCIRC/66) hitherto used as a basis for safeguards agreements also determine the four well-known procedural elements for safeguards work:

1. The provision of design information to supply the inspectorate with a defined and limited knowledge of the facilities in which nuclear material is produced, used, processed or stored

2. The requirement for the operators of such facilities to keep records on material production, change and movement

3. The provision of reports on material production, change and movement to the safeguarding authority

4. The independent verification, by inspections, of recorded and reported data as well as of material flow and inventory. These four procedural elements are common to all safeguards systems presently in use; they appear in domestic and bilateral safeguards as well as in the regional systems of the European Nuclear Energy Agency and the European Community (Euratom). Naturally, they were taken over as the main procedural part for non-proliferation safeguards.

An important novelty of the proposed agreements to meet the safeguards requirements of NPT is the obligation of the Parties to the Treaty to establish and maintain a system of accountancy for and control of all nuclear material. Technical and organizational provisions to be made by such a system are enumerated in detail in the agreement. Safeguards shall be applied in such a manner as to enable the Agency to verify, in ascertaining that there has been no diversion of nuclear material from peaceful uses to nuclear weapons or other nuclear explosive devices, findings of the State's system. The Agency's verification shall include, inter alia, independent measurements and observations conducted by the Agency in accordance with the procedures specified in the technical part of the Agreement. The Agency, in its verification, is obliged to take due account of the technical effectiveness of the State's system.

Within the frame of the defined technical objective, the international safeguards system, superimposed over national or regional systems for accountancy and control of nuclear material, is basically an information system. It must provide the inspectorate at any time within a defined period with a complete picture of the whereabouts of all nuclear material in a State and it must fulfill a great number of boundary conditions, such as being unintrusive, guaranteeing protection of information received, making use wherever possible of the fact that nuclear material is for long periods safely contained, providing for the use of statistical measuring techniques and random sampling, and providing for the utilization of the accountancy system of the States by verifying its findings, e.g., by independent measurements and observations. Thus, the real problem is not to lay down the need for information—that would be simple—but to define what minimum of readily available information and what minimum amount of additional measurements will fulfill the purpose of the IAEA system. Therefore, the description of that system looks rather like an enumeration of its limitations.

These limitations vary with the type of information. The information called for in the first procedural step, i.e., design information, which should provide the Agency with the more or less static picture of a chain of facilities through which nuclear material may flow, is limited in three ways. The first limitation is the general condition that it should be the minimum necessary for safeguards; the second limitation is contained in a positive enumeration of the specifications that must be given—geographic location, type, nominal capacity, and so forth; and the third and sharpest limitation is given in the definition of the purpose for examining this design information.

The most important result to be achieved by this examination is
to determine <u>material balance areas</u> to be used for IAEA accounting
purposes and to select those <u>strategic points</u> that are <u>key measurement
points</u> for determining nuclear material flow and inventories. The
Committee even specified detailed criteria for material balance area
selection. For instance, on the request of a State a particularly small
material balance area may be established around a process step
involving commercially sensitive information. The idea is that, if
there is only a small hold-up of nuclear material within such an area
and continuous input and output flow measurements can be made, it
would be possible to avoid inspection access to the area itself.

Thus, in connection with the provision of design information two
principles are established for the protection of commercial and industrial secrets. In fact, there are two classes of such secrets:

1. Those that must in any case be disclosed to the inspectorate
which, in turn, must guarantee their protection: these consist of information related to nuclear material flow, such as the capacity of a fuel
fabrication plant.

2. Industrial secrets, mainly process know-how, for which
disclosure to the IAEA inspectorate can be avoided. The criterion
for selection of a particularly small material balance area around a
sensitive process is an example of this second principle.

Other results expected from the examination of design information are the establishment of: records and reports requirements
and records evaluation procedures; requirements and procedures for
verification of the quantity and location of nuclear material; and
nominal timing and procedures for physical inventory-taking. In
addition, the selection of appropriate combinations of containment and
surveillance methods and techniques and the strategic points for their
application should result from the examination of design information.

This enumeration shows how far the Committee went in formulating precise technical procedures and the reasons for them.

However, there is one step more to be taken: quantification.
For practical reasons the agreement itself, which must be concluded
independently of the quantity of nuclear material required to be safeguarded and the number and type of facilities through which this might
flow, cannot give all the quantitative values involved. Therefore, in
the agreement the quantification step is relegated to "Subsidiary
Arrangements"; these will be described later. At this stage it should

be mentioned that the results of the examination of the design information, like the selection of material balance areas, key measurement
points, and so forth. must be included in such Subsidiary Arrangements.

With regard to the information on nuclear material flow and
inventories, the limitations could be handled in a much simpler way.
Both the new record system, dealing with information that must be
accumulated continuously at the facilities, and the new reports system,
covering the information to be provided regularly to the IAEA are
straightforward developments from the Agency's existing safeguards
system. What in the latter was a skeleton has now become much more
fully formalized by stating all types of records and reports and pre-
scribing their content. Thus the concept of transaction or inventory
change reports also has been formally incorporated into the system.
Again, quantification takes place in the Subsidiary Arrangements;
these should, for instance, specify the amounts of nuclear material
that, if inadvertently lost, would trigger the submission of a special
report to the IAEA.

A great step forward in formalization also was made concerning
inspection procedures. Clear limitation of inspection rights without
curtailing verification efficiency was one of the major concerns of the
Committee. A complete definition of the purpose and scope of inspection was used to indirectly establish the limitations.

There are three types of inspections connected with different
purposes: (1) ad hoc inspections which include verification of the
initial report on nuclear material, verification and identification of
changes before the routine scheme of inspection is established, and
verification of nuclear material before and after international transfers;
(2) routine inspections with the purposes of verifying consistency between records and reports, verifying location, identity, quantity and
composition of nuclear material, and possible causes for MUF; and
(3) special inspections which obviously are concerned with the verification of special reports but also with such additional investigations
as are needed when the information obtained through normal means
is not adequate for achieving the technical objective.

The scope of inspections is determined by giving a long list of
permitted actions to the inspector. Typical examples are independent
measurements of nuclear material, verification of the functioning and
calibration of instruments, observation of sampling and anlysis, and
arrangement for the receipt of duplicate samples—but described with
a higher degree of precision than in this incomplete enumeration.

The first direct limitation concerns inspection access. The decisive element is that routine inspections are limited to strategic points specified in the Subsidiary Arrangements and to the records. There is a safety valve for additional access under special circumstances, but this must be preceded by consultations between the State and the Agency.

The second direct limitation on inspections is given by stating the maximum yearly workload (in man-years) to be deployed per group of facilities. For reactors and sealed stores this is one-sixth of a man-year of inspection for each such facility in the State. For all other types of facilities, the inspection workload is made dependent on throughput or inventory of nuclear material, expressed in effective kilograms to take care of the graduation in the diversion risk. For facilities involving plutonium or more than 5 percent enriched uranium, the annual workload may be as high as thirty times the square root of the number of effective kilograms in inventory or throughput, whichever is the greater, and not lower than 1.5 man-years. This is valid for, e.g., reprocessing plants, whereas fabrication plants for power reactor fuel are covered by a simpler formula: one-third of a man-year plus 0.4 times the amount of effective kilograms.

Such is the frame of inspection rights; again quantification is left to the Subsidiary Arrangements in which, for example, the number and location of strategic points will be fixed. On the other hand, it is not possible to determine the actual inspection workload in advance. This must be left to future experience, but criteria to be taken into account already are enumerated in the agreement.

The Committee also succeeded in precisely determining the fields of activity within which nuclear material must be followed by safeguards. There were a number of functional boundaries to be defined, such as exemptions for small quantities or non-nuclear use. The most important boundary is given by the definition of that point in the nuclear fuel cycle at which nuclear material must come under safeguards for the first time. After careful consultations, it was set as the point where any nuclear material reaches a purity and composition suitable for fuel fabrication or enrichment.

An essential feature of the proposed agreement is the complete description of a versatile feedback system from the Agency to the State. Three types of statements are required from the Agency: (1) a semiannual statement of the nuclear material inventory on the books of the Agency, which permits a check on the completeness of the information flow; (2) information on the result of inspections in the

State, at intervals to be specified in the Subsidiary Arrangements; and (3) a statement on the technical conclusions drawn from verification activities, i.e., the difference between book inventory and physical inventory or, expressed in another way, the MUF, as well as the accuracy with which this quantity can be known. Through this feedback system the safeguards information flow gains an additional justification.

Finally, a word of explanation must be said on the Subsidiary Arrangements. In the Agency's safeguards practice up to now, this kind of document has figured as an additional protocol concluded between the Secretariat of the Agency and a State party to a safeguards agreement in order to fix all the detailed procedures and technicalities left open in the agreement itself. In the new and more complete type of agreement, many of these details are incorporated. But Subsidiary Arrangements are still necessary to lay down those quantities, dates, and numbers which, within the validity of the agreement, undergo a steady development parallel with the growth of nuclear activities. In some twenty agreement articles the following phrase appears: "as specified in the Subsidiary Arrangements." Contrary to previous practice these Subsidiary Arrangements do not contain any rights or obligations additional to those in the agreement but consist of a series of tables, information sheets, report forms, and of course indicate the mechanism for keeping them up to date. As mentioned before, Subsidiary Arrangements are the instrument for quantification of safeguards as far as this is at all possible at this stage.

THE NEED FOR FUTURE DEVELOPMENT

The foregoing presentation of the IAEA safeguards to be applied in the frame of the Non-Proliferation Treaty brings out the best sides of the improved system. Naturally, any presentation in the light of the development work applied tends to emphasize the progress made. However, this should not blind anybody to the fact that there is much left to be done.

The IAEA is aware of the need for further development of safeguards technology which must move along with the development of nuclear technology in theory. In practice it must move faster for some years because it is lagging behind. The safeguards development division at the IAEA is working under high pressure and includes at present almost as many "inspectors" as the implementation division.

As an example, I would like to mention a particular field of investigation: the technique of correlating nuclear material flow measurements in States where a more or less complete fuel cycle is being safeguarded. By comparing, e.g., the U-235 content of fuel leaving the fabrication plant with its content at the head-end of the reprocessing plant and correlating this ratio with the U/Pu-ratio, an extremely valuable cross-check is obtained. This ultimately should permit lowering the inspection workload in nuclear power stations.

Some thirty similar development projects are being pursued actively both within the IAEA Secretariat and in cooperation with Member States. Every effort is made to meet the heavy responsibility that has been placed on the IAEA in a favorable international climate.

The uncertainty in material unaccounted for (MUF) was of concern to <u>Manuel Kanter</u> (Argonne National Laboratory) both in regard to limits on its magnitude and whether the design of material balance areas should be based on this uncertainty in MUF. The latter, Kanter felt, was implied by the measures given in IAEA document INF/CIRC 153.

In response to the inquiry whether limits of error possibly might be stipulated in the future, Rudolf Rometsch noted that the agreement in document INF/CIRC 153 was carefully arranged to leave this open. Otherwise, a trickling type of diversions could be made within stated values. A plausible MUF—one that is acceptable or not— should be defined only on the basis of all the judgment that is needed in a technical conclusion.

Several factors were cited by Rometsch for choosing the extent of the materials balance areas. On the measurement side, the accuracy of measurements and the accuracy with which a balance can be made for each material balance area are factors. In regard to the processes, the techniques involved in an area and the flow within an area are factors. However, clearly a whole country cannot be taken to be one material balance area.

ORGANIZATIONAL CHANGES

Since the summer of 1971, when I was asked to cover the topic "U.S. Safeguards Overview," there has been a change in the Atomic Energy Commission (AEC) safeguards organization. As a result of this change, the regulatory organization under C. D. W. Thornton now has policy responsibility for safeguards for U.S. licensees. I retain responsibility for license-exempt safeguards operation and policy, research and development, and the international interfaces.

Therefore, my observations will be confined to the international interfaces, research and development progress and programs, and safeguards as they relate to government contractors, i.e., the license-exempt sector. It should be borne in mind that some of the AEC contractors also are licensees. Safeguards for these are currently under Thornton's control.

U.S. DOMESTIC SAFEGUARDS OBJECTIVES AS COMPARED WITH INTERNATIONAL SAFEGUARDS OBJECTIVES AND INTERFACES

In the past few years as both the U.S. domestic safeguards program and the International Atomic Energy Agency (IAEA) program have begun to crystallize, I have noted ever-increasing concern with respect to the objectives of the two programs. I shall therefore

attempt to clarify their respective roles to clarify understanding of
the interface between the U.S. system or, as a matter of fact, any
domestic system and the IAEA system.

From the very inception of the U.S. nuclear program, the major
domestic safeguards objective has been to carefully guard bomb and
bomb-type nuclear materials to ensure that they do not fall into the
hands of unauthorized persons. Although this objective has remained
unchanged, the nature of the threat and the program scope and dimensions have changed as the availability of materials and the dissemination of information relative to nuclear weapons increased and, particularly, as peaceful programs for application of nuclear material expanded.

Within this broad objective we have developed an embryo "graded"
approach that provides for the most intensive efforts to be applied to
highly enriched uranium or plutonium in readily useable form to make
one or more nuclear explosive devices. Less intense efforts are
applied to smaller quantities, lower enrichments, and such forms as
spent fuel elements which are difficult to handle and require considerable further processing. We use a mix of physical protection, surveillance, and accountability elements. Our specific objectives are to
systematically define the optimum mix of all three elements and to
improve the accountability element by continuing to develop a capability
to have closed measured materials balances, to improve measurement
accuracies, and to shorten the time in which missing materials are
detected.

Although international safeguards will achieve a credible level
of deterrence for diversions, they do not and cannot incorporate
physical protection and police and criminal sanction elements. These
would be necessary to achieve a credible level of diversion prevention, particularly with respect to small volume diversions of low
international military significance.

The international and domestic systems are basically designed
and will have to deal effectively with different kinds of threat problems
using different tools to some extent. Therefore, the systems are not
duplicative or overlapping but rather complement each other as so
effectively explained by Craig Hosmer in Chapter 2.

The principal product of the IAEA safeguards system will be a
reasonable degree of assurance to the international community that
no single state subject to IAEA safeguards has diverted a substantial
portion of its peaceful nuclear materials to a nuclear weapons program.

It is obvious, however, that in addition to accountability safeguards, which are the prime tools available to the IAEA, prevention of diversion also must include a physical protection element, a rewards element, and a search, seizure, arrest, and severe sanctions element in those cases where a diversion does take place within a state.

Since the international agency by its very nature will not have police-related powers, the very best that we can expect is that the IAEA will develop a set of recommended standards for these important elements of safeguards which would then be incorporated within a state's domestic safeguards program.

Hopefully, this brief analysis of the difference in objectives between the IAEA and national safeguards systems serves to emphasize the necessity for an effective national system, particularly one that accommodates a wide variety of nuclear materials, including privately owned materials, and appropriate regulatory powers on the part of the state to insure effectiveness. Also required is a system responsive to subnational threats, the environment in which the materials are involved, and the strategic value of materials. It must be sufficiently sensitive to promptly detect a diversion of strategically important materials. These attributes of a national system are a convenient way of restating the U.S. domestic objectives.

THE IMPORTANCE OF A DOMESTIC SYSTEM

There has been some concern that in most states participating in the IAEA system evidence of the existence of effective domestic safeguards systems, independent of but complementary to IAEA systems, may only be in the formative stages. Most national systems I have heard about seem to be designed only to be responsive to IAEA system input requirements. If it is true that only a few states have a truly independent domestic system, this is a very serious matter. The United States has a reasonably effective independent domestic safeguards system, and efforts to upgrade its effectiveness are continuing. I hope that others will be in a position to provide comparable assurance with respect to the attention being devoted to independent domestic systems in other states.

It is also important that the domestic system be tied in with the IAEA system and other national domestic safeguards in such a way as to assure international exchange of intelligence and operational type information relative to evidences of the development of a black market and the police type measures being implemented.

SAFEGUARDS RESEARCH AND
DEVELOPMENT

Having stated the U.S. objectives, it is important to outline how it is proposed to meet them and the effectiveness of the measures involved.

The United States has pioneered in the field of research and development of safeguards, including systematic analysis. There are several reasons for this. First, we recognized the need early and later saw that the U.S. system could be an effective and defensible model for worldwide safeguards. Second, we wanted the safeguards procedures and techniques that were developed to be applicable to plant conditions and operations on a realistic scale. Third, we wanted the program to be responsive to the problem areas that existed, particularly in achieving a measured material balance on a time scale that would permit the timely indication of problems. We also wanted to assure an appropriate mix of physical containment, accountability, surveillance, and transportation safeguards to meet the threats to the materials in their normal environment—a so called "graded" safeguards system. It was thought that these kinds of objectives and the results achieved would help in technical discussions with the IAEA, Euratom, and individual countries, particularly in regard to the installation of other effective national and international systems of safeguards.

How well have we done for the amount of resources committed? The starting point in achieving a measured material balance was to attack the hard-to-sample items—scrap and discards—so that it would not be necessary to wait for recovery to close the material balance. A number of techniques have been developed and tested; active and inactive interrogation and measurement techniques have been employed (see Tables 1 and 2). The results of the in-plant instrumentation program have been covered in progress reports, and the results of the integrated experiment with a plutonium plant were discussed at the 1971 conference of the Institute of Materials Management (INMM) in Palm Beach.

Norman Rasmussen, G. Robert Keepin, Richard Bramblett, William Higinbotham, Herbert Kouts, and others have reported on the research, applications, and results from applying nondestructive measurement techniques to a wide variety of nuclear materials. D. Gupta, at the International Meeting on Nondestructive Measurement and Identification Techniques in Nuclear Safeguards at Ispra on September 20-22, 1972, traced the development of nondestructive

TABLE 1

Accuracies of Typical Fissile Material Assay Methods

Fissile Material Assay Method	Percentage Accuracy of Methods			
	Plutonium		Uranium-235	
	Feed and Product	Scrap and Waste	Feed and Product	Scrap and Waste
Chemical analyses of samples	0.2	inaccurate	0.1	inaccurate
Neutron-induced fission	0.5	10 to 30	0.5	10 to 30
Gamma-induced fission	1 to 2	5 to 10	1 to 2	5 to 10
Normal gamma emission	0.2	5 to 10	0.2	inaccurate

36

TABLE 2

Summary of Nondestructive Assays by Active and Passive
Methods with Representative Accuracies

Fissile Material	Inventory Samples		Scrap and Waste		Fuel Material			
					Cold		Hot	
	Active	Passive	Active	Passive	Active	Passive	Active	
Pu	16 1-2%	16 2-4%	32 10-30%	421 2-15%	25 1-2%	27 2-5%	Planned	
235U Highly enriched	254 1-2%	158 5%	302 5%	382 5-15%	112 0.4-1.5%	14 2.5%	9 0.8-2%	
235U Low enriched	82 1-2%	Planned	176 5-15%	456 2-10%	9 2%	88 5%	10 3%	

Legend:

Active	Passive
Number of Independent Assays	Number of Independent Assays
Active	Passive
Range of Representative Accuracies	Range of Representative Accuracies

measurement techniques and closed by paraphrasing a principle that
the United States adopted some time back and that was first enunciated
by Keepin as the KISS principle at the Los Alamos Scientific Laboratory
(LASL) Research and Development Symposium in October 1969, namely,
Keep It Simple, Stupid.

In keeping with the KISS principle, measurement capabilities
have been demonstrated on such products as uranium fuel rods and
waste materials. In summary, we have satisifed ourselves that the
state of the art of nondestructive measurement of nuclear material is
now either adequate or approaching adequacy to start toward a measured
material balance and to be able to start to abandon by-difference accounting. However, there are some major problems remaining, such
as how to reduce the burden of inventory taking in large continuous
processes without a plant stoppage and clean-out. There probably are
a number of trade-offs possible. As yet we have not clearly mapped
out how dynamic inventory and verification procedures can be accomplished to meet the requirement for early warning of missing
material.

Under the KISS principle, the problem of standards and calibrations required for nondestructive analyses, which are as important
as those required for chemical analytical problems, must be solved.
A standards, instruments, and calibrations organization must be established in the IAEA.

As to the system analytical results, we have produced a comprehensive analysis of a conceptual safeguards system. However, we
need to further identify alternatives, costs, risks, and time scales
before proposing major changes to upgrade the U.S. system. One major
item requiring identification is what is being safeguarding against and
why, and therefore what intensity of inventory, inventory frequency,
physical protection, number of samples taken, and form of inspection
and verification are needed to provide a desired level of countermeasure
effectiveness. It seems counterproductive to implement an intense and
frequent inventory without specifying the necessary quality of inventory.
Also, it seems useless to require intense physical containment for
materials that have little priority on the threat list. Although there
are many alternatives for nonweapon grade materials, the alternatives
seem greatly reduced for weapon grade materials. It may well be that
physical protection will provide the best cost-benefit ratio. On the
other hand, physical protection alone does not assure 100 percent of
necessary early detection.

To date I think we have identified and plugged the most obvious holes in the safeguards system. We have sorted out most of the alternatives and developed technology for most of the measurements and flows. What remains is to continue to get the techniques applied in both government and industry. We would expect that this application might lower material unaccounted for (MUF) by as much as 50 percent; however, as Shakespeare wrote, "Ay, there's the rub" (see Table 3). The absolute quantities of MUF are important only when related to the throughput of the plant. Therefore, public understanding of the term MUF in its proper context is absolutely necessary, particularly the understanding that in most cases the MUF is well within the propagated measurement errors (and what this means as to diversion probabilities) and estimates for a particular process or plant. One can expect responsible critics to demand, and reasonably so, that there be a carefully conceived safeguards system that gives a high degree of assurance that nuclear material is where it should be and in the right quantities. So one of our major problems is to put MUF in the appropriate context or to devise another more meaningful term so that the public does not generally conclude that MUF literally means suspiciously lost.

A NATIONAL NUCLEAR MATERIALS
DATA SYSTEM

One cannot overemphasize the necessity for national safeguards systems to include a well conceived, functioning nuclear materials data system. The same admonition goes for plant safeguards systems. Such a system requires timely submission of accurate data to permit analysis of the problem areas that in turn would identify actions needed to be initiated by the plant as well as by the national system authority.

The United States has a national data system, and many U.S. plants also have their own plant data systems. To date, the national system has served very well as a single data bank for the location of materials within the system.

For those who are comtemplating the installation of a data system, we will be happy to share our experiences on timeliness and accuracy of reports required, measurements and computations to be reported, and in general the problem of getting the reports to the users and regulators in time to be of value. We have learned that unless you can complete a measured material balance in a timely manner and appropriately report the results, you can expect to have a data bank of great historical interest but little practical value in safeguards. To get practical safeguards value from the data system, we are devoting

TABLE 3

Average Six-Month MUF Experience
(license-exempt contractor facilities,
July 1, 1966–June 30, 1971)

Facility Type	U-235 in Enriched Uranium (percentage)	Plutonium (excluding Pu-238) (percentage)
Enrichment plants—cascade operations	0.03 to 0.12	—
Conversion, fabrication, and scrap recovery	-0.03 to 0.09	-0.07 to 0.15
Large-scale multipurpose (including chemical reprocessing)	0.05 to 0.24	-0.23 to 0.19
Research and development laboratories	0.01 to 0.05	0.23 to 0.79

Note: The percentages reflect the division of the averages for the ten reporting periods of the MUF by the beginning inventory plus receipts [i.e., (ave. MUF)/(ave. BI+R)].

the considerable resources necessary to insure the timeliness and
accuracy of input.

TRANSPORTATION

Many have heard me comment on the special safeguards problems
in transportation. I continue to believe that when nuclear materials are
placed in the transportation environment they become more vulnerable
to diversion and theft than when they remain in the environment of a
plant using these materials. Many have stated that transportation
safeguards of an effective type will never be achievable without the
expenditure of enormous resources. If they are right, then it will be
necessary to examine the possibilities of planning nuclear industry in
such a way as to eliminate the need for transporting materials outside
a nuclear complex. Although such planning may be worth consideration,
I do not share the view of those who look upon the achievement of effective transportation safeguards using common carriers as relatively
impossible. In the United States efforts by many different government
agencies and private industries are under way to strengthen the protection of all kinds of goods exposed to the transportation environment.
I will not discuss in detail the nature of specific efforts to which I
allude. However, I do believe that, due to the combined efforts and
attention of shippers, shipping companies, and government agencies,
marked improvements in transportation security of all kinds in the
United States can be expected to come rapidly in the foreseeable future.
This development can only benefit safeguards.

SAFEGUARDS AS APPLIED TO LICENSE-
EXEMPT CONTRACTORS

Within the license-exempt operations, we have implemented a
safeguards system incorporating physical protection, surveillance,
and accountability elements. We believe our system is reasonably
effective. Monthly inventory activities are carried out for the most
strategic materials in the system. Although the extent of measurements, their accuracy, and the sample analysis practices related to
these frequent inventories are not yet optimized, we are working toward that goal. We do have physical protection, personnel screening,
and surveillance requirements applicable to license-exempt operations,
and we are now examining possibilities of appropriate trade-offs among
all the elements, together with possible upgradings for selected ones.

I previously mentioned MUF as a performance standard, when
expressed in the context of throughput. The range of five-year

averages for MUF as a percentage of beginning inventory plus receipts for the indicated type of license-exempt operations shows that the average six-month MUF experience for enriched uranium varies from a low of 0.01 percent to a high of 0.24 percent and for plutonium from a low of 0.07 percent to a high of 0.79 percent. These figures are cited only to make the point that both industry and government will have to do better, particularly in regard to plutonium. We are working hard on this area to insure that when large flows of plutonium appear we will have the necessary capabilities to safeguard this strategically important material.

CONCLUSION

In conclusion, I wish to summarize in somewhat reverse order the salient features of my overview of the U.S. safeguards program.

1. The performance and overall concept of the U.S. domestic safeguards system for a license-exempt operation are now reasonably effective but efforts must continue to provide for an assured higher degree of effectiveness. We must always look for the holes in the system.

2. Our safeguards research and development effort has now come close to demonstrating the feasibility of achieving a fully measured and consequently a more accurate and timely materials accountability balance.

3. Our analytical studies have identified the need to provide for an appropriate mix of physical security, surveillance, and accountability, depending on the strategic value of the material and the nature of the threat.

4. Since there is a changing nature of the threat to nuclear materials, effective domestic safeguards programs oriented at subnational threats are essential in all states in addition to, and complementary with, the application of IAEA safeguards in those states.

5. Transportation safeguards with the expected addition of monitor service probably have gone about as far procedurally as can be expected. Work on secure containers and vehicle communications and locating systems and application of these ideas to the problem should introduce some additional preventive measures.

    Referring to the observations of both Inspector General Rudolf
Rometsch and General Delmar Crowson, John Van Hoomissen (General
Electric Company) asked Crowson to comment on the future of the
relationship between U.S. and international safeguards. Crowson
pointed out that the NPT is in effect and that the U.S. President has
offered to place under international safeguards the parts of the U.S.
nuclear industry not having national security significance. However,
Crowson emphasized that, while the United States is in favor of the
full implementation of NPT safeguards, the extent to which nuclear
industries in the United States eventually will come under the jurisdiction of international safeguards remains to be determined. Specifically, much depends on subsidiary arrangements, the negotiations
concerning which have already begun for certain foreign states. Subsidiary arrangements for the United States will be important as far
as the U.S. nuclear industry is concerned. The United States plans to
involve representatives of the nuclear industry in the negotiations of
subsidiary arrangements when their plants are under discussion so
that they can have some say in the arrangements adopted as well as
in the implementation of these arrangements. This follows from the
meetings held between the AEC and the nuclear industry which discussed
the problems of implementing IAEA safeguards in the U.S. nuclear
industry. In these meetings many issues, especially concerning reporting arrangements, i.e., which material balance areas (MBA) are
reported and how, were met in a fairly definitive, straightforward
manner. Crowson emphasized that, in the planned discussions presently under way, the U.S. nuclear industry views would help the IAEA
select the strategic points at which safeguards measurements will
be made. As the subsidiary arrangements are completed, Crowson
expects that certain contractor operated facilities will fall under the
same arrangements as will apply to licensees.

    Lawrence Scheinman (University of Michigan) asked both Rometsch
and Crowson whether subsidiary arrangements between the IAEA and
a given nation would be priviledge information or whether they would
be generally available. Rometsch responded that subsidiary arrangements had to be considered on two levels. First, the IAEA has developed a model subsidiary arrangement which contains no specific
data but clearly maps out the data that must be fixed. The model
subsidiary agreement is obviously generally available. However,
final subsidiary agreements will contain specific data, such as plant
capacities, and therefore will contain privileged information that must
be carefully protected.

Scheinman wondered whether or not the fact that subsidiary arrangements contain specific privileged information might in some manner affect the perceptions of a state that might negotiate with the IAEA at some time in the future, but the discussion failed to resolve this question.

Raymond L. Jackson (Battelle Columbus Laboratories) asked Crowson to be more specific on what his office planned to do in the area of transportation. Crowson replied that one need is to monitor fissile materials at transfer points, as contemplated for licensees in the proposed amendment to 10 CFR 73. Thought is being given to the design of shipping packages that, if penetrated or if moved from a specified location, would emit a signal to bring law enforcement agencies into action. Thought also is being given to the utilization of sophisticated communication systems for tracking vechicles and possibly packages.

Following up on these comments, Theodore Taylor (International Research and Technology) asked whether effort was presently involved in identifying appropriate countermeasures to involve progressively stronger forces as needed when a clear signal is received that fissile materials are being stolen either in transit or from a facility. Crowson replied that appropriate countermeasures are being studied for a national recovery system entailing the right amount of force in the right place at the right time.

II

NATIONAL
SAFEGUARDS
SYSTEMS

**NUCLEAR SAFEGUARDS
POLICY:
A CASE STUDY
IN REGULATION**

David Brady

INTRODUCTION

Regulatory politics are characterized by conflict between the agency regulating and the interests being regulated. The central area of disagreement involves the degree of control (stringency) to be exercised over the regulated interests. The following are some classic examples of the politics of regulation: the control of meat packing firms by the Department of Agriculture, the regulation of labor-management disputes by the National Labor Relations Board, and the regulation of the mass media by the Federal Communications Commission. The case of regulating the safeguards system of the nuclear industry by the AEC is a study in the politics of regulation.

In this chapter the extent and degree of disagreement between the regulators and regulated over general safeguards policy is ascertained. After the parameters of the general disagreement are ascertained, the decision-making theory of Brunswick, Hammond, and others is applied to determine both the various cuing factors that determine

Research for this chapter was supported under the Research Applied to National Needs (RANN) Program of the National Science Foundation. The author wishes to express thanks to the following individuals who contributed to the researching and writing of this paper: Robert B. Leachman, F. A. Costanzi, Clifford Rudy, and Dean Zollman.

the disagreements and the possibilities for trade-offs in the bargaining process. In short, the investigation attempts to delineate the scope as well as the specifics of the differing viewpoints in the nuclear safeguards field.

METHODS

The Research Design

The fundamental question underlying our survey is as follows: In what manner are safeguards policies agreed upon? We assume that the crucial variable relevant to this question is the degree of control that a regulated facility will allow the AEC to exercise over its safeguards program. Thus, the stringency of external control over the safeguards program of a regulated facility is the focal point of our analysis. Specifically, our primary purpose is to ascertain the extent of the differences between the regulator and the regulated as well as the nature of the variables that cue the various responses concerning regulation. To collect the data necessary to realize this purpose, we devised a structured interview instrument that was pretested at Kansas State University, revised with the assistance of the Survey Research Center at the University of Michigan, and then taken into the field for interviewing purposes.

The Survey Instrument

Since degree of control was assumed to be the crucial variable relevant to safeguards policy agreements, we devised five hypothetical systems reflecting in each case five differing degrees of external control. The five systems concerned AEC control over regulated facilities. In each case the five systems ranged from System I, which provided for the least stringent set of controls, to System V, which provided for the most stringent set of controls. Each respondent was asked to respond to each of the five systems in general as well as in terms of specific likes and dislikes. Then each respondent was asked which system he would prefer as the actual safeguards system and which system he felt most closely resembled the present safeguards system. This segment of the interview thus produced data concerning preferences and perceptions of the overall safeguards system.

Since in practice degree of control depends upon the development of specific methods of control that are of a more or less technological nature, each of the five systems referred to the same specific methods of control, albeit in terms of differing degrees of stringency. In this survey (see Table 4) the following specific methods of control were mentioned in each of the five systems:

1. The extent to which the AEC should be involved in the process of designing safeguards procedures for a regulated facility

2. The extent to which the AEC should be involved in changing plant practices in order to insure good safeguard procedures

3. The extent to which the AEC should be involved in the measurement of fissile material

4. The extent to which the regulated facility should be allowed to deny access to AEC inspectors due to the loss of proprietory information

5. The manner in which diversions should be reported to the AEC

6. The manner in which the AEC should react to reports of missing fissile material

7. The manner in which the safeguards program of a regulated facility program should be funded

8. The manner in which general accounting records should be reported to the Division of Nuclear Materials Safeguards (DNMS)

9. The method by which special nuclear materials should be transported

10. The nature of the relationship between IAEA and AEC safeguards systems

11. The number of physical inventories per year to be required by the AEC

12. Whether the purpose of the AEC and the IAEA safeguards systems should be to detect or to detect and deter the diversion of fissile material.

In addition to including these twelve specific methods of control in each of the five systems, the respondent was requested to respond

TABLE 4

Variation in the Most Important Topics Considered in the U.S. Hypothetical Systems

TOPIC	SYSTEM				
	I	II	III	IV	V
Safeguard design and procedures	DNMS certifies and reviews periodically	AEC establishes recommendations	AEC reviews design information before licensing	AEC reviews design before construction; can require changes before licensing	AEC approves before construction; inspects during construction
Changes in plant practices	DNMS recommends voluntary changes	DNMS requests improvement	DNMS can require changes	AEC orders changes	AEC orders immediate changes
Independent measurements	none	at input-output; using random, passive and nondestructive measurements	at strategic points; using active or passive nondestructive, and random measurements; resident inspector in reprocessing	at strategic points; using destructive and nondestructive random measurements; resident inspector in fabrication and reprocessing	continuous survey by nondestructive; random destructive; resident inspection at all facilities
Denial of access due to proprietary information	facility can withhold information	facility may restrict access to certain areas	AEC has access if plant has more than 5 effective kgs.	AEC has access to all areas of all facilities	AEC has access to all areas of all facilities
How diversions are reported to AEC by facility	diversion is confirmed and then reported	diversion reported when discovered even before confirmation	all missing material reported as soon as discovered	all losses reported including NOL as soon as discovered	resident inspectors report irregularities
Commission reaction to reported MUF	aid in determining where it went; inform appropriate agencies	send investigators; if necessary, inform Justice Department	same as II, plus may require inventory and obtain court injunction to change practices	same as II, plus will require physical inventory and may request injunction to close plant temporarily	same as IV except plant may be closed permanently

	Column 1	Column 2	Column 3	Column 4	Column 5
Commission reaction to unreported MUF	Same as above plus complete review	same as above	same as above	same as above	same as above
Funds for facility	AEC provides funds	AEC defrays costs	AEC provides equipment but no funds	AEC pays cost of inspection only	all costs borne by facility
Safeguards purposes	detection	verification; facility can detect	ensure detection of loss or diversion	detect and possibly deter diversion or loss	detect and deter diversion or loss
Paperwork to DNMS	keep records that are reviewed periodically	interfacility transfers reported and records reviewed on random basis	interfacility transfers reported and records reviewed on random basis	interfacility transfers reported and detailed records reviewed on random basis	records reviewed continuously by resident inspectors
Physical inventories	none	none	annual	semi-annual	semi-annual
Transportation	not mentioned	shipping facility responsible for safeguards; shipped by common carrier	safeguards responsibility of shipping facility and carrier; shipped by approved common carrier	carrier responsible for safeguards which are approved by DNMS	AEC personnel accompany all shipments
IAEA safeguards	will not duplicate DNMS; accept system as sufficient	IAEA reviews DNMS and facility procedures; may request repeat of measurements	IAEA cooperates with DNMS; makes joint measurements	IAEA performs independent measurements at strategic points and reviews AEC and facility records and procedures	IAEA safeguards independent of AEC but procedures set up in agreement with AEC

to a specific question related to each one by selecting the response
that most closely reflected his attitude in terms of stringency of control;
further, the respondent was queried concerning the strength of his commitment to his response. These questions therefore served to probe
the specific attitudes of the respondent as related to certain specific
methods of control.

The value of the approach outlined above to the construction of
our questionnaire is that, by combining data on the five hypothetical
systems with data on the twelve questions, a 12 x 5 matrix can be
generated for each respondent. From these matrices are obtained
not only a general overview of relevant attitudinal preferences but
also an indication of specific attitudes. Further, and of prime importance to the problem of attitude measurement, the matrices allow for
checks on the response consistency of a respondent.

The Population

Our population included 85 individuals in government, industry,
and academia (all of whom have been interviewed) who are in either
policy determining or policy influencing roles in relation to safeguards
in the United States. The interviews were sessions of approximately
one hour in length.

FINDINGS

The Scope of the Disagreement

If the case of diversion safeguards is a study in regulatory
politics, then the obvious expectation is that the AEC and the nuclear
industry will differ in regard to the preferred stringency of the safeguards system.

The industry should prefer a safeguards system that is less
stringent than the system preferred by the AEC. Such a finding would
not be unexpected but would establish that there is disagreement over
what the safeguards system should be. However, in this section we
also test for a second dimension of disagreement. The hypothesis is
that the industry and the AEC respondents will perceive the present
system as the opposite of their preference. That is, the industry
sample will perceive the present system as more stringent than the
one they prefer while the AEC sample will perceive the present system

as less stringent than the one they prefer. Thus, the general hypothesis is that the AEC and the industry respondents not only will prefer different systems but will perceive the present system in opposite directions along the stringency continuum.

In order to test this hypothesis, each of the respondents was asked to state which of the five hypothetical systems he preferred as well as which of these systems most closely resembled the present safeguards system. Table 5 shows the results. It should be noted that the higher the mean average the more stringent the safeguard system.

The results verify the hypothesis. The industry respondents prefer a system less stringent than their perception of the present system's stringency while the AEC respondents prefer a system more stringent than they perceive the present system to be. The t test for significant differences between mean averages was applied to these findings, and the results showed that the differences were statistically significant. On the basis of this analysis, the conclusion is that significant differences do exist between the regulated and the regulators concerning the stringency of safeguard systems.

TABLE 5

Perceptions of Safeguards Systems:
The Industry and the AEC

	Industry	AEC
Preferred system		
$\overline{x}$ =	2.10	3.90*
Variance =	1.30	.66
Present system		
$\overline{x}$ =	3.00	2.20*
Variance =	1.14	.71

*Significant difference at .01 level (t test).

Cuing Factors in Safeguards Preferences

The Brunswick-Hammond theory of conflict resolution holds that conflicts result from a combination of factors underlying the ostensible general differences.[1] For example, disagreement over the question of urban renewal in a community can be shown to be the result of such underlying factors as economic improvement civil rights, law and order, and community beautification. Agreement in regard to a program of urban renewal for a community has been relatively difficult to achieve since the various participants emphasize one or more of the underlying factors at the expense of the other factors.

However, discussions regarding agreements on urban renewal programs seldom are cast in terms of the underlying factors but rather in terms of the general problem as though all the participants shared a common understanding of the term. Thus, conflict situations are difficult to resolve because the bargaining and compromise processes are characterized by a general broad terminology that neglects the weightings that the participants place on each of the underlying factors.

It has been shown that, when the participants in the conflict situation are made cognizant of the underlying factors and the weighting or cuing of the factors in determining their positions, the conflict is more easily resolved.[2] Once the disagreement has been shown to be the result of the fact that participant A favors position X because he cues on factor X_1 rather than on X_2 or X_3 and that participant B favors position Y because he cues on X_2 rather than X_3 or X_1, then with this information the participants are more readily able to bargain and compromise. All of the above, of course, implies that, by pinpointing the factors underlying disagreements, compromise is facilitated and the result is a more reasonable solution (policy). The decision model of Brunswick and Hammond is now applied to the safeguards problem. The safeguards system is examined in terms of its component parts, and the underlying factors are isolated and analyzed.

If the differing preferences of the nuclear industry and the AEC respondents concerning safeguards stringency are the result of a number of different underlying factors, then an analysis of the component parts of the safeguards system should reveal differences in the emphasis placed on the separate parts. To test for this relationship, each respondent was asked what degree of stringency he favored on each of the twelve variables that comprised the five hypothetical systems. The respondents were told that response I was always the least stringent while response IV was always the most stringent. Thus, in effect each respondent could build his own safeguards system emphasizing the areas where he felt AEC regulation needed to be most stringent or least stringent. The answers to these questions provide a method by which the researchers could analyze the specifics of the variables underlying the general safeguards preferences.

To test this hypothesis, the respondents were categorized into three groups: AEC personnel, those in the nuclear industry working with reactors, and industrialists working in the area of reprocessing and fabrication plants (academics are excluded in this analysis). The nuclear industry was separated into reactor and reprocessing-fabrication categories because of the nature of the technological processes involved with fissile materials in the different facilities. The hypothesis is that, due to the relatively more complex nature of technological processes and the concomitant problems raised, the reprocessing-fabrication respondents would favor less stringent AEC control in more questionnaire content areas than would those in the reactor category. Table 6 shows the results of this analysis (the higher the mean the more stringent the response).

On twelve of the fourteen variables, the reprocessing-fabrication respondents disagree with the AEC respondents and the direction of the disagreement is as expected, i.e., the AEC respondents prefer more stringent controls. The differences between the reactor sample and the AEC personnel are not as severe as the above differences. On eight of the fourteen variables, there are significant differences between the AEC and the reactor samples; however, on six of the fourteen variables there is substantial agreement between the two groups. This is in contrast to the comparison of AEC and reprocessing-fabrication respondents where there is agreement on only two of the fourteen variables. The general pattern on the stringency continuum is that the reprocessing-fabrication sample is located at the least stringent end of the continuum while the AEC sample occupies the most stringent end of the continuum.

Turning to the specific areas of agreement and disagreement among the three groups, we find that an underlying pattern exists. The greatest disparities regarding safeguards occur in the areas of AEC reaction to reports, the funding of safeguards, and where measurements are to be taken. In the area of controlling plant design, what types of measures to take, the denial of access, reporting diversions, AEC reaction to written reports, IAEA relationship to AEC safeguards, and the number of inventories, the disagreements are less severe but statistically significant. Thus, across almost all of the variables in the survey the AEC and the reprocessing-fabrication samples are in disagreement. However, the intensity of the disagreement varies from issue to issue.

TABLE 6

The Component Parts of the Safeguard System with
Preferences of Industry and Government

		Reprocessing	Reactor	AEC
System choice	$\bar{x}$ =	2.2	2.7	3.9
Control of design	$\bar{x}$ =	2.6	2.6	3.8
Power to change practices	$\bar{x}$ =	2.3	2.3	3.0
Measurements where	$\bar{x}$ =	2.1	3.1	3.8
Measurements what	$\bar{x}$ =	2.7	2.7	3.6
Denial of access	$\bar{x}$ =	3.0	3.4	3.9
Reporting diversion	$\bar{x}$ =	2.4	3.2	3.6
AEC reaction to report	$\bar{x}$ =	1.1	1.7	2.0
Funding	$\bar{x}$ =	1.6	2.1	3.4
Reporting accounting records	$\bar{x}$ =	1.4	2.0	2.0
Transportation, who carries	$\bar{x}$ =	2.5	2.5	2.4
Transportation, responsibility for	$\bar{x}$ =	2.6	2.6	2.7
IAEA relation to AEC safeguards	$\bar{x}$ =	2.1	2.7	3.0
Inventories	$\bar{x}$ =	2.9	2.8	3.9
Detect or deter*		Detect	Detect	Detect & deter

*Majority of respondents favored the response listed.

The industry samples, i.e., the reactor sample and the reprocessing-fabrication sample were in agreement with each other and
in disagreement with the AEC sample on the following variables: the
AEC's power to change plant practices, the AEC's right to control
plant designs, the kind of measurements that ought to be taken, and
the number of inventories. The pattern for the remaining variables

was that the reprocessing-fabrication sample preferred the least stringent controls while the AEC preferred the most stringent controls with the reactor sample occupying the middle ground.

The above analysis shows that there is reason to believe that differing degrees of disagreement exist between the regulators and the regulated as one moves from one system variable to the next. However, such differences do not constitute proof of underlying factors that determine the overall safeguard system preference. The following section deals with the question of the factors underlying the general disagreement over safeguards.

CUING FACTORS

The purpose of this section is to determine what, if any, are the underlying clusters of variables that cue the different system preferences. In order to accomplish this, the data used in the previous section were intercorrelated using the Tau b statistic. The assumption is that, if there are factors underlying the decisions regarding system preference, there will be clusters of intercorrelated variables. The correlation matrix was then fed into the Guttman-Lingoes non-metric factor analysis program.[3] This program was specifically designed to determine the factor structure present in any given correlation matrix. In this analysis, the system preference variable was included in the correlation matrix in order to determine which of the underlying factors was most closely related to or determinant of system preference. Figures 1 and 2 show the variable clusterings for the nuclear industry and the AEC, and Table 7 shows the mean importance for each factor. The variable groups are labeled in the order of the strength of their relationship to system choice. Thus, variable group 1 is most closely related to system choice and so on.

Figure 1 reveals that for the nuclear industry the group of variables most closely related to the preferred stringency of the safeguards system (hereafter termed systems choice) is what we have labeled an intrusiveness factor. That is, the cluster of variables in group 1 all deal with actual AEC physical presence in the facility. In the open-ended section of the survey instrument, many industry respondents commented on this phenomenon:

> It is difficult to run an efficient business with AEC personnel running about the plant.

> We cannot show a profit if the AEC is continually present poking about.

FIGURE 1

A Two-Dimensional Clustering of Variables
in Relation to System Preference: Industry Sample

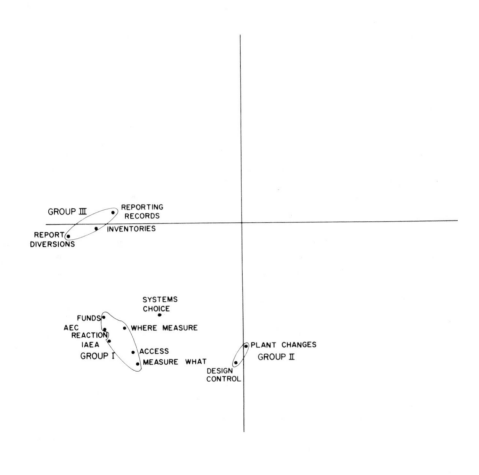

FIGURE 2

A Two-Dimensional Clustering of Variables
in Relation to System Preference: AEC Sample

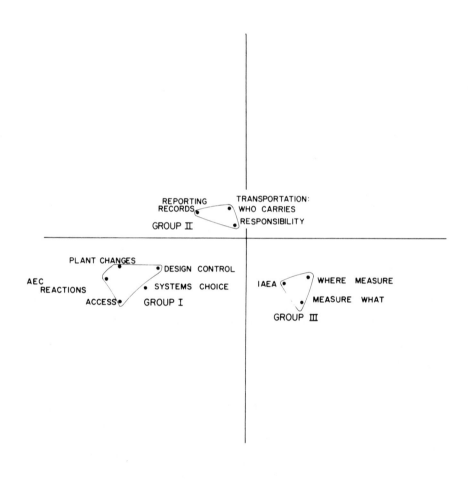

TABLE 7

Mean Scores for Cuing Factors
by AEC and Industry

Factor		AEC	Nuclear Industry
AEC regulatory power	$\overline{x} =$	2.6	2.1
Transportation	$\overline{x} =$	2.0	n.a.
Measurements	$\overline{x} =$	1.8	n.a.
Intrusiveness	$\overline{x} =$	n.a.	2.4
Record-keeping	$\overline{x} =$	n.a.	1.9

Note: 1.0: not too important; 2.0: important; 3.0: very important; n.a.: not applicable, i.e., no such factor for the group.

Production schedules are impossible to meet if the AEC insists on being present measuring this and that and in general disrupting orderly procedures.

In short, the most important determinant of the industry respondents' systems choice appears to be their concern that the presence of AEC personnel in the facility disrupts orderly business procedure.

The second factor related to system choice for the industry respondents is a straightforward concern for the AEC's power to regulate. That is, the variables in this cluster deal with the power of the AEC to close facilities for improper safeguards methods as well as to control the plant designs of the industry.

The third factor related to the industry's systems choice is a safeguards accountability factor. The variables in this cluster deal specifically with the methods by which accounting records are to be reported to the AEC.

Thus, for the industry the three factors on which the industry cue their system preference are as follows: (1) Intrusiveness, (2) the AEC's power to regulate, and (3) safeguards as accountability.

These findings, of course, agree with common sense in that the variables in each cluster seem to have a common underlying content and, taken as a whole, reflect the industry's concern for making a profit. In short, all three cues are related to the following general underlying problem: Can the industry "run a business" if the AEC's safeguards requirements are too stringent?

Figure 2 reveals that for the AEC sample the first group of variables relates to the AEC's power to regulate. That is, the variables in this cluster all tap a dimension of the extent to which the AEC can regulate the industry. However, whereas this factor is most closely related to systems choice for the AEC, it was the second most important determinant of systems choice for the nuclear industry sample.

The second factor related to the system choice of the AEC respondents included two questions on transportation of special nuclear materials as well as one question on reporting records. This factor does not appear to have any readily identifiable underlying content such as intrusiveness. Further analysis of this factor indicates that it is simply a general concern for safeguarding materials during transportation.

The third factor reflects a concern for measurements and the extent to which the IAEA would duplicate DNMS measurements. Analysis of the structure underlying this factor revealed that, rather than a common underlying content, the factor reflected AEC organizational role differentiation. That is, the third factor was the result of the fact that those individuals in the sample who work for DNMS virtually unanimously responded with the same pattern on the questions concerning measurements. This is not surprising in view of the fact that one of the chief functions of the DNMS is detecting diversion through measurements.

In sum, Figure 2 reveals that the prime cue determining the AEC sample's position on safeguards stringency is the extent to which the AEC can regulate the industry. Further, the results show that the question of detecting diversion through measurement is of great importance to the DNMS sample.

The results in Table 7 show that the factors discussed above are perceived as important to the two samples (industry and AEC). In the nonmetric factor analysis for the industry, the intrusiveness factor was closest to the system choice and the industry sample viewed their responses to the various components of that factor as between

important and very important. Next to intrusiveness, AEC power and
record-keeping were viewed with decreasing importance. In short,
the results show that both the factor analysis and the respondents'
perceptions of the relative importance of the factors agree in the case
of the industry sample.

The results from Table 7 show that the same pattern observed
above for the industry holds for the AEC sample. That is, for the AEC
sample the factor analysis and the respondents' evaluation of the factors
are in agreement insofar as regulatory power, transportation, and
measurements, in that order, are most closely related to safeguard
systems stringency preferences.

Comparison of the results shows that for the industry the most
important factor cuing responses to safeguards preferences is the
extent to which the AEC can "intrude" in the operation of the facilities.
For the AEC the prime factor cuing safeguards preferences is the
scope of the AEC's regulatory power. This same factor concerned
the industry sample and was the second most important cue for it.
Overall, the findings show that indeed the regulators and the regulated
cue on different factors. Thus, disagreements between these groups
may be mediated by focusing discussions regarding safeguards on
these specific aspects of the overall safeguards problem.

REACTOR-REPROCESSING DIFFERENCES

The final section of this chapter deals briefly with some aspects
of differences between the reactor and reprocessing-fabrication samples. The hypothesis in this section is that for the reactor sample the
most important factor cuing responses to safeguard stringency will
be the record-keeping factor (see Figure 1), while for the reprocessing-
fabrication sample the most important cuing factor will be intrusiveness.
Figures 3 and 4 show the results.

The results show that the two samples cue on different factors.
The most important factor for the reactor sample was a record-keeping,
or safeguards as accountability, factor, while for the reprocessing-
fabrication sample the most important cue was intrusiveness. This
finding is in keeping with the argument that technological differences
between these two components of the nuclear industry affect both
general preferences regarding stringency and attitudes about which
specific parts of the safeguards system should be most stringent.
That is, not only does the reactor sample show a preference for a
more stringent system than does the reprocessing-fabrication sample

FIGURE 3

A Two-Dimensional Clustering of Variables
in Relation to System Preference: Reactor Sample

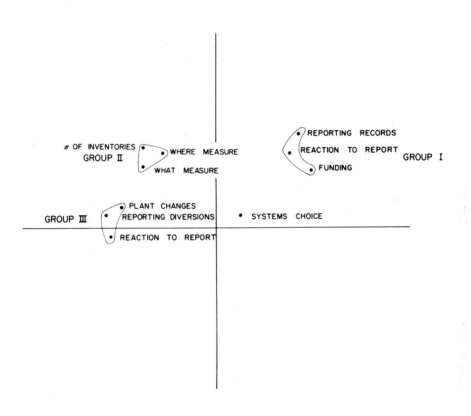

FIGURE 4

A Two-Dimensional Clustering of Variables
in Relation to System Preference: Reprocessing Sample

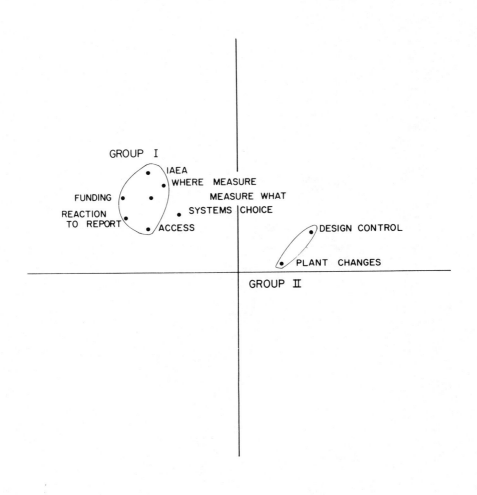

but the two samples disagree over which of the facets of the system should be more stringent. Again, attempts to mediate disagreements between industry and the AEC could be facilitated by recognizing that within the nuclear industry different types of facilities prefer different types of safeguards. Of course, there have already been discussions that considered graded safeguards systems.

OBSERVATIONS AND CONCLUSIONS

In this section a brief summary of the results will be given and a brief remark on the implications of these findings put forward.

The basic premise of this work was that the study of implementing nuclear safeguards systems could be characterized as a case study of regulatory politics. The findings demonstrate that there are differences of opinion between the AEC and the nuclear industry in regard to the strength (stringency) of the safeguards systems each preferred. It also was shown that a gradation of opinions existed rather than two polarized opinions. Reprocessing and fabrication personnel were most opposed to strong regulatory practices while reactor personnel were less opposed to strong regulation than were the reprocessors and fabricators. As expected, of the three groups the AEC sample preferred the strongest regulatory practices. However, while these disagreements were substantial there were component parts of the safeguards systems, such as transportation, where there was substantial agreement.

The aforementioned differences of opinion were shown to be related to differing perceptions of the safeguards problem. Specifically, the nuclear industry's main concern was that safeguards would interfere with their right to "run a business" and the AEC's prime concern was with its right to regulate.

In view of these observations, one major suggestion seems to be in order. The suggestion is simply that the parties involved continue to take into consideration the gravity of the problem, thereby realizing their joint responsibility to the public. In short, it would seem that, if the industry could focus more on the gravity of the problem than on "running a business" (a very special kind of business indeed), the public interest would be better served. On the other hand, if the AEC would concern itself less with preserving its position, a better solution would be reached. This does not imply that the industry is only concerned with "running a business" or that the AEC seeks only to maintain its position as regulator, but rather that efforts directed at a good safeguards system may well be aided if both parties continue to keep the ultimate objective in mind.

NOTES

1. Kenneth R. Hammond and P. J. R. Boyle, "Quasi-rationality, Quarrels and New Conceptions of Feedback," Bulletin of the British Psychological Society, 24(1971); Kenneth R. Hammond, "Computer Graphics as an Aid to Learning," Science, 172(1971), 903-8.

2. Ibid.

3. Louis Guttman, "A General Nonmetric Technique for Finding the Smallest Coordinate Space for a Configuration of Points," Psychometrika, 33(1968), 469-506; J. C. Lingoes, "An IBM -7090 Program for Guttman-Lingoes Smallest Space Analysis-I," Behavioral Science, 10(1965); J. C. Lingoes, "An IBM-7090 Program for Guttman-Lingoes Multidimensional Scalogram Analysis-II," Behavioral Science, 12(1967); J. C. Lingoes, "The Multivariate Analysis of Qualitative Data," Multivariant Behavioral Research, 3(1968), 61-94; J. C. Lingoes, "Some Boundary Conditions for a Monotone Analysis of Symmetric Matrices," Psychometrika, 37(1972), in press.

After pointing out that David Brady's findings implied the existence of extremes—one being the AEC and the other being the nuclear industry—concerning the safeguards question, Theodore Taylor (International Research and Technology) asked Brady whether or not he had given any thought to a third category, namely, the general public, including its representatives in Congress and in the executive branch outside the AEC. Taylor implied that individuals in this category might hold an even more extreme view of how detailed the safeguards system should be.

Brady replied that, while he had interviewed individuals in consulting firms and in academia as well as members of the Joint Committee on Atomic Energy, he had not presented findings resulting from these interviews because he had chosen to emphasize the extremes on the safeguards continuum. He also pointed out that the findings from individuals in consulting firms and in academia as well as from members of the Joint Committee on Atomic Energy would suggest that a middle ground on the safeguards question does exist.

Taylor replied that his concern was that the general public would take a more extreme view than the AEC on the safeguards question. He pointed out that comments from the general public suggested that it was quite upset concerning, for example, the methods of physical security now applied to nuclear materials.

Brady stated that he had no random sample of the general public upon which to base a conclusion but suggested that, if the general public responds to the safeguards issue as it does to most policy issues, the conclusion would be that it is relatively uninformed concerning the problem. He also emphasized that one of the shortcomings of safeguards attitude research concerns the lack of knowledge of the opinions of the general public.

Frank Morgan (United Kingdom Atomic Energy Authority) pointed out that the cardinal requirements of such surveys were (1) that the questions asked should be mutually exclusive and (2) that they should cover the range of possibilities. These had not been met. Further, is it desirable to determine general attitudes from the survey instruments rather than obtaining answers on details?

Brady pointed out that, in his opinion, the five hypothetical safeguards systems included in the questionnaire allowed for the elicitation

of the respondents' attitudes concerning general policies while the
questions relating to specific details allowed the respondents to reply
to the more or less technical aspects of safeguards, all of which were
incorporated into each of the five hypothetical systems, albeit in terms
of differing degrees of stringency. Brady emphasized that, even though
the questionnaire utilized to collect the data was a good one by social
science standards, it was up to those involved in day-to-day decision-
making concerning the safeguards question to decide the extent of the
utility of the data analysis resulting from it.

Richard Butler (Australian Mission to the United Nations) stated
that he was concerned over the extent to which the statistical differences
between the various perceptions identified are likely to have any bearing
at all on the sort of negotiation that must take place between a regulatory authority and a regulated concern. Brady responded, "all that was
meant by statistically significant differences is that the differences
were numerically such that they did not occur by chance. The effect
of these differences on negotiations could not be exactly determined
because the power quotients for the two groups were not available."

5

SETTING NEW STANDARDS
FOR SAFEGUARDING
THE PEACEFUL ATOM

C. D. W. Thornton

Safeguards was born by the application of advanced science and technology to war. Peacetime safeguards could be characterized as a floundering odyssey while government and industry, with the public virtually absent, sought correct objectives, size, role, and importance for safeguards.

Preservation and maintenance of safeguards must somehow be developed within the competitive climate of the business world. Near term profits, which provide widespread benefits in our capitalistic system, must be realized as other necessary national objectives are concurrently attained by business.

Unfortunately, in the economist's terms, safeguards may be an externality whose costs should be internalized, if any particular business or other activity is to fairly and currently pay for all of its costs and the impacts created through its operations.

Like other environmental impacting activities, safeguards failures by industry and government may yield both incipient and deferred consequences. In addition, protection is necessary against potentially more catastrophic results. Other activities where low level risks and hazards to the public occur also are searching for mechanisms to optimize or minimize them equitably in relation to the benefits that will be produced from the activity.

Society generally has played only a very peripheral role in safeguards. Meanwhile, the activities and the inherent low level risks have grown during the course of postwar weapons programs. They are now spurting as nuclear power grows.

Fortunately, the general framework for providing safeguards was laid down by prudent legislators, beginning with the first and subsequent enactments of the Atomic Energy Act.

For many years large governmental nuclear activities were carried on under the compulsion of producing and maintaining a nuclear arsenal. Safeguards compromises were necessarily made in plant designs, control systems, and measurements. These still appear justified in the interest of national security since we were buying the telescoping of weapon schedules, always against future possible war dates. Fortunately, our nuclear prowess has maintained the peace.

But the most intensive programs of personnel investigations, polygraph examinations, perimeter physical protection systems of guards and continuous patrolling, and the death penalty threat were imposed. These may have prevented the clandestine diversion of significant quantities of weapon material to undisclosed nuclear stockpiles that could be in existence somewhere. The absence, to date, of international blackmail threats from apparent nuclear have-nots may indicate that we were fortunate in not actually losing dangerous quantities of materials from our largely unmeasured operations.

But there is a serious aftermath of our great wartime and postwar nuclear materials manufacturing successes, which produced today's escalated nuclear weapon stalemate. Both the facilities and a large output-oriented corps of engineers and plant designers resulted. They had little or no experience in peaceful requirements, which should include designing facilities for appropriate safeguards. Such designers, skilled in attaining weapon objectives but novices in safeguards designs, teamed up with businessmen newly interested peaceful uses of nuclear energy to design and operate our new peaceful power complex. This new complex will have flows dwarfing even those of our earlier inherently dangerous weapons operations.

Unfortunately, our newer plants have many of the characteristics of the older ones because so little safeguards innovation has occurred. The development efforts that had been undertaken were aimed largely at improving the measurements technology. The more crucial system problems stemming from poor plant design remained unrecognized and unsolved. This perpetuation of postwar emergency plant designs and the new key positions held by traditionally oriented operators is an unfortunate characteristic of our present peaceful nuclear business. Indeed, it might have been better if we had found younger and less experienced designers and given them responsibility of designing safeguardable facilities of low holdup and more frequently inventoriable types.

Society could require and pay for minimization or reduction of all risks if it can clearly understand the problems. Thus, our country undertakes large defense expenditures to minimize the risk of war. But, just as preparation for an unrealized war requires large expenditures on a hypothesis, so safeguards expenditures might have to be based on hypotheses.

There are today vested and committed groups who must initially pay any incremental costs for safeguards. As parties to the arguments involving the degree of safeguarding required, they necessarily state the problem in terms of their particular prejudices and insights.

Because correct and consoling language has been set down in the Atomic Energy Act, in writing incidental to the NPT, and in the public pronouncements incidental to the IAEA, society appears to have made the assumption that safeguarding special nuclear materials is in good hands and needs little of society's attention. Also, there has been a great deal written concerning how results from dramatic research can be applied to markedly improve controls and the closing of material balances. This has led to further possibly invalid public assumptions concerning the exact status of safeguarding and the current ability of the industry to cope with the problems of tightly and frequently closing its operating material balances.

In the 1940s even mention of the word uranium by the "uncleared" was suspect. Today, hundreds of thousands of tons of uranium later, no great safeguards significance is attached to relatively large quantities of normal uranium. Yet a quantity of only 2,000 kilograms contains enough uranium-235, even with poor separations processes, to make an atomic weapon. But limited separations capacity and the attractiveness of plutonium as an illicit weapons material makes it a more preexemptive target.

The economics of separating uranium isotopes cause the U.S. power program to be largely based on uranium of about 3 percent U-235 content. It has about ten times the cost per kilogram of normal uranium. About half of the separative work necessary to take normal uranium to weapon level U-235 has already been done on the material, at 3 percent concentrations, so it is far more than ten times as dangerous as normal uranium. However, to make atomic weapons from such material requires further enrichment at considerable cost. Because isotopic enrichment facilities are not yet common around the world, the potential danger associated with the conversion of three percent uranium to weapon material for illicit use is deferred.

The AEC's Division of Nuclear Materials Safeguards announced an interim standard limit of error for MUF of 0.5 percent of through-put for new license applicants for low enriched facilities. By 1980 there will be 300,000 kilograms of U-235 available to the nuclear industry. That material could still largely be as low enriched uranium fuel. If it were recycled only once in two years, through the fuel fabrication plants operating within the 0.5 percent standard, a loss of about 750 kilograms of contained uranium-235 could be camouflaged each year. Also, other parts of the fuel cycle would each have their own share of system insensitivity. They could similarly mask potential losses, which would be added to the 750 kilograms noted above.

Our research indicates that measurements through the cycles could be made much better than this sensitivity indicates. MUF could be more promptly and precisely evaluated if plants closed balances more frequently. Accountability would become the diagnostic tool it should be to localize and solve problems.

But such systems improvements cannot be made at zero cost. Safeguarding costs, which are presently very low because managements have set them there, will not be cheap in existing plants. Major improvements in system designs and some retrofitting may be needed. Nor will the improved safeguarding generate much profit, in terms of recoverable material, when the processes are already well optimized to the existing market prices, even for newly designed plants.

But to guard and verify materials and tightly close balances is a national security and safety matter. Intensity and cost levels should not be set only by what the current market will bear and certainly not on a short term profit motivational basis. Safeguards should not be an ad hoc activity in which we indulge as long as it costs little.

The licensing authority of government usually guarantees the public against public risks and hazards that are discernible and can be evaluated. But there is a difference between licensing an aircraft for safety when the plane will only carry a limited number of people and licensing a nuclear pipeline facility. Each nuclear facility has immediate low level potential incipient impacts which, fortunately, are steadily being reduced. In addition, it may have another increment of deferred or close-up cumulative risk arising as materials

unaccounted for are encountered in the pipeline plants to support the
facilities. Such threats from MUF do not vanish even when facilities
are closed down; they continue to mount as the industry grows. So
any government nuclear licensing authority is licensing both an escalating and a nondisappearing risk.

We are now designing nuclear reactors to standards, and at
substantial incremental costs, to keep major accidents below the one
in a million probability. Society will pay an out-of-pocket cost for
each reactor to avoid a very low probability of a nuclear incident
having destructive consequences. At the same time, we have not yet
been able to get standards we can afford to minimize escalating risks
from nuclear MUF in reactor pipeline plants. One illicitly fabricated
and used atomic bomb would be far more disastrous than a runaway
reactor. Certainly the probability of one or more illicit bombs or of
blackmail material dispersal threats must be relatable directly to the
MUF from all facilities.

No sensible analyst would assume that each weapon quantity of
material diverted—which may need further enrichment, further conversion, and some weapon fabrication expertise—will become a lethal
weapon. No prudent man can assume that each weapon quantity unaccounted for in a plant is a priori diverted to some potential illicit
use. Neither should one assume that, because one material is an
easier route to weapons, it is the one on which to concentrate all safeguards resources. The latter particularly should not be done if the
material flows and accessibility ratios between the material requiring
the most work and the most pristine weapons material is over 1,000
to 1, as is presently the case.

If we are to make progress in reducing the risk contribution
per new nuclear plant licensed, we must require considerably better
safeguards performance than we have seen for existing plants. Mankind's continuing security requires that, since the overall risk is
directly relatable to some fraction of the cumulative quantities of
nuclear materials that are unaccounted for, we decrease the rate of
escalation, if possible, each time we add an increment of new plant
to our peaceful nuclear complex. Perpetuation of current performance
would require admission that many times the single bomb quantities
of material could be outside the purview and sensitivity of our control
systems in the near future.

The combinations of capital and operating costs that are necessary to yield forecastable and concrete improvements in the degree of
control in all facilities are clearly calculable costs. For new facilities,

these real costs can be related to the forecast limits of error. The present guideline letters from the Division of Nuclear Materials Safeguards request a facility calibration during which the actual limit of error for the materials unaccounted for will be determined and compared to the forecast limits of error based upon the earlier submitted materials "proforma" which reflected the efficacy of the facility design.

It is the sense of our times to require industry to show costs that are incurred in order to optimize or minimize particular risks or impacts. Clearly, cumulative MUF in a complex of peaceful atomic plants represents a potential risk to society. The quantities that become significant risks, per unit of time, differ depending upon such factors as the following: how much material is necessary to fabricate a weapon; the degree and nature of further processing required to increase the damage potential of the material; the accessibility of the material in the various unit processes, plants, transportation links, and storage areas; and the value of the particular material in ultimate damage potential as related to other available materials that will provide equivalent damage potential.

For plutonium, the materials protection and containment safeguards aspects should be intensified because quantities of this material that are well below weapon significance levels pose a major toxicological risk to society. Fortunately, plutonium is a better signal emitter than uranium. Much promise exists for a suitable and comprehensive array of electronic portal monitors, vehicular and package inspection devices, and sensitive instruments for exercising surveillance over every recognizable diversion pathway. In addition, tight closing of material balances is needed to indicate that cumulative weapon quantities are not being diverted and that the material protection matrix is apparently working.

With regard to plutonium, we have a little time to permit innovative design improvements for unit process equipments, so segmented containment of plants can be provided. Such segmented containment of unit processes would permit the use of automated storage vaults to contain in-process lots of buffer inventory material in sealed containers. These could be automatically selected, presented, and rapidly verified by automated weighing with the contents validated automatically, using nondestructive instrumentation. Management auditing could be virtually continuous and unannounced.

It is unfortunate that historical and current performance provides too poor a data base for safeguards standards. Both AEC and

industrial managements long failed to take sufficiently bold and innovative steps to improve safeguards performance. Until the last three
years virtually the only impetus to improve process yields and reduce
MUF has been the economical duress. I have repeatedly emphasized
that the nuclear business can afford losses and immobilizations
considerably in excess of necessary safeguards limits. Because of
this, system studies of historical yields and the MUF in existing
facilities merely confirm that such facilities should not be perpetuated
if we are to kept the cumulative MUF suitably low.

There are obvious limitations in setting numerical standards
related to throughputs for particular classes of facilities. If such
limits are truly related to ultimate levels of risk, they may not be
attainable in present facilities with their poor materials handling,
process, and measurements designs. Even though cogent arguments
can be put forward defending such proposed standards, a large body of
the industry, already frozen into a pricing structure, will object
because costly backfitting would be involved.

However, in new facilities the basic costs for large increments
of safeguards improvement are small. The regulator could implement
dynamically adjustable standards that would require improved performance in newer facilities while permitting the upgrading of existing
facilities in due course.

But concerning numerical standards there is another body of opinion that objects to specifying an acceptable quantity level for MUF.
They feel that such a level inherently permits the specified or acceptable amount to be diverted without concern on the part of the operator.
This argument is particularly forceful in the case of plutonium where
gram quantities of material are inimical to the public health and
safety and diversion of many gram quantities will mount to kilogram
quantities, which are then inimical to the national security.

Since both groups of people would argue against numerical
quantitative standards for different reasons, the proposer of such
standards is impeded.

As the regulatory agency, we have continued to explore a variety
of standards, all related to the comprehensive safeguards system.
There is a differing degree of obtrusiveness and detail inherent in
each level of standards that we have studied. An early obvious set
of standards appeared to be facilities design guidelines. When it
became apparent that precise and enforceable design standards would
require an array of government experts, equivalent in competence to

those of industry, to evaluate proposed designs, it was clear that it was necessary to devise some criteria better reflecting the efficacy of the operator's proposed design.

We therefore proposed the materials "proforma" concept which requires forecasting the materiality aspects of a proposed design for an operating campaign. This has become an evaluation document incident to new license applications. The "proforma" had the elegance of not requiring a forecast of expected MUF for the proposed facility. Rather, it required a calculation of the cumulative limits of error by component. These included sampling, weighing, chemical, and isotopic analyses incident to individual lots or batches. The interim limit of error standards for MUF at low enriched facilities of 0.5 percent of throughput apparently have been met by talented designers who have indicated that more frequent inventories also can be taken.

When the limit of error rationale is combined with short operating campaigns, it provides management with various options for efficient optimization. Suitable operating breakdowns into material balance areas yields such insights as the following: where better lot homogenization might permit easier sampling and more precise measurements so that limits of error would be small; whether inventories should be reduced or increased depending upon how well they were measured; whether the main streams in a plant should be very precisely and accurately measured so that larger imprecisions might be accepted in the waste streams so long as they were a small fraction of the flows.

Statisticians have been increasingly employed by management. They can assess and assure control of MUF risks by focusing their attention on material balance accounting problems. Recently, new plant designers have used their statisticians to prediagnose alternative plant designs so that new safeguards optimums can be found, concurrent with high yield processes. Using statisticians to arrive at design optima is far superior to using them in the post mortem diagnoses of later anomalies involving MUF from poorly designed facilities.

I appeal again for the industry to take steps beyond what it deems necessary with regard to specific regulatory requirements. The industrialists must evaluate the sufficiency of their systems. Progress has been made in discerning the magnitude of the measurement "noise" being encountered in various processing stages. Some have accumulated this into the limit of error for their facility. Considerable accomplishment is evident in improving the correctness of some of the material stream flows. But we still do not have the sampling

intensity nor the composite measures of all of the flows necessary
to assure the completeness of the data.

Material balance closings must be far more frequent, at least
by campaigns within segregated Materials Balance Areas (MBA).
Figure 5 is entitled "Cost Effective Safeguards as an Interacting
System." Such a system could involve standards for every principal
parameter, and I have spoken already concerning many of these
areas.

Physical protection still provides a major opportunity for the
industry. The nuclear plants can add, at relatively low cost, those
monitors and devices that produce large gains in material and facilities
protection and that can be adversary tested. Without discussing these
in great detail, I should state that, whatever level of safeguarding is
ultimately required on the basis of gradations of risk, we are assuming
that a much higher level of material protection will be required as a
prerequisite to the rest of the safeguards system.

The section of Figure 5 entitled "physical protection" indicates
the relationship between physical protection and the prevention of
diversion. The section entitled "design improvements" emphasizes
that design improvements can minimize losses and would be much
facilitated by the frequent closing of balances. The section entitled
"process improvements" indicates several parameters that, if designed
into newer facilities, will minimize retrofitting. The section entitled
"promptness" indicates the importance of frequent inventories, rapid
analyses, and the use of automatic data processing in facilitating
effective safeguarding. The section entitled "better measurements"
indicates some of the parameters to obtain better measurements so
that accuracy will be assured. The section of Figure 5 entitled
"making measurements" indicates how measurements, combined with
more material balance areas, can be crucial to improving precision.
Finally, the section entitled "statistics" shows some of the sources
of data that, when appropriately evaluated and statistically analyzed,
provide the confidence we need in our safeguards systems.

Figure 6, "Better Measurements," indicates how improvement
in particular areas improves the quality of measurements. Figure
7, "Promptness," shows how the ability for precise remedial action
is greatly improved as various parameters are put on a more timely
basis. Figure 8, "Statistics," indicates how the risk devolving from
uncertainty can be reduced by improving a number of areas following
appropriate diagnostic use of statistics.

FIGURE 5

Cost-Effective Safeguards Is an Interacting System

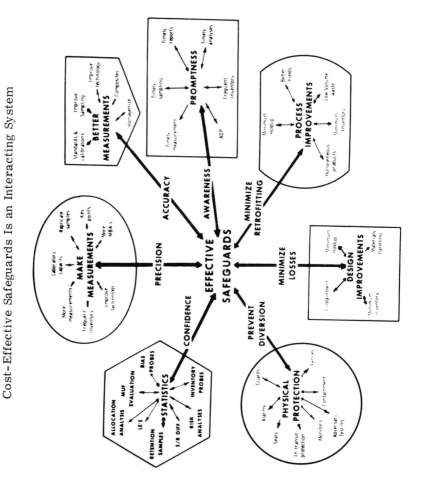

78

FIGURE 6

Better Measurements

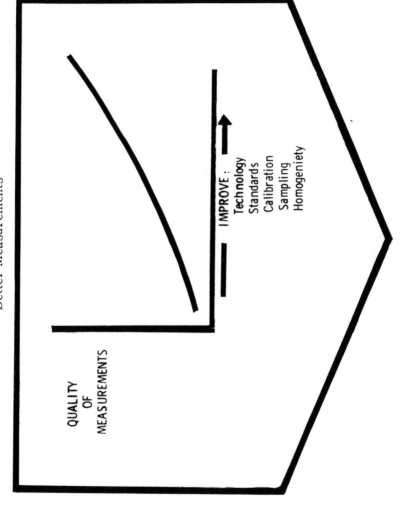

QUALITY
OF
MEASUREMENTS

IMPROVE :
Technology
Standards
Calibration
Sampling
Homogeniety

FIGURE 7

Promptness

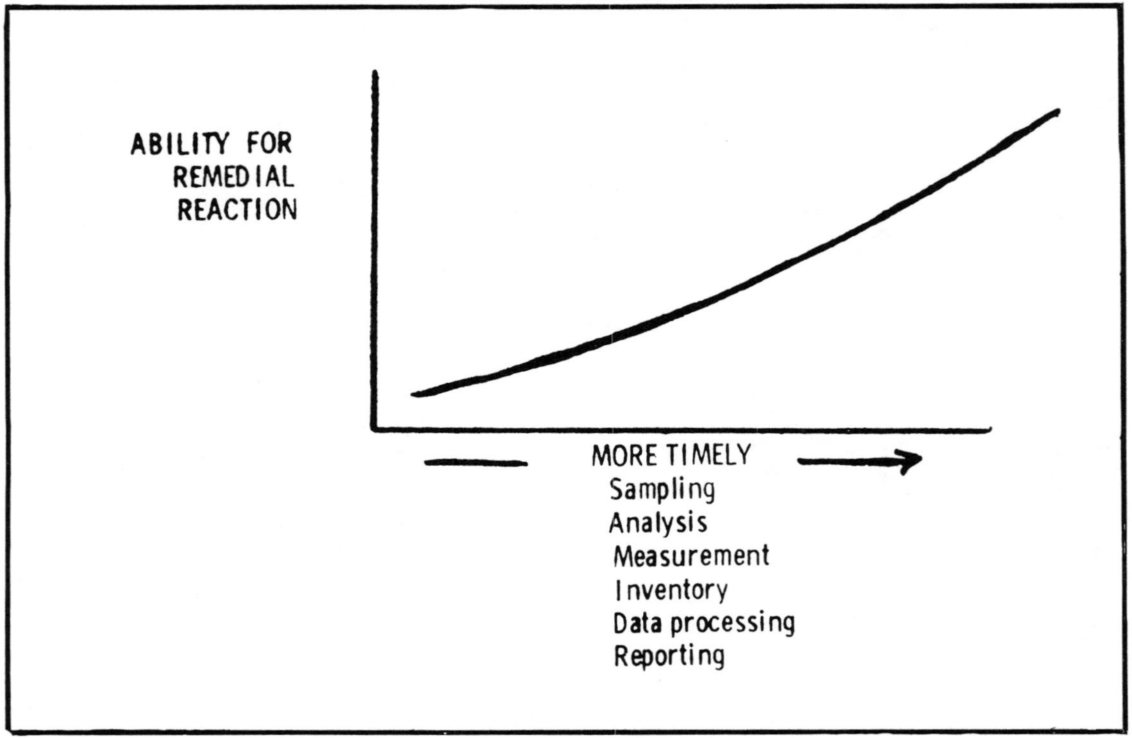

ABILITY FOR REMEDIAL REACTION

MORE TIMELY

Sampling
Analysis
Measurement
Inventory
Data processing
Reporting

FIGURE 8

Statistics

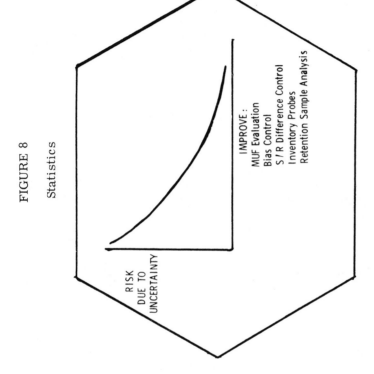

RISK
DUE TO
UNCERTAINTY

IMPROVE:
MUF Evaluation
Bias Control
S / R Difference Control
Inventory Probes
Retention Sample Analysis

Is the safeguards enemy a strawman or a paper tiger that should be demolished and discredited because we are unwilling to pay the insurance premium costs to close our balances better and more frequently? We are now producing and circulating the most dangerous commodities we have ever handled at large volumes that shortly will become extremely large volumes.

What is the appropriate level of discipline that we should impose on ourselves as our brothers' keepers entrusted with minimizing their risks? Was all the atomic weapon insurance we have bought during the past 25 years wasted because since Japan we have never used a weapon to guard our nation? We can spend some of our current riches to minimize the growth of diversion risks to mankind. If we are successful, we may prevent even a small fraction of the large cumulative MUF that can now be forecast from being used as actual threats by outlaws to mankind. If we never have such incidents and are thus successful, is our money wasted?

Obviously, we should not expend irrational costs to bring safeguards risk levels down to much below other risks society may be taking, as it builds new plants and devices of every type to provide desired services. We should only incur that cost level necessary to contain potential impacts at consistent levels.

What industry and government must strive for and persons working in regulation must finally impose are safeguards standards that will be rational, equitable, and economical. Then a great, viable, safe, and contributary industry can be created and grow.

■ DISCUSSION

Craig Hosmer (U. S. House of Representatives, Joint Committee on Atomic Energy) inquired whether the risk of diversion of nuclear materials is expected to be linearly related to the amount of these materials available. In the opinion of C. D. W. Thornton, the risk is nonlinearly related to the amount. The risk escalation rate ultimately decreases to zero at the margin, but the cumulative threat never decreases. In any event, a common weighting factor that needs to be included in risk of diversion involves such aspects as the statistics of crime.

Early in nuclear operations, the risk of diversion from a particular facility is considered. One observes that risk initially increases at an escalating rate with the amount of material in the facility because many more opportunities for diversion are camouflaged in control imprecisions. The concern at this operations level is with diversion of quantities to fabricate the first illicit weapons.

After nuclear operations become large, the risk levels follow ordinary market theory as applied to possible forecasts of nuclear weapons utility. Obviously, the first weapon is worth very much to a diverter, but the hundredth or thousandth is worth progressively less. Thus, Thornton felt that the rate of risk escalation approaches zero with increasing amounts of worldwide material subject to possible diversion after longer operations. Also, the rate of risk escalation is less important if there has been a cumulative history of material unaccounted for that presents an ever-present and irrevocable risk that can only be kept minimal by requiring stringent material balance closings of continuing nuclear operations.

The risk element for low-enrichment uranium was a topic raised by Manuel Kanter (Argonnne National Laboratory). In terms of vulnerability, Thornton viewed low-enrichment uranium as a more attractive target now than plutonium, although plutonium is admittedly a more attractive target in terms of its immediate utility in weapons fabrication. The present larger risk originates from the fact that 2,000 times more low-enrichment uranium than plutonium is flowing in fuel cycles. Indeed, shortly a number of plants will be so immense that they will have one million kilogram flow quantities of low-enrichment uranium. Then the material unaccounted for could reach tonnage quantities.

Further enrichment of diverted materials also was considered by Thornton. At this starting enrichment, capital costs are much lower for plants needed to raise the enrichment to weapons levels. Furthermore, as enrichment technology, particularly of modern design, is dispersed in the world, the possibility of clandestine enrichment increases rapidly. Thus, overall the low risk inherent in low-enrichment material converts to an appreciable risk situation in view of these other factors.

6

U.S. NATIONAL SAFEGUARDS SYSTEM: AN INDUSTRIAL VIEW

A. E. Schubert

As the outgoing Chairman of the Nuclear Material Safeguards Committee for the Atomic Industrial Forum of the United States, the following will be a distillation of the views of the various industrial representatives in the Forum Safeguards Committee rather than a summary of the thinking of General Electric, the firm with which I am professionally connected. I begin by emphasizing that industry fully understands the importance of nuclear materials safeguards. There is no hesitancy in supporting the objectives: namely, to limit the possibility of unlawful diversion of strategic quantities of special nuclear material from peaceful uses to nuclear weapons or other nuclear explosive devices and to promptly detect any such diversion should it occur. There is also meaningful industrial support of the offer originally made by President Lyndon B. Johnson, and reaffirmed by President Richard Nixon, to place all civilian and government nuclear facilities in the United States, excluding only those with national security significance, under the international safeguards system. We have made it known to the AEC that the Forum Safeguards Committee, as representatives of the nuclear industry, is ready and willing to cooperate with the government in its effort to develop a suitable system of materials safeguards.

Specifically on this point, we made a formal offer in August 1971 to join with the regulatory arm of the AEC in establishing a joint working group that could be charged with establishing mutually acceptable objectives for the U.S. safeguards system. On request, we are also prepared to work with the AEC on the plans for implementation of IAEA safeguards in U.S. facilities that will be subject to them.

GENERAL CHARACTERISTICS
OF THE SYSTEM

Let us now turn to the major subject of this chapter: the national safeguarding system. We will first consider what some of the general characteristics of that system should be. These observations will be followed by a more detailed coverage related to nuclear fuel fabrication plants handling low-enriched uranium, power reactors, reprocessing plants, and the transportation link. With the maturing of the nuclear industry, experience has been rapidly gained in the safeguarding of special nuclear material. Most of this experience has been associated with handling low-enriched uranium in nuclear fuel factories, but the system in its entirety is beginning to take a more discernible form. From this experience, we are beginning to identify what the characteristics of the system should be. First, it should keep its prime objective in view. That objective, as stated before, is to protect against the diversion of nuclear materials for use in nuclear weapons or other nuclear explosive devices. Often in day-to-day operations we find ourselves intruding in the domain of the health physicist and his rightful concern for the well-being of people and the quality control engineer and his professional concern for the quality of the product. We must restrain ourselves from expanding from safeguards into these interesting areas in order to be sure that we are in fact concentrating on our assigned task, i.e., safeguarding.

Much has been said and written in the last several years concerning the concept of graded safeguards. As a philosophy, we believe that the national system should proportion the expenditure of its efforts on a given segment of the fuel cycle in relation to the diversionary risk in that segment. The translation of this philosophy to a specific action plan turns out to be difficult to accomplish. What should be done about source material? How tightly should low-enriched uranium fuel plants be controlled? To what degree should the safeguarding of the transportation link be strengthened? How do we conclusively safeguard the output of reprocessing plants? These are difficult questions with no easy answers. What is needed here is the definition of a set of objectives for the national safeguarding system, particularized for the various segments of the fuel cycle. Through the Atomic Industrial Forum and other associations, industry continues to work with the AEC to develop a mechanism whereby these objectives might be defined. In the meantime, there is a certain uneasiness in the nuclear industry because it becomes difficult to measure the potential impact, financial and otherwise, on the various contributors to the industry due to the lack of resolution in the safeguards picture.

Special nuclear materials are valued assets. Industry over the years has developed techniques and procedures for the control of such assets. Much of the development of measurement systems and the handling of the resulting copious data has come about due to management's need for adequate materials controls. The processing of the data and its rapid reduction into useful forms to provide information for industrial management have resulted in innovative use of computerized equipment. This dexterity in measurement and processing of information has allowed, and will allow, industry in general to function with smaller supplies of special nuclear materials on hand. Physical protective means, both active in the form of guards or passive in the form of alarms and monitors, have long been part of industry's tools in protecting assets. Modern technological developments are strengthening these older techniques.

Industrial management learned long ago that independent auditing by professional, objective outside organizations is invaluable in reviewing the performance of any factory operation, including the materials control system. All of these techniques and procedures, starting with original measurements of the materials, working through the data processing and inventory control operation, and including the final audit of the control system, owe their major development impetus to the industrial concern about the control of assets. In an analagous manner, the same set of techniques and procedures are being utilized most effectively in safeguarding. It is probably true that in some segments of the fuel cycle the intensity of safeguarding called for by the diversionary risk of the material may well exceed the assets control effort dictated by the intrinsic value of the material. However, a realistic safeguards system will make maximum use of the economic incentive rather than attempt to stress the weakness of the economic incentive as a motivation for safeguarding.

If the concept of a definition of the safeguards objectives is combined with the economic incentives of plant management, the conclusion can be reached that an effective regulatory system would give industrial management the responsibility for conforming with performance standards in its plant. The AEC regulatory system then would be free to spend a larger amount of its time improving the balance of the total safeguards system in such areas as the following:

1. A genuine concern to both industry and government is the exposure of special nuclear materials to the risk of diversion during the transportation from one segment of the fuel cycle to another.

2. Research and development programs proceeding at a promising pace continue to need attention.

3. Resolution with the IAEA of detailed safeguards procedures responsive to the Non-Proliferation Treaty certainly will take some time.

Seeing to it that safeguarding on a national scale is applied in an equitable fashion to the various plants in the fuel cycle bears examination. All of these broad systematic interfaces and concerns could, and in our opinion should, occupy the energies of the regulatory agencies as the industry itself concentrates more on the policing in the plants in the fuel cycle according to the objectives as established by the regulatory agency.

LOW-ENRICHED URANIUM
FUEL FABRICATION PLANTS

Turning now to a discussion of some of the specific elements of the fuel cycle, let us first direct our attention to the low-enriched uranium fuel fabrication plants. As stated earlier, some form of a graded safeguards system is desirable. On the other hand, it has not been easy to develop a set of criteria for a graded system, and indeed no highly detailed criteria have yet evolved. However, in any scheme industry finds it difficult to ascribe a serious diversionary risk to the low-enriched uranium fuel fabrication plants. It seems highly improbable that a political entity sufficiently sophisticated to develop enrichment and device fabrication capabilities would at the same time be naive enough to base the feed stock for that plant on an ability to steal from a U.S. low-enrichment fabrication plant. This is not to say that low-enriched plants should not be safeguarded but rather that the intensity of safeguarding should not be the intensity that the system intends to impress on plants of higher diversionary risk.

It is appropriate at this point to comment on some ideas concerning standards of performance that might be impressed on low-enriched uranium plants. As is well known, one philosophy suggests control of special nuclear materials to amounts less than a critical mass of that nuclear material. It is unlikely that this concept would be applicable to smaller plants, and the throughputs associated with the larger plants would require a sensitivity of control that is extremely expensive if not impossible. Rather, it appears more sensible to base the performance of the low-enriched uranium plants on a throughput standard such that the material unaccounted for over the accounting period would be some low and acceptable percentage of the throughput of the plant. Another approach might well be that chosen in the IAEA working groups where the amount of enriched material is stated in terms of effective kilograms. In this scheme, the intensity of regulation is inversely related to the degree of enrichment of the uranium. To summarize with regard to low-enriched uranium plants, we encourage a national safeguarding system that has as its objective of plant performance an acceptable percentage of throughput or some equally acceptable alternative, related to enrichment level and with independent verification of performance.

NUCLEAR POWER PLANTS

A few comments about reactor power plants and the attitudes of their owners, the utilities, are necessary. As the nuclear industry has matured, two points are coming more to the fore with each passing month.

First, because the utilities generally own the uranium fuel they are interested in a good materials control and quality assurance system throughout the fuel cycle for the protection of their assets. Second, the growing dependence of the electrical utility industry, and ultimately the general population on nuclear power generation means that any delays in the scheduled delivery of fuel from nuclear fuel suppliers, including delays that might originate from an unreasonably stringent safeguards program at the fuel plant, will be unacceptable if they interfere with the orderly production of electric power.

As stated earlier, the intrinsic value of the fuel material will aid immeasurably in the safeguarding of that material. A direct manifestation of this fact has been the employment by the electric utility industry of a materials auditing capability that is being implemented at all stages of the fuel cycle from source material through the reprocessing of the fuel and the reclaiming of the valuable nuclear material in the spent fuel. The electric utility does not want to lose its assets either. This system of checks and balances on the nuclear industry is beginning to come into play in a stronger and stronger fashion. Certainly, a perceptive safeguarding system will take advantage of this natural tendency.

The actual safeguarding of the nuclear material in reactor power plants does not seem to present any undue difficulty. Indexed

fuel bundles make piece counting an accurate control method. Once
the fuel is irradiated, it is self-protected by the resulting high radiation
fields. It is correct to stress that each delay in the fuel cycle either
at the fabrication plant or at the input end of the reactor power plants
due to safeguarding steps will cause, at the very least, uncertainty
in reliable electric power generation. The nuclear industry can get
along without any further delays or uncertainties coming from the
regulatory side.

FUEL REPROCESSING PLANTS

Fuel reprocessing plants offer a unique set of challenges, not
only to safeguarders but also to their operators and their customers,
because the amounts of recovered uranium and plutonium from these
plants determine the economics of the fuel cycle. At the output point
of the reprocessing plants the customer, usually the owner of the fuel
being reprocessed, gets the information upon which he bases his
conclusions about many events that have already occurred, some of
them years previously, as original enrichment, burn-up, and plutonium
content. His interests, and that of the other participants in the fuel
cycle, in a first-class nuclear material control system in those reprocessing plants is of the highest. Here is another case where the
natural driving forces of economics and good management accountability are completely consistent with the objectives of a reasonable
material safeguards program.

The quantity of the input material to the plant is particularly
difficult to determine because of the high activities associated with
it and the need for working behind shielding walls. This leads to a
lack of certainty about the input material which is not helped by the
accompanying difficulty in taking inventory throughout the process
flow. The front end of the reprocessing plant, then, presents a real
opportunity for research and development of safeguarding devices.
One major output of the reprocessing plant, the plutonium, is certainly
one of the most sensitive materials from the standpoint of risk of
diversion for explosive devices. Because of this fact, exceptional
precautions are being taken with plants coming on line to assure that
the diversion potential of the end product plutonium is minimized.

It might be appropriate at this point to consider a possible performance plan for reprocessing plants. Here, rather than a percentage throughout, an MUF standard based on a few critical masses of
plutonium might be established. If the MUF is larger than this relatively small amount, suitable techniques could be brought to bear
to reduce it to a more acceptable amount.

TRANSPORTATION

Any discussion of a national system of safeguards would be less than complete without the inclusion of a few words concerning the transportation link. The nuclear industry is concerned that its transportation link will not be ready to properly safeguard the predicted large amounts of plutonium moving from one site to another in the fuel cycle. We do not have solutions as yet for this particular problem, but we expect to cooperate with the government to establish procedures for the transportation end of the business such that the public can rest assured that the significant nuclear materials being transported are covered by a protection system commensurate with their diversion potential.

To close this chapter in a positive tone, it can fairly be said that much progress has been made in the safeguarding of nuclear material on the national scene. We on the Atomic Industrial Forum Committee are certainly aware of the need for safeguards. We feel we have raised the level of awareness of the importance of this issue at all management levels including the top. This awareness in management is not due solely to our own efforts, however. The regulatory arm of the AEC has been diligent in expressing to nuclear industrial management its deep concerns associated with safeguarding. As a result, new techniques are beginning to be applied in the plant, new discipline is being exerted on the operational floors, and in general the sensitivity of the safeguard system on the domestic level is increasing.

I am confident we are evolving to a sensible, practical, useful safeguards system that will be consistent with all of our expectations for performance from the nuclear power industry.

Much of the discussion centered on difficulties in industrial operation as a result of safeguards needs. Possible delay in industrial procedures was one of these, with clarification of the industrial attitudes sought by Samuel Edlow (Edlow International). Commenting on this, A. E. Schubert pointed out that some delays can seriously affect the health and safety of the public as, for example, any lack of electrical power resulting from delays in refueling a nuclear power plant. These cannot be tolerated. To avoid these delays, regulations should be well under way and include necessary checks and balances. These regulations should have been thought through sufficiently so as not to cause abnormal and unnecessary delays.

The industrial outlook was sought by Frank Morgan (United Kingdom Atomic Energy Authority) as to where safeguards needs might impose the greatest costs on industrial processes. While acknowledging that industrial views vary, Schubert was most concerned about a possibly high frequency of inventory shutdowns which decrease the capacity of a production plant and thereby increase the capital costs per unit of output.

Herbert Scoville (Carnegie Endowment for International Peace) broached the feasibility of an incentive-type approach to this problem in which the inventory frequency would be lower for plants with higher quality of operation in regard to safeguards. In effect, this principle is being followed in some of the General Electric fuel fabrication plants, according to Schubert, but only for their own material accountability purposes. However, he acknowledged that their frequency of taking inventory for this purpose is considerably less than what is understood to be the goal of the Division of Nuclear Materials Safeguards (DNMS). Leaving fuel fabrication plants, Kenneth Osborn (Allied Chemical Corporation) cited the extremes of difficulty involved in plant inventories. A small batch plant that recovers the scrap it makes could be inventoried each shift, while the inventory difficulty for an AEC diffusion plant is the other extreme.

Industrial plants can be designed to accommodate safeguards needs; any added cost for this was one of industrial costs about which Morgan inquired. Although General Electric's experience is limited, Schubert felt that designing a plant for these safeguards provisions did not affect the construction cost appreciably. With each successive plant designed, the deficiencies in regard to safeguards are progressively reduced. The third possibility of added industrial costs for safeguards mentioned by Morgan, namely measurement costs, did not receive attention in this session of discussions.

Part of the discussion dwelt upon reprocessing plants and the difficulty of determining the fissile input in the spent fuel elements entering these plants. Inspector General Rudolph Rometsch (International Atomic Energy Agency) mentioned the method of isotopic ratio measurements as being useful in input analysis at a reprocessing plant. The need for input measurements was emphasized by Schubert in noting that the customers paying $5-9 a gram for the fissile output of the plant are likely to be as demanding as a regulatory agency about knowing with great precision what is entering the plant. Research and development opportunities are believed to be rich in this needed area of improved measurements.

Low-enriched uranium in unirradiated fuel elements was of some concern to Stephen Lawroski (Argonne National Laboratory). Uncertainties in MUF could mask the diversion of such fuel elements which could be irradiated and processed elsewhere for the production and separation of plutonium. However, Schubert cited a difficulty in this route that would be encountered at the reprocessing plant. Here the plant knows the plutonium amounts at least for payment purposes. Lawroski observed that industry has experienced occasionally large uncertainties in its estimates of plutonium in spent fuel elements. Schubert felt that in a new industry of this sort some problems are only now being managed. This is being enabled through the cooperation of the AEC. A particular incentive in this is the need of fuel managers at power reactors to know exactly the fuel rod contents both for reactor operation and for rearrangement of fuel rods.

Another aspect of the discussion centered on what the safeguards situation will be when plutonium recycle becomes prevalent. Theodore Taylor (International Research and Technology) was particularly concerned about the amount of plutonium that would then be available in the fabrication of fuel elements and their storage before use in a power reactor. He inquired whether the magnitude of the safeguards problem would not then be drastically changed. While agreeing that the fuel pool will then require more stringent control, Schubert did not feel that plutonium recycle would produce a discontinuity in the safeguards problem. In his opinion, the value to a potential diverter is reduced by the fact that the plutonium will be mixed at a low percentage with uranium oxide. Individual fuel pellets of plutonium would overheat if used, and so mixing of uranium and plutonium is required. Later, William Higinbotham (Brookhaven National Laboratory) expressed a reservation about any difficulty in separating plutonium from uranium fuel being a deterrent.

REMARKS OF W. A. HIGINBOTHAM

I shall begin with a technical comment. I do not agree with Schubert about the plutonium recycle. Although the fuel will be a mixture of 2 percent plutonium oxide with 98 percent uranium oxide, I have seen small facilities that could take the mixture apart rather rapidly. It is not nearly as safe as natural uranium, where you need an enormous plant to separate ^{235}U from ^{238}U. I do think plutonium recycle is going to pose a problem, not just at the end of the reprocessing plant but also at the fabrication facilities. At the reactor, safeguards are a problem of physical security: good vaults and guards. I do not think physical security at reactors is too hard.

The direction that I would hope we could take is to try to arrive at not just throwing out challenges but seeing if there is not some way that we can make some progress toward resolving our difficulties. I might remind you that there is a long history in this field. The time when the problem looked simple and when there was a very simple solution was in 1946 when Bernard Baruch proposed that we put all the dangerous activities under the United Nations international operations. We do not have that kind of a world anymore. We have an enormous number of nuclear weapons in five different countries, and we are developing an industry that is putting nuclear materials in greater abundance all around the rest of the world. Whether or not we believe in certain scenarios, the whole situation is frightening.

One thing I think that we should all bear in mind is that this is not just a question of diversion of materials. In fact, any measures

in terms of limiting the nuclear arms race among the major powers
depend on finding some solution to the problem of non-proliferation.
I do not think that there is going to be much in the way of strategic
arms control or limitation if it is easy for people to steal nuclear
materials and to make them into weapons anywhere. Conversely, I
think that unless there is progress made in limiting the arms race
between the major nuclear powers, there is little likelihood the NPT
and the IAEA will be successful in preventing further proliferation.

The other thing that bothers me, and has bothered me for the
past four years, is that I certainly feel that the AEC put off worrying
about the problem of nuclear materials safeguards until pretty late
in the game. It was not until Ralph Lumb and his panel finally made
strong recommendations (1967) that there began to be some real
action in the United States. We have had an awful lot to do in a short
time. I think part of the difficulties was that differences of opinion,
resulting from the fact that different people put emphases in different
places, existed. It is always easier to see how to fix the other guy's
bathtub than how to fix your own.

The time is running out; we must negotiate now with the IAEA
on how its inspection procedures will be overlayed with those of the
AEC and the operations of the U.S. industry and the contractors.

There is no question that the controls that apply to contractors
should be just as stringent and just as thorough as those applied to
private industry. If there is any lack of exchange of information, and
I know there is, then it is time to do something about it. So what I
would like to say is this: Okay, let's argue about these things, but
let's get on with it because we have to have something, you know,
starting fast, It may not be perfect. We all recognize it is going to
change in time and so are the problems; so let's get with it.

REMARKS OF K. R. OSBORN

I shall comment on just one facet of our national safeguard system.
This facet usually is considered to be out of bounds for a discussion
of this type. However, I believe the subject not only is pertinent but
at this point in time is the most pertinent of all to those of us who are
truly interested in improving our national safeguards. I refer to the
phrase Craig Hosmer has used: "separate but unequal treatment."
He used it in discussing the Non-Proliferation Treaty signers versus
the nonsigners. I am going to borrow Hosmer's phrase and apply it
to the application of national materials safeguards in terms of separate

but unequal treatment of the AEC's contractors and licensees. I
happen to fit into both of these categories.

I agree with C. D. W. Thornton that at that time, which was
several years ago, there was good reason to direct, shall we say, less
attention to safeguards than appears appropriate today. That good
reason had to do with military necessity. We applied two standards
in the reactor safety area as well. I also am impressed by the fact
that there are people from outside the United States who have this
same kind of a problem because their industrial and their military
operations are conducted in the same facilities.

I must avoid, for security reasons, revelation of any information
not already in the unclassified public record, but on the other hand I
will attempt to convey to you information of value. We want to consider
all the aspects of safeguards, potential for diversion, security methods,
and so forth. To be more specific, Delmar Crowson has stated that we
will soon be handling large quantities of recycled plutonium. I am
amazed! We have been doing that in this country for many years.
The AEC has been producing and recycling large quantities of plutonium
and highly enriched uranium for about 25 years. Why cannot the
benefits of this experience be made available to the licensees? As of
today, AEC rather than licensees essentially handles all plutonium.
Certainly light water reactors do not use highly enriched uranium for
the production of electric energy.

Schubert reaffirmed his proposal that the AEC and the industry
cooperate in formulating effective safeguards measures and regulations.
However, there are indications within AEC circles that Schubert's
proposal will be unacceptable because this might imply connivance
between the regulators and the regulated. I find this a little unfortunate
and a little strange. I am compelled to comment that at present this
is another most peculiar situation wherein the AEC exercises both
police power and law-making functions. The laws, or more properly
the regulations—sometimes called guidelines—are only very slowly
being evolved and re-evolved.

To turn to AEC practices and how they relate to our present and
proposed regulations affecting a licensee, the first that comes to mind
has to do with a personal experience several years ago when I first
learned about shipper-receiver differences. I was "taken" by this.
My company constructed a rather large facility in Metropolis, Illinois.
It bid competitively to convert government-owned material. It was
bidding not only against others in industry but also against the AEC
itself and AEC practices. We were led to believe that the total losses—

the gross losses—in the AEC's operations were one-half of one percent.
We were successful in obtaining that business, guaranteeing 99.5
percent recovery. Losses beyond that were to be out of our pocket.
Some time later, when the AEC's Weldon Springs plant ceased to be of
use to the AEC and was "put on the block," I visited that plant and
looked at the operating records. I found that the 99.5 percent figure
we had used in good faith a few years earlier did not include the
shipper-receiver differences which the AEC held in a separate "kitty."
That was my first experience that things were not quite the same within AEC operations as they are in the business world outside.

Because of general knowledge on the subject, I will not go into
detail about fairly recent discussions concerning sampling and analytical procedures in some of the AEC's facilities. There also exists the
question of in-process inventories and their difficulty of application
in many large continuously operated facilities. Not only would the
Metropolis UF_6 plant truly be inoperative under such a requirement,
but diffusion plants would also be inoperative. In the case of the
Barnwell reprocessing plant, I think in-process inventories would
reduce the throughput of that plant by 50 percent.

On the other hand, the following question has been raised within
an AEC operating area: How might we apply some of the proposed
methods of treating industry to our own operations? I do know that in
the case of the Idaho chemical plant such a study was made recently
and duly reported to the authorities. The penalty there was one year
outage time for retrofitting and $16 million.

I touched upon plutonium recycle above: not recycle through
reactors but recycle through the weapons complex. Perhaps this is a
delicate subject, so let me just ask a few question. I wonder whether
or not the AEC applied imputed values of the type we have heard about
in minimizing waste from such operations. I wonder if the AEC samples
and analyzes all materials in the plutonium area as it believes a
licensee should. I wonder how good the records are on the wastes that
have been generated and are being generated currently.

There is a public report in existence that indicates that at a single
location the AEC stores material containing plutonium exceeding, by my
calculation, the total plutonium production of more than a thousand-
megawatt power reactor running for a year.[1] From the descriptions
and the reports, it is not clear that any normal security measures
are employed in the storage of this material. In summary, I think
there should be some consistency between the measures that are
applied to the privately owned material and the measures that are
applied to the larger quantities of material owned by the AEC.

In the field of transportation, we have a situation that some of us on the industry side would say is intolerable to live with. I am speaking of the methods of transportation that have been employed in the past by the AEC. This subject has been discussed in considerable depth by Samuel Edlow as well as others before other forums.[2] I think the dollar value alone of this material is such that much more rigorous security measures are required.

I think industry is groping for ways of developing better security measures, and I have been giving a lot of consideration to reprocessing plants and the extraction of plutonium therefrom. I think this is the most critical part of the cycle, and I find it the most frustrating because neither from the AEC nor from outside have I really found answers that appear to be reasonable.

I have been perhaps a little critical of the AEC. Let me suggest two alternate, simple solutions to this question which is really a dichotomy at present. Obviously, one of them is to apply licensee regulations to the contractor-operated facilities. If this is too logical or too simple, the second is to have the contractors assume financial liability for losses. I know many would object to that, and needless to say that method could not be applied overnight without the AEC running the risk of running out of contractors.

REMARKS OF R. F. LUMB

Craig Hosmer, Delmar Crowson, and Rudolf Rometsch touched upon points dealing with physical security. It is clear that the charter of the IAEA places physical security in the hands of the nations as their responsibility. Obviously, the prime responsibility rests with the particular facility that has the materials, but there is indeed a need for some national action and I would like to point out a few areas where I believe action needs to be taken.

First, I believe there is a need for some formal coordination of all of the intelligence and enforcement agencies within a nation in order to develop some sort of a national action for the apprehension of materials diverted to unauthorized uses. Beyond that, similar coordination between nations is needed in order that it be possible to act internationally. The situation within the United States is such that it is extremely easy to move across the borders north and south. As a consequence, I believe that in the best interest of international relations we need this kind of international coordination and cooperation.

Another area that needs some attention is that of penalties and rewards. Currently, I cannot speak for other nations, but in the United States the penalty for diverting these materials—provided there is no intent to harm the United States—is about equivalent to the penalty for stealing an automobile. We also need some sort of a reward system to encourage the flow of information into our intelligence and enforcement agencies.

Going on to materials unaccounted for and limits of error about such materials, I believe Delmar Crowson commented that he was looking for a different word to put this into better perspective. I should caution him that we have gone through that once before. I do not think we need any better word; perhaps we do need better perspective.

In any event, it struck me that one of the discussions in industry and one of its real concerns is what the impact of the IAEA inspection program will be and what the United States will commit the industry to do. Some reference has been made to the fact that it might be on some sort of selective basis or perhaps even a round-robin basis. I would simply like to throw out the concept that perhaps we should leave the decision as to the inspection requirements to the IAEA and that its decision in this area probably would be based upon the limit of error associated with the materials unaccounted for experienced by the industry. If indeed those inspections are a burden on the industry, this might get at C. D. W. Thornton's hope that we could do something about improving the limit of error on material unaccounted for.

Finally, Schubert and Thornton have commented on the industry's capacity for protecting its assets. I think this economic incentive is indeed a real incentive although I have heard it derided many times. I would like to make a couple of comments about it. First of all, part of the problem is that indeed the fabricator and the reprocessor are not protecting their assets: the assets happen to be the utility's assets. Schubert has pointed out that utilities are beginning to be concerned about these assets and that they are moving in the direction of attempting to better protect these assets. I would propose to the utilities that they need to direct a good deal more attention to techniques for improving protection of their assets in the hands of fabricators and reprocessors. The first place to start is at the contract stage, i.e., to write contracts providing for the protection of those assets. I think this is something that has taken a bit of time for utilities to appreciate. I do see signs that they are appreciating it, and I think part of our problem today is that we are operating under contracts that were written a long time ago under circumstances of little experience, i.e., when the utilities had not had extensive experience in this area. I did want to introduce these thoughts, and I hope that some of them might be provocative.

NOTES

1. Special Report to the Governor's Task Force on Radioactive Waste Disposal at the National Reactor Testing Station. Prepared by the Idaho Operations Office of the Atomic Energy Commission for Governor Samuelson of Idaho, July 8, 1970.

2. S. Edlow, Proceedings of the AEC Symposium on Safeguards Research and Development, Los Alamos Scientific Laboratory Report WASH-1147, 1969, 29.

Attitudes shown by regulator and regulatee of licenses was of concern to <u>Samuel Edlow</u> (Edlow International). Although the survey research reported by David Brady specifies for both parties the areas of differences that can be useful in bargaining between them, Edlow was concerned that some regulators might be reluctant to bargain, even to the point of believing bargaining to have an air of danger.

This question was clarified by <u>William Higinbotham</u> (Brookhaven National Laboratory), who considered bargaining to be essential to the success of safeguards. Safeguards must be a cooperative effort in order to be successful. Specifically, he noted that all participants have the same objective of making diversions difficult but that, if diversion is accomplished, their objective is then timely detection. Bargaining is necessary in the sense of comparing different ways of achieving these objectives. Toward this goal, if industry feels the requests of the Division of Nuclear Materials Safeguards of the AEC are unreasonable, industry should counter with different methods for reaching the objectives.

The fact that bargaining is essential to effective regulation and that it does occur was confirmed by <u>Kenneth Osborn</u> (Allied Chemical Corporation). He expressed the caution that effective bargaining requires the regulator to fully understand the facility, the process, and the operation being considered. He felt that perhaps progress has not yet been made to this point. In general, every opportunity should be made available so that both regulator and regulatee understand the problems and the objectives.

In response to an assessment request from <u>C. D. W. Thornton</u> (Director, Division of Nuclear Materials Safeguards, AEC), the ease of detecting plutonium compared to ^{235}U was noted by Higinbotham. The higher-energy and increased number of gamma rays and the neutrons from spontaneous fission make its detection easier but also make plutonium the greater health hazard. Therefore, he felt that plutonium detection by area monitors, door monitors, and pollution monitors is easy. In contrast, detection of low-enrichment uranium in large use is more difficult as a result of negligible neutron emission and a low-penetration 185-keV gamma ray. However, Higinbotham was surprised that only after they were demonstrated in such plants by the AEC did these instruments come into use in industry. He thought quality control experts in the plants would have taken the

initiative of introducing those instruments, for which construction
knowledge is widespread.

The question of whether severe criminal penalty would be a
deterrence to nuclear materials diversion was raised. In response,
Ralph Lumb (Nuclear Surveillance and Auditing Corporation) expressed
the belief that every means available should be used to minimize the
probability of diversion and maximize the possibility of detection.
However, he recognized the limitations, as evidenced by the failure
of the death penalty to eliminate homicide from society. Later, Leon
Rappoport (Kansas State University) confirmed these limitations of
criminal penalties. He cited current studies in psychology by B. F.
Skinner on the use of rewards and punishments to shape behavior
through operant conditioning. Rewards are found to be much more
effective than punishment in shaping behavior. Applying this to the
case of safeguards, he suggested that some punishment is needed, i.e.,
offenders should not go completely free of punishment; however, rather
than increase the punishment as a deterrent, a much more effective
method, in his opinion, would be the offer of large rewards for anybody who turns in someone guilty of a theft.

Theodore Taylor (International Research and Technology) asked
about the industry's concerns over aspects of physical security
designed to prevent thefts from happening. In response, Osborn
concentrated on protection of plutonium. In his evaluation, the reactor
itself is probably the most effective vault that man has ever constructed.
The large level of radioactivity from fission products continues to
make the plutonium inaccessible as it is discharged from the reactor,
transported, and passed through the reprocessing plant. Particular
attention to physical security should start at the point where plutonium
is separated from the fission products. Until recycling of plutonium
becomes appreciable, plutonium storage at reprocessing plants is a
factor worthy of concern. Reprocessing plants do not particularly
want to be in the storage business, but alternatives are lacking. The
most effective physical security systems are needed at this point, in
Osborn's opinion, particularly until the mid-1970s when plutonium
use should reduce the large amounts in storage. Industry still is
looking for the type of physical security systems that will be most
effective in view of the fact that plutonium should have greater
protection than materials of less strategic or monetary value. In his
outlook, transportation is perhaps an even more difficult problem.
Although this material cannot be trusted to the conventional methods
of truck or rail shipment, Osborn pointed out that we have learned
how to transport large amounts of other valuable materials.

The vulnerability of such experimental facilities as demonstration reactors to outright theft of plutonium or highly enriched uranium was emphasized by Taylor. Not being behind massive shields, these facilities are more exposed; furthermore, is achieving the objectives of a critical facility, the fissionable materials of which they are made frequently are "reshuffled," with a resulting increased difficulty in accountability. Moreover, the amount of materials for one of these facilities is large, as much as a ton of highly enriched uranium. Frank Morgan (United Kingdom Atomic Energy Authority), in a study in conjunction with the IAEA, found that accessible nonirradiated pieces weighing not more than 50 grams were used to make these assemblies, which total the better part of a ton. Not only are pieces "shuffled" but the users of these facilities require "weird" combinations of such materials as thorium and natural uranium as well as plutonium. Knowing precisely where all these fissionable materials are at any one time is difficult, short of a computerized accounting system.

Information on the magnitude of this problem was provided by Ralph Page (Division of Nuclear Materials Safeguards, AEC). Some fifty private facilities in the United States are authorized by license to possess more than five kilograms of ^{233}U, ^{235}U of greater than 20 percent enrichment, or plutonium, and thereby are subject to the physical protection requirements of 10 CFR Part 73. Most are critical facilities or university reactors. From the physical security point of view, the critical facilities present a greater safeguards risk for two reasons: the fissile content is larger and the material is more attractive for theft than irradiated fuels having high radiation levels.

PART

III

**INTERNATIONAL
SAFEGUARDS
SYSTEMS**

8

POLITICAL ASPECTS
OF NPT SAFEGUARDS

Lawrence Scheinman

When in 1945 the nuclear genie was let out of the bottle, fore-sighted men recognized that nothing short of comprehensive international control over the development and use of nuclear energy could ensure its devotion to exclusively peaceful purposes. The international political system of 1945 was not amenable to so comprehensive a control system, and the number of nuclear weapon states grew as the coincidence of technological capacity and political will to achieve nuclear status manifested themselves in particular nation-states.

Structurally, the world of today is not significantly different from that of 1945: the basic units of international politics remain the nation-states, and dedication to the principle of sovereignty is no less pronounced today than it was a generation ago. However, both at the level of the superpowers and of a large plurality of the world's non-nuclear weapon states, the conviction has grown that a world of nuclear weapon powers is neither safe nor desirable. The maximum attainable consensus on the matter of nuclear proliferation was codified in the Non-Proliferation Treaty (NPT) of 1968. The Treaty created a more comprehensive framework than heretofore for coping with the problem of the dissemination of nuclear weapons through the establishment of relevant norms, procedures, and mechanisms.

Although the NPT with its reciprocal commitments of nuclear and non-nuclear weapon states not to transfer or receive nuclear weapons or to manufacture or assist in the manufacture of such weapons is important in its own right, one of the most significant features of the Treaty is the provision for the application of

international safeguards on the peaceful nuclear programs of all non-
nuclear weapon states that ratify the NPT. Although the concept of
safeguards is not new, heretofore they were applied variously through
bilateral, regional, or international arrangements and limited, except
in the case of Euratom, to source or fissionable materials that were
the subject of international transactions. Indigenously mined or
manufactured nuclear material thus remained beyond the pale of most
of the prevailing safeguard systems. NPT safeguards, on the other
hand, apply to all source or fissionable material within the safeguarded
state or under its control anywhere regardless of origin, and responsibility for verification of the adherence of states to their Treaty
obligation not to divert nuclear materials from peaceful uses to
nuclear weapons is vested in a single central organization, the International Atomic Energy Agency (IAEA).

The value of an international safeguards system depends in
large measure on its capacity to satisfy two criteria: acceptability
and credibility. There is a respectable body of opinion that supports
the proposition that the more credible a system is the more intrusive
on national sovereignty it must be, and the more intrusive the system
the less likely it is to secure the voluntary adherence of the largest
possible number of states. Since, it is argued, there is a close relationship between the level of nuclear development on the one hand and
the probable intensity of intrusion on the other, the states most likely
to resist implementation of a truly credible safeguards system are
precisely those that are industrially and technologically most capable
of converting their peaceful nuclear program to military ends. This
resistance is attributed not so much to sinister motives as to perceived concerns of advanced non-nuclear weapon states over the
implications of safeguards for their competitive industrial and commercial nuclear status. One must remember that the safeguards in
question are obligatory for all signatory non-nuclear weapon states
but only voluntary for signatory nuclear weapon states. The conclusion drawn by skeptics of safeguards is that any operational system
that is acceptable to all or nearly all non-nuclear weapon states by
definition must be of dubious credibility from the point of view of
effectiveness and reliability. Paradoxically, they are concerned lest
a widely accepted international safeguards system generate false
expectations regarding national and international security and lull
states into maintaining less vigilance than they might regarding the
continuing growth of nuclear capacities and sophistication. Proponents
of this line of thought consequently tend to deemphasize international
safeguards and to assert that the principal value of the NPT lies not
so much in the safeguards provisions it contains as in its very acceptance and ratification. This, rather than safeguards, is viewed as

the principal building block for impeding the further dissemination
of nuclear weapons.

The purpose of this chapter is to try to offer, in a selective
rather than an exhaustive fashion, an assessment of the political utility
and limitations of NPT safeguards and to suggest possible supporting
policies that might be implemented to enhance the value of the safeguards system under discussion. I will accordingly look first at some
of the positive features of the projected NPT safeguards as well as
at some of its lacunae, second at possible ancillary non-proliferation
policies that might enhance the value of diversion safeguards, and
finally at some considerations that should be borne in mind as we
move from the stage of principle to the stage of implementation. In
so doing, I hope to introduce some balance and modification into the
"realpolitik" view of international safeguards sketched above.

POSITIVE FUNCTIONS OF SAFEGUARDS

Even if we accept the proposition that 90 percent of the value
of the NPT lies in its ratification, it is certain that safeguards
operate as a reinforcing mechanism for the obligations undertaken
in the Treaty. They serve as a constant reminder, symbolized by
the international inspector, of those obligations and of the risks of
detection and possible sanction inherent in their violation. The
measure of that risk ultimately may lie in the probability of sanctions
being applied against violators, which raises the problem of enforcement. For present purposes, it suffices simply to suggest the possibility of sanctions as a factor that national decision-makers contemplating diversion must take into account.

The fact that safeguards are assumed in the context of a multilateral treaty rather than in bilateral agreements or as byproducts
of commercial transactions conducted by selected supplier states
also adds to their importance and authority, for it raises to the level
of international commitment what were previously discrete contrac-
tual agreements. Although these elements are not easily quantified,
I think they are profoundly important and contribute to the creation
of a psychopolitical climate favorable to the promotion and maintenance of non-proliferation policy.

If we grant that nation-states are not the single-minded mono-
lithic actors we sometimes characterize them to be but consist rather
of competitive bureaucratic and organizational elites each seeking to
define particular national interests and to develop appropriate

supporting policies, then other positive features of international
safeguards emerge. Perhaps the best way to demonstrate this aspect
is to draw on the experience of one of the states that already has pro-
liferated: France.

The initial French "decision" to acquire nuclear weapons was
the product of a series of many small incremental decisions made
by a limited group of persons operating through informal channels of
communication outside the mainstream of political activity. In a very
real sense, the final decision to exercise the nuclear option imposed
itself on the responsible political authorities virtually as a fait
accompli.

NPT safeguards are based on the establishment and maintenance
of a national system of accounting for and control of all nuclear
material subject to safeguard. In such circumstances, future incipient
patterns similar to those that obtained in France would quickly be
forced to the surface: in the context of NPT safeguards, diversion by
default would seem to be a rather remote possibility; only a conscious
and considered decision by responsible political authorities could
start the ball of diversion rolling. The point is that NPT safeguards,
while not preventing a diversion or a decision to proliferate, place
that decision in a significantly different context than that portrayed
for France, and to the extent that NPT safeguards force the issue
into the open they complicate the process of national proliferation.

The NPT and its operational safeguards system thus can be
seen as contributing two elements to the diversion-proliferation question. First, they reinforce the hand of those domestic elites who are
opposed to proliferation. Opponents of the allocation of nuclear
resources to weapons purposes can point to the NPT obligations and
to the risk of being detected in trying to divert. Second, the internally
generated debate would be unlikely to go unnoticed and this would
give external actors (the superpowers, for instance) an opportunity
to respond to the incentives apparently compelling the state in question
toward proliferation to nuclear weapon status. These effects may be
limited, but they are not insignificant.

Finally, safeguards play a valuable role as vehicles of communication. On the one hand, acceptance by a state of safeguards and
international inspection communicates intentions to use nuclear technology and material for peaceful purposes only. A state bent on proliferation from the outset is not likely to place itself under the constraints of treaty commitments and safeguard procedures. Hence,
one may assume arguendo that states that ratify the NPT intend to

abide by its provisions. Safeguards offer them a way of demonstrating their peaceful intentions to other states. On the other hand, acceptance of safeguards and international inspection by one state enables it to communicate its expectation that other states will do likewise. It is a way of saying that the state in question recognizes that safeguards may contribute to the reduction of mutual mistrust and help to build a climate of confidence in which even the option of acquiring nuclear weapons would become less attractive and that it expects its neighbors to undertake similar obligations if they wish to minimize the risk of a local nuclear arms race. In the case of communication as in the above situations, safeguards can play only a limited role but that role nevertheless is useful and of potential value in furthering the objective of non-proliferation.

THE GAPS

Despite these positive functions, safeguards have, as suggested, only a limited role in the fulfillment of non-proliferation policy: they may detect a diversion but they cannot prevent diversion. Even in the context of detection, there are a number of lacunae in the projected NPT safeguards system—lacunae that at least in part reflect compromises related to negotiation of the guideline principles on safeguards set forth in INFCIRC 153 of the IAEA.1 For one thing, international inspectors cannot seek out undeclared clandestine facilities. Safeguards extend only to those facilities declared at the time agreement is negotiated with the IAEA. The probability that a signatory state has a facility whose identify is unknown either to the international agency or to the intelligence offices of one of the major or other powers is low, but it is a hypothetical possibility that cannot be overlooked. The IAEA itself, however, is intended as a verification and inspection agency, not as a spy network.

Second, IAEA inspectors cannot follow nuclear material that is removed from safeguards for declared nonproscribed military purposes. The NPT extends only to nuclear weapons or explosives; it does not prohibit the development of such things as nuclear submarines. Any state may legitimately undertake a nuclear submarine program and withdraw nuclear material from safeguards in pursuit of that program. The possibility always exists that the material in question may be diverted from the declared purpose to a clandestine nuclear weapons program, and this falls beyond the pale of NPT safeguards. Yet this very gap exemplifies the value of international safeguards: their existence forces the state in question to declare that it is removing a stated amount of material from safeguards for the

nonproscribed military purpose, thus alerting the international community to the fact that observation and monitoring of that state may
be in order. The possibility of surprise proliferation is thus reduced.

Third, safeguards cannot meet the problem of denunciation by
a state once it has attained a level of sophistication and/or a stockpile of fissile material enabling it to rapidly convert such material
to the manufacture of nuclear weapons. Numerous commentators
have pointed out that one of the perverse effects of international safeguards is that they cloak safeguarded nuclear material and programs
in the mantle of legitimacy precisely because they are safeguarded
but are powerless to prevent a state from shedding that mantle in
the interest of proliferation.

ANCILLARY POLICIES

International safeguards, then, are powerless in the face of a
government decision that the benefit of having nuclear weapons out-
weighs the political, economic, and social costs associated with their
acquisition. This logically leads to the question of how we can supple-
ment safeguard systems so as to have not only a plausible system of
detection of the fact of a loss of material (thus raising perhaps a
presumption of diversion) but also a higher degree of assuredness
that safeguarded material will not be converted to proscribed military
ends.

Before proposing possible ancillary non-proliferation measures,
I think it would be helpful to ask what impels governments to make
a decision to acquire nuclear weapons? We can identify two broad
categories of incentives: security and prestige. Security embraces
belief in the effectiveness of nuclear weapons as deterrents and as
means of defense should deterrence fail. However dubious propositions of the credibility of deterrence theory may be, we would do well
to remember that sophisticated strategic analysts in the United States
have propounded the deterrence theory for several decades now and
that American strategic policy remains wedded to the validity of
those theories even today. We also might keep in mind the strategic
theory voiced a decade ago by the French General Pierre Gallois:
that "thermonuclear weapons neutralize the armed masses, equalize
the factors of demography, contract distance, level the heights, limit
the advantages which until yesterday the Big Powers derived from the
sheer dimensions of their territory." [2] This theory still has a popular
ring in countries faced with serious security interests and convention-
ally more powerful neighbors.

Prestige, on the other hand, encompasses a range of considerations such as the following: (1) expectations that a state's voice will be more clearly heard and accorded greater weight in international forums if it is a member of the nuclear club; (2) beliefs that a state's general status and influence are enhanced by the possession of nuclear weapons; or (3) assumptions that greatness is measured in nuclear weapon terms and that their possession constitutes a precondition to such things as regional leadership or the revision of responsibilities in military alliances. France, of course, is a striking example of the power of prestige thinking on the nuclear decisions a country might make.

Given these considerations, how can we minimize the probability that state with the capacity to do so will decide to acquire nuclear weapons? At least three courses of action would appear open at the present time: (1) devaluation and further delegitimization of nuclear weapons, (2) policies of sanction for diverters and denunciators, and (3) ancillary non-proliferation policies.

Devaluation and Delegitimization

Devaluation of nuclear weapons entails deemphasizing the deterrent capacities of such weapons. At the very least, we ought not to encourage other countries in the same beliefs as those expounded in the past by great powers spokesmen. What applies to the great powers may not apply to lesser powers whose size, location, or technological capacity affects the relevance of having nuclear weapons. Stress should be placed on the possibility that nuclear weapons not only may not enhance national security but may even detract from it by encouraging other states to consider preemptive action or preventive war against an incipient or weakly endowed nuclear weapon state. The nonuseable nature of nuclear force, so eloquently demonstrated by the American experience in Vietnam, is also a lesson worth reiterating. Finally, devaluation should mean not rewarding prestige-oriented proliferators. The American policy of not rewarding France in the early 1960s through refusal to grant the French increased recognition and stature in the context of the North Atlantic alliance is a useful precedent that might be profitably applied in the future.

Further delegitimization of nuclear weapons essentially means further agreement among the nuclear weapon powers on arms control measures. Many non-nuclear weapon states that have signed the NPT and several that have not have stressed the importance of winding down vertical proliferation as central to the success or failure

of the NPT. Constant pressure from the non-nuclear weapon states
during the negotiation of the NPT led to the inclusion of specific
undertakings on arms control and disarmament in the Treaty by the
major powers. Measures such as agreement on a comprehensive
test ban, on a cutoff in the production of fissile materials for weapons
purposes, on the limitation and reduction of offensive and defensive
strategic delivery vehicles (SALT-type objectives), and eventual
nuclear disarmament all come to mind. It should be sobering to
remember that five years after the entry into force of the NPT a
review conference is' to be held to assess the operation of the Treaty.
If the nuclear weapon states have failed to make serious efforts to
contain and reduce vertical proliferation, then the survival prognosis
of NPT will be very dim indeed.

Sanctions

Steps also should be taken to minimize rewards for evasion and
proliferation and to maximize penalties for those who take such action.
Sanctions can be interpreted as nonrewards in the sense noted in discussing the devaluation of nuclear weapons; as security guarantees
by nuclear superpowers against actions threatened by diverting states
(similar guarantees might serve as a disincentive to proliferation in
the first place by offering to substitute the nuclear umbrella of a
major nuclear power for the less credible weapons system the proliferator might create); or as punitive measures against diverters
or denunciators.

The sanctions contained in the statute of the IAEA (curtailing
or suspending assistance from the IAEA to the state in question,
demanding the return of materials or equipment given to the state,
and suspending the rights and privileges of membership of the delinquent state) are not sufficient. The most effective punitive response
would be the concerted economic or political action of the superpowers
against the delinquent state. If proliferators can get away with diversion and proliferation "cost-free," then states desirous of acquiring
a nuclear weapons capability will feel that much less constrained to
do so; if the nuclear weapon powers fail to rise to the challenge of
proliferation, then the policy of non-proliferation will quickly become
obsolete.

Other Ancillary Policies

Sanctions based on threat can play only a limited antiproliferation role. Additional measures of a more constructive nature are

still necessary. Here, it seems to me, several possibilities exist. One objective might be to create a network of international interdependencies in the context of the nuclear fuel cycle by encouraging the establishment of multinational facilities. An abiding concern of many of the advanced non-nuclear weapon states has been the matter of fuel supply. Fuel for the current generation of nuclear reactors comes almost exclusively from the United States and, as developments in Europe and elsewhere attest, economic or political willingness to continue to rely on this source for enriched fuels is rapidly eroding. The European Economic Community is investigating the possibility of building a gaseous diffusion facility; Japan, Canada, and Australia are engaged in similar discussions; and rapid progress is being made in the development of the gas centrifuge technique of isotopic separation. It would seem that the United States in particular, as the leading nation in peaceful nuclear technology, has a unique opportunity to influence the direction that the spread of nuclear technology takes by using its technological capacities to channel development in the direction of the creation of multinational isotope separation facilities or reprocessing facilities.

One possibility that comes to mind is fostering the emergence of regional fuel cycle clusters instead of national fuel cycle infrastructure. While private American enterprise or the AEC might have partial involvement in the development and management of such clusters, it need not, and in the interest of minimizing the perception of dependency it probably should not; the key objective should be to minimize the development of self-sufficient fuel cycles and to encourage the economically attractive alternative of shared facilities on the part of several states. In a sense, there should be an attempt to decouple politics and economics, to emphasize the economic values that accrue from shared facilities, and to minimize the political costs of interdependence. Unquestionably, multinational clusters raise problems of long-distance transportation thus opening possibilities of diversion or theft outside the safeguarded facility, but this problem too should be manageable as states develop security systems to cope with this range of risks. Fifteen years ago the United States dissuaded the Europeans from building an enrichment facility in the framework of Euratom; nevertheless, today there is a French national plant as well as renewed European interest, as represented in the centrifuge, in finding alternative means for enriching uranium. Serious thought should be given to changing our philosophy on the scope and conditions of technological transfer.

A second type of ancillary policy that might be worth consideration is the development of arrangements for plutonium stockpiling. The risk of stockpile diversion is as great as the risk of diversion in enrichment or reprocessing facilities. Obvious political problems are raised when it comes to determining where plutonium should be stockpiled, but at least one possibility is the creation of international islands on national territory for such stockpiling, which islands would be outside national sovereignty and under the control of international authorities.

Whether one is considering stockpiling alternatives or those designed to generate interdependencies and to diminish complete self-sufficiency, I think that they hold out the promise of facilitating the objective of non-proliferation and as such should be given careful thought and deliberation. The more internationalized and interdependent the nuclear fuel cycle is, the more difficult it becomes for any one state to strike out on the path of complete independence and the more complex the decisions and effectuation of diversion or denunciation become.

FROM PRINCIPLE TO IMPLEMENTATION

Let us return from these considerations to safeguards. I suggested at the outset that safeguards performed a number of valuable functions but that they also were characterized by some real and serious limitations. Some argue that the distinction between two classes of states created by the NPT and the intrusion on national sovereignty that safeguards entail constitute irritants and that, in view of the limited effectiveness one may attribute to safeguards, irritation should be kept minimal. In other words, an added unit of intrusion will not yield an equal added unit of effectiveness.

If safeguards could perform preventive functions as well as those of detection, I would disagree with this line of thought. But to the extent that safeguards do perform only limited, if valuable, functions I agree. Our objective should be to avoid a system that irritates disproportionately to what it provides and to attract as many states as possible to the obligatory safeguards system. INFCIRC 153 appears in principle to meet the criterion of providing a balance between acceptability and credibility. It is important that the operational system developed under the aegis of INFCIRC 153 maintain this balance. Polarization must be avoided, and we should strive for the development of intermediate situations in which widely accepted safeguards are reinforced by auxiliary measures such as those suggested above.

I would go beyond this general statement, however. I believe that a plausible case can be made for the argument that the United

States ought to take the lead in establishing and implementing model-type agreements with the IAEA on the operational side. The technologically competitive non-nuclear weapon states pressed for <u>equality of misery</u> in Vienna during the negotiation of INFCIRC 153. I see little evidence that having won the principle they will sacrifice the implementation. We are speaking of the real political world, not about a parlor game. C. D. W. Thornton's observations (see Chapter 5) are particularly appropriate in this regard: in establishing exacting yet economically acceptable standards of safeguards and security for ourselves, we can insist on nothing less for others. Japanese and German industry seem concerned about reprocessing and fuel fabrication facilities in particular, but these are our own internal concerns as well. I see no reason why we cannot turn a social good established for the benefit of our own society into a tool of international policy for the ultimate benefit of mankind.

NOTES

1.   IAEA document INFCIRC/153 (Vienna, 1971).

2.   Quoted in Raymond Aron, <u>The Great Debate</u> (New York: Doubleday, 1965), p. 102.

E. M. Kinderman (Stanford Research Institute), commenting on Lawrence Scheinman's suggestion that the internationalization of nuclear-oriented corporations is a method of making safeguards more effective, stated that the resulting international cartels might essentially become weapon states without regard to national policy. Scheinman replied that, in weighing the problem of the state versus the international cartel, he was more concerned about the state. While international cartels may have lives of their own, their lives are not conducted without regard to the environment in which the international controls operate. Certainly, an ideal situation with respect to nuclear facilities would be one in which a mix exists between private and public enterprises across national boundaries. Thus, private, public, and cross-national values would be in competition; Scheinman felt that this would reduce to a minimum the kind of consensus involved in a decision to go nuclear.

C. D. W. Thornton (Director, Division of Nuclear Materials Safeguards, AEC) made several observations and asked how they might fit into the context of Scheinman's statements. Thornton pointed out that timeliness should be considered in regard to the dispersal of many nuclear activities. Timeliness is a function of the access to technology for nations that are not yet near the degree of maturity needed for controls. On this basis, the argument can be made that it is not a good policy for the United States to lubricate the international growth of nuclear technology prior to possessing the means of controlling the output of this technology. Along these lines, a possible reason for a given nation's becoming party to the NPT might be to gain peaceful access to technology that might enhance its means of achieving weapons objectives at a later date. During these developments, the nation can observe whether controls are effective. If these arguments are plausible, deferment of the dispersal of nuclear technology might well be based upon the argument that such dispersal, particularly for isotope separations facilities, should wait upon the development of better methods of control.

Scheinman agreed with Thornton's comments but asked Thornton whether or not other nations would acquire nuclear technology regardless of U. S. attempts to facilitate or not facilitate their acquisition of that technology. Thornton responded that, under the circumstances, other nations should not be encouraged by aiding them in their attempts to acquire nuclear technology whose results cannot yet be controlled. Thornton added that his comments were not made solely with the national interest of the United States in mind but in the belief that, both internationally and domestically, ability to control should be ahead of the general dispersal of nuclear technology.

Scheinman pointed out that, during a recent trip to Europe, he had spoken to officials concerning their interpretation of Article 4 of the NPT. Their interpretation was that they could do anything in developing and acquiring nuclear technology as long as it is safe-guarded and not utilized for weapon purposes. Their feeling was not that the United States should turn over technological developments but rather that the United States should not impede them in their developments and that impediments would be regarded as violation of the spirit of the NPT.

9

EURATOM
SAFEGUARDS
Enrico Jacchia

Since the end of World War II, efforts have been made to establish international control over nuclear weapons and the activities that enable them to be produced.

International support of the concept of international nuclear safeguards increased rapidly as more people became aware of the critical dangers inherent in the further, ineffectively controlled dispersal throughout the world of nuclear materials of the type required for the construction of nuclear explosives.

In addition to the strong endorsement of the Non-Proliferation Treaty (NPT) by a large number of nations, there are many reasons to believe that it will be possible to operate an effective system of international nuclear safeguards in the very near future. Among these reasons, and not the last, I like to mention that most of the world's peaceful nuclear facilities and specific nuclear materials are now subject to safeguards administered by organizations that have substantially the same objectives and that develop their system along similar lines: accountability, containment, and a corps of inspectors.

Therefore, it is not extravagant to believe that a gradual transition to an international system can be achieved in a way that preserves and even strengthens the assurances now provided by the national and regional systems and in particular by the system operated by the European Atomic Energy Commission (Euratom). It is the structure and activities of this safeguards system that I now wish to illustrate.

The Communities Safeguards System, which has now been in operation for more than ten years, is based on the acceptance of rules and a common authority and possesses certain distinguishing features that warrant emphasis:

1. It is mandatory and directly applicable on the territory of each Member State.

2. The body exercising supervision—in this case the Comission—is placed in a direct relationship with the holders of materials subjected to control, and this enables the Commission, and more particularly its duly authorized inspectors, to have direct access to the enterprises.

3. Finally, this system applies, without any restriction as to time, to all activities connected with the peaceful uses of nuclear energy in the member countries.

In order to underline the special aspect of the features enumerated above, it is desirable to point out, inter alia, that under the IAEA safeguards system, which was in force hitherto, the IAEA is not empowered to contact directly the holders of materials subject to control but must approach them through the intermediary of the Member State concerned; furthermore, its safeguards system applies only to those cases of the peaceful use of nuclear energy that the Member States voluntarily submit to safeguards, and even in these cases it applies only during the period provided for in the safeguards agreement concluded. With the entry into force of the NPT and the conclusion of new safeguards agreements with the Member States, the IAEA system becomes mandatory and all-embracing for non-nuclear weapon states party to the Treaty with respect to the undertaking regarding the peaceful use of nuclear materials. Consequently, the IAEA's system has just acquired one of the essential characteristics of the European Community's safeguards system.

The Commission's safeguards system relates to uranium, thorium, and the special fissile materials deriving therefrom; in addition, by virtue of commitments entered into with non-Community countries, it relates to such other materials as heavy water and tritium. The surveillance does not apply to the testing, development, manufacture, or storage of either nuclear weapons or the means of delivering them. It results from the implementation of the provisions of Chapter VII of the Euratom Treaty and of the Regulations made for the purpose of their application.

To date, the Commission has made two Regulations: Regulation 7, published in the Official Gazette of the European Communities dated March 12, 1959, and Regulation 8, published in the Official Gazette of May 29, 1959. As has just been stressed, these texts are directly binding on the firms and the public and private institutions subjected to them without any intervention by the governments or public authorities of the Member States.

The aims of the Commission's safeguards are defined in Article 77 of the Euratom Treaty, under the terms of which the Commission must satisfy itself that in the territories of Member States ores, source materials, and special fissile materials are not diverted from their intended uses as declared by the users; that the provisions relating to supplies are complied with; and that any special control obligations assumed by the Community under an agreement concluded with a third country or an international organization are observed.

To enable the Commission to fulfill its obligations in their entirety, the Treaty stipulates that anyone setting up or operating a plant for the production, separation, or use of source materials or special fissile materials or for the processing of irradiated nuclear fuels shall be required to declare to the Commission the basic technical characteristics of such a plant (Article 78). It also lays down that operating records shall be maintained and produced in order to permit accounting for ores, source materials, and special fissile materials used or produced (Article 79). These provisions are reinforced by the right that the Treaty confers on the Commission to send into the territories of Member States inspectors who shall at all times have access to all places and data and to all persons who deal with materials, equipment, or facilities subject to the safeguards.

It can be seen that the provisions described above are aimed at furnishing the Commission with appropriate means of carrying out the task of surveillance assigned to it by the Treaty, but that—and this must be stressed—they do not restrict the freedom of the firms or institutions to determine their investments or the operation of their plants in the light of technical or economic considerations.

The essential elements of the safeguards system are on the one hand the declarations made by the firms to the Commission and on the other the on-the-spot checks carried out by the inspectors.

Through the application of Regulation No. 7, made in implementation of Article 78, the Commission is provided with the means of keeping abreast of plans and data regarding the capacities of the installations, the nature of the materials used and produced, the technical processes employed, and the methods adopted for measuring and checking the quantities and nature of the materials held in the installations subject to control. As a result of the information it receives in implementation of Regulation 8, the Commission has knowledge of the stocks held by those covered by these provisions, the location of the materials, transfers from one installation to another, and imports to and exports from third countries. The materials-accounting organized by the Commission comprises accounts in respect of each installation and each material, broken down according to the origin and status of the latter.

The Commission of the European Communities ensures compliance with the provisions of the Treaty and if necessary can record infringements and impose penalties. These can take the form of a warning, the withdrawal of such special benefits as financial or technical assistance, the placing of the firm under administrative control for a period not exceeding four months, and the total or partial withdrawal of source materials or special fissile materials. The Member States are required to ensure that these penalties are enforced.

Moreover, since the safeguards are an integral part of the European Communities' institutional system, it is the Commission that, in this sphere as in others, is accountable for its actions to the European Parliament, and in case of dispute the parties concerned can institute proceedings against its decisions before the Court of Justice of the European Communities. The underlying purpose here is to effectively combine the necessary power of decision of the Commission and the guarantee of individual rights against arbitrary action.

THE STRUCTURE OF THE SAFEGUARDS DEPARTMENT

The Safeguards Department at present comprises about sixty employees divided between two divisions: Accounting and Inspection and External Commitments. The Commission's inspectorate consists of thirty-two inspectors and assistant-inspectors who have duly been given security clearance and appointed to their posts by the Commission after consultation with the Member States. The inspectors possess appropriate qualifications for the tasks they have to perform: some of them carry out the accounting checks, others the technical checks. The former have an economic and legal training; the latter are for the most part from the Joint Research Centre Establishments and their training has been in such fields as nuclear engineering, nuclear physics, electronics, nuclear chemistry, metallurgy, and radiation protection.

Materials Accounting

It has already been stated that the data supplied by persons subject to the system requirements under the provisions of Regulation 8 provides the Commission with the information necessary for it to keep track of the use of nuclear materials in the six Community countries.

On the basis of the statements submitted by persons subject to the aforementioned requirements, the Commission of the European Communities has set up and maintains a system of accounting for all ores, source materials, and special fissile materials in actual existence in the Community as well as for stocks, movements, and losses. This accounting is done with IBM machines.

Examination of the statements sometimes reveals the need for explanations or corrections. In such cases, the Commission communicates directly with the plants. This procedure has always had the advantage of setting up personal contacts between the Safeguards Department and the firms concerned.

The periodical statements submitted by the various plants are assessed from two different angles:

1. From the accounting angle, a check is carried out on the accuracy and concurrence of the statements. The check focuses in particular on whether the increases and decreases recorded in relation to an installation's initial stock are equal to the variation shown by this stock and whether inter-installation deliveries in the Community balance out and offset each other.

2. From the technical angle, the following points in particular are studied and examined: the composition of the monthly return; the nature of movements of materials; and reported material losses.

As a matter of interest, it may be pointed out that on December 31, 1970, a total of 250 installations had submitted statements of their basic technical characteristics. Moreover, at the same date 22 mines and 67 installations not involved in the nuclear fuel cycle were registered with the Safeguards Department.

Inspection

The Commission of the Communities carries out on-the-spot inspections which, depending on the case, may be "intermittent," "continuous" or - according to a decision taken recently by the Commission—"intense." This last type of inspection applies to certain installations for the production of fuel elements.

The inspection programme, which is based particularly on a statistical weighting of the installations, groups in one "mission" several installations situated on the same site or in the same area so as to minimize travel and save time. A mission is usually completed within one working week. An inspection team usually consists of two or three inspectors, depending upon the size and complexity of the installation to be visited. As indicated above, these inspectors enjoy very wide powers of investigation. At the request of the country concerned, they may be accompanied by representatives of that country acting as observers.

Before leaving the Commission headquarters, the inspectors receive a detailed program in the preparation of which they themselves participate. This program defines the scope and limitations of the checks to be carried out and gives details of the following: (1) the installations to be inspected; (2) the date of the inspection; (3) the substances and/or materials to be inspected; (4) the accounting checks to be made; and (5) the physical checks to be made.

As regards the accounting checks, the Commission's inspectors ask for the materials account and the documents originating from the suppliers and carriers. They make an accounting inventory of the installation's stocks on the date of the inspection. They compare the company's accounts and the documents received from other parties with the declarations made to the Commission under Regulation 8.

The technical checks include the establishment of physical inventory on the date of inspection. The operations to be carried out are detailed in the special manuals for each type of installation. These checks have the following main objectives:

1. To verify, if necessary, that the basic characteristics of the installation are in fact those that have been declared to the Commission in implementation of Regulation 7.

2. To check partial stocks by the type of substance (or by the technological type of material, e.g., U/Al kernels, pins of enriched

UO_2, fuel elements, UO_2/PuO_2 plates) and by the location in the installation. This is done either by physical measurement (weighing, volume measurement and sampling, and gamma spectrometry) or from internal "operational" documents (receipt vouchers, with corresponding delivery forms, weighing slips, fabrication slips, fabrication control slips, dispatch notes with handover slips, and so forth).

3. From the results obtained, to compile an overall inventory of the material(s) subject to inspection.

4. To check that the materials and the finished products correspond, as regards their characteristics, to their declared uses and also to confirm, where necessary, that external commitments are being observed.

Following Inspection

On returning to the Commission headquarters, the inspectors draw up an inspection report setting out point by point, with reference to the mission order, the results of the checks, inspections, and observations made at the plant. Depending upon the case, this report is either forwarded to the installation for comments or circulated within the Department and filed. When the installation does not receive a copy of the report, it is at all events informed by letter of the results of the inspection. Thus there is always an opportunity to comment on the inspections.

Ray Heinisch (Nuclear Assurance Corporation) asked Enrico Jacchia to comment on how Euratom supplements its inspection of nuclear facilities with the safeguarding of nuclear materials in transit. Jacchia replied that, since hijacking has not been a serious problem in Europe, and in this he was supported by other participants, he did not feel that there presently existed a real danger of diversion of nuclear materials in transit. Thus, Euratom has taken no special precautions in this area except for a normal system of requiring notification that such materials are to be transported and that they have arrived. Jacchia added that Euratom has no immediate plans for the additional precaution of nuclear materials in transit.

The question of illicit markets for fissile materials received lively discussion. Herbert Scoville (Carnegie Endowment for International Peace) held the belief that fissile material is not now a particularly attractive commodity to steal. He supported this with the contention that simply stealing fissile material is far from having a weapon; even though weapon technology is not now highly secret, a tremendous effort is still required to fabricate a nuclear explosive that could actually be used. In this regard, E. M. Kinderman (Stanford Research Institute) cautioned that a distinction should be made between construction of a weapon system and of a nuclear explosive, the construction of the latter being relatively simple.

The belief that a black market in fissile material does not now exist was expressed by Ralph Lumb (Nuclear Surveillance and Auditing Corporation). This contention is based on the fact that none has been lost in transportation in the United States, although some has been temporarily misplaced. For the future, Scoville was worried about the possibility that a country would want weapons and decide, rather than to make the material, to purchase it on the black market and thereby help create such a market. An even more realistic danger, in his view, was the theft of existing nuclear weapons, a theft that in one step replaces both stealing material and fabricating weapons.

Samuel Edlow (Edlow International) asked whether he understood Jacchia to say that the prevention of diversion was beyond the mission of safeguards. Jacchia stated that for Euratom the mission of safeguards is the detection of diversion. Inspector General Rudolf Rometsch (International Atomic Energy Agency) agreed that the IAEA follows the same policy. Edlow pointed out that the approach of Euratom

and of the IAEA differed from both the recommendation of the Lumb
Panel and the approach of the AEC, which are that the mission of
safeguards is the prevention of diversion. Scoville observed that a
good feature of an international safeguards system is in tying itself
to the national systems in order to let nations do the police work, which
is clearly beyond its responsibilities. In this connection, Lawrence
Scheinman (University of Michigan) asked how Euratom safeguards
could then be treated as the equivalent of a national system. Of course,
police action on a multinational basis is impeded by national sovereignty.

In the international case, the delicacy of the distinction between
deterrence and prevention of diversion was illustrated by Rometsch.
The NPT states that verification is for the sole purpose of fulfilling
the obligations of preventing diversion of nuclear energy from peaceful uses to nuclear weapons or other nuclear explosive devices. At
the more practical level of the safeguards agreements of the IAEA,
the corresponding sentences are slightly changed. In this case, the
objective of safeguards is timely detection of diversion of significant
quantities of nuclear material and deterrence of such diversion by the
risk of early detection.

A question about the completeness of Euratom safeguards was
raised by C.D.W. Thornton (Director, Division of Nuclear Materials
Safeguards, AEC). Rather than "eyeball" inspections, he believed
diagnostic probes provide needed effectiveness. He then asked
whether any Euratom facilities had been shut to review abnormalities.
Jacchia said that this has not occurred.

10

INTERNATIONAL SAFEGUARDS:
A STUDY
OF THE INFLUENCE
OF TECHNOLOGY
ON POLITICAL DECISIONS

Dean Zollman

INTRODUCTION

The safeguards program of the International Atomic Energy
Agency (IAEA) had its practical beginning in 1956 when Japan requested
three tons of natural uranium for a research reactor. This first
safeguards agreement, as have all agreements since then, represented
a compromise between the technical requirements of the IAEA and
political reality.[1] This pattern of compromise between political and
technical considerations was incorporated into the IAEA Safeguards
System formally established in 1961, reconstructed in 1965, and
revised in 1966 and 1968.[2]

The ratification of the Non-Proliferation Treaty (NPT) has
opened a new phase in the safeguards to be applied by the IAEA. This
phase is far from complete since very few countries have signed the
safeguards agreements required by the NPT. However, a major step
toward these agreements was accomplished early in 1971 when, after
lengthy negotiations, a model safeguards agreement was published.[3]
As in the earlier agreements, many compromises between the political
and technical aspects of safeguards were necessary. In this chapter
I will examine the relations between the political and technical variables
involved in this future safeguards system.

Research for this chapter was supported under the Research
Applied to National Needs (RANN) Program of the National Science
Foundation. The author thanks R. B. Leachman and R. F. Kruh for
assistance in this research.

RESEARCH DESIGN

The central question underlying this study is: How are safeguards policies agreed upon? As in the similar study of the U.S.
safeguards program described in Chapter 4, the crucial variable was
assumed to be the degree of external control over safeguards procedures, i.e., the degree of external control the various nation-states
would allow the IAEA to exercise over the nation's nuclear energy
program.

Clearly, the degree of control the IAEA may exercise over a
safeguards system is intimately related to both the political and
technical considerations of a safeguards system. For example, to
assure that no proprietary information is revealed, a nation may wish
to limit the areas of a plant in which an IAEA inspector may perform
the measurements and review the records involved in the safeguards
inspection. On the other hand, the staff of the Department of Safeguards and Inspection may consider entering some of these restricted
areas in order to obtain additional highly desirable data. The question
becomes the following: Which is more important, the protection of
proprietory information or the obtaining of additional data on the
material in the plant? Thus, a compromise must be reached between
a technical variable, obtaining data, and a political variable, protecting
information. Clearly, the degree of external control exercised by
IAEA becomes more limited as the area within a plant that is not
open to inspection increases.

THE SURVEY INSTRUMENT

To investigate the interaction of the political and technical aspects
of safeguards, a structured survey research questionnaire was developed. This instrument is similar to the one for the U.S. safeguards
system described earlier by David Brady (see Chapter 4). The first
section of the questionnaire contains five hypothetical international
safeguards systems. Each of the five systems includes the following
set of twelve topics:

1. The extent to which the IAEA should be involved in the process
of designing safeguards procedures for the facilities of a signatory
nation

2. The extent to which the IAEA should be involved in changing
plant practices in order to insure good safeguards procedures

3. The extent to which the IAEA should be involved in the measurement of fissile material

4. The extent to which a facility in a signatory nation should be allowed to deny access to IAEA inspectors due to the loss of proprietory information

5. The manner in which suspected diversions should be reported to the IAEA

6. The manner in which the IAEA should react to reports of missing fissile material

7. The manner in which the IAEA's safeguards office and the safeguards program of a facility should be funded

8. The manner in which the IAEA should license a facility

9. The manner in which disputes over the findings of IAEA inspections should be settled

10. The manner in which general accounting procedures should be reported to the IAEA

11. Whether or not the IAEA should require regularly scheduled physical inventories

12. Whether the purpose of the IAEA safeguards system should be to detect or to detect and deter the diversion of fissile material.

By increasing the degree of external control the IAEA exercises for each of these components of a safeguards system, each system becomes more stringent than the one before it. (The manner in which the stringency increases for each variable is shown in Table 8.)

As a specific example, consider the topic discussed above, denial of access due to the loss of proprietory information. In System I the nation, the nuclear industry, or the individual nuclear facility may deny the inspector entry to the facility if it believes an inspection will result in the loss of proprietory information. At the other end of the spectrum in System V, the nation has no denial rights and the IAEA inspectors have complete freedom to move about any facility.

Since a similar gradation was constructed for each of the twelve aspects of safeguards, System V gives the greatest degree of external

TABLE 8

Variation in the Most Important Topics Considered in the International Hypothetical Systems

TOPIC	SYSTEM				
	I	II	III	IV	V
Safeguard design and procedures	IAEA certifies and reviews periodically	IAEA requests minimum design and information and review by nation	IAEA requires design information by nation	IAEA reviews design before construction and licenses plant	IAEA approves designs, inspects construction, and issues licenses
Changes in plant practices	IAEA could request voluntary improvement	IAEA requests improvement	IAEA requires improvement	IAEA requires changes	IAEA orders changes
Independent measurement	none	at input-output, using random, nondestructive, and passive measurements	at strategic points, using random, nondestructive, active or passive measurements; resident inspection at reprocessing	at strategic points, using random, destructive and nondestructive measurements; resident inspection at fabrication and reprocessing	continuous survey; resident inspection at all facilities; random destructive and nondestructive measurements
Denial of access due to proprietary information	plant industry nation has veto	nation has veto	nation may deny access to facility or areas within facility	nation may deny access to areas within facility with good reason	nation has no denial rights
How diversions are reported to IAEA	plant or nation confirms then reports	plant reports as soon as discovered	plant reports all missing material as soon as discovered	plant reports all losses (including NOL) as soon as discovered	reports made by resident inspector
IAEA reaction to reported MUF	aids facility in determining what happened; informs member states if peace and security threat exists	sends investigators; informs member states if peace and security threat exists	may request inventory; sends investigators; may inform UN committee and Board of Governors	requires inventory; sends investigators; informs UN committee and Board of Governors	performs immediate physical inventory; may close facility, may request removal of SNM and technological aid

IAEA reaction to unreported MUF	above, plus review of safeguard practices	same as above	same as above	same as above	same as above
Funds for facility	can be obtained from IAEA	some can be obtained from IAEA	equipment only obtained from IAEA	none	none
Funds for IAEA	from special nuclear materials (SNM) suppliers	by UN formula	more than UN formula by states with nuclear facilities; less by those states without	from inspected and supplying states only	nation pays cost of inspection
Licensing	none required	IAEA requests nation to license	IAEA may require nation to license	IAEA licenses	IAEA licenses
Board of Review (for disputes)	none	none	mediation board	arbitration board	arbitration board
Safeguards purposes	to certify nation can detect diversion	to verify facility can detect	to ensure detection of loss or diversion	to detect and possibly deter diversion or loss	to detect and defer diversion or loss
Paperwork to IAEA	keep records which are reviewed periodically	report inter-facility transfers and keep records which are reviewed randomly	report inter facility transfers; keep records which are reviewed on random schedule	detailed intra-facility records; interplant transfers reported at once	records reviewed "continuously" by resident inspectors
Physical inventories	none	none	regularly scheduled	required annually	required annually

control to the IAEA while System I represents a safeguards system that is almost completely controlled internally (i.e., by the nation-state).

The respondents were asked specific questions about each of the five systems. Further, each respondent was asked which of the systems he preferred to be the actual system as well as which system he believed was likely to be the actual safeguards system.

In addition to including the twelve specific components of safeguards in each of the five systems, the respondent was requested to reply to a specific question related to each one by selecting the response that most closely reflected his attitude in terms of stringency of control; further, the respondent was queried concerning the strength of his commitment to his response. These questions therefore served to probe the specific attitudes of the respondent as related to certain specific methods of control.

From the responses to the questions concerning the hypothetical systems and the specific questions about each component, a complete description of each respondent's attitudes toward safeguards control has been generated. Further, the consistency of each respondent's comments and replies is determined.

THE POPULATION

The sample for this survey includes 84 safeguards experts of 23 different nationalities as well as safeguards experts in relevant international organizations. The population was distributed among the various nations with two considerations in mind: the nuclear power projected for the nation and the influence that knowledgeable nuclear experts from nations without plans for large-scale use of nuclear power exert at international meetings. Thus, the population includes experts ranging from nations with no plans to generate electrical energy by nuclear means to those with large-scale nuclear energy programs.

RESULTS

An important aspect of the technological interaction in the overall safeguards system is the elementary proposition that the experience of a nation in the generation of nuclear energy will influence the nuclear elites' perception of a safeguards system. Their perceptions should

be affected in two ways: in how much external control they would
prefer the IAEA to exercise and in the amount of external control
they feel the IAEA's safeguards system will ultimately have.

Experience in generating nuclear energy can be classified in
two ways: (1) the length of time a nation has been generating electricity
through nuclear energy or (2) the capacity of the nation to generate
energy by nuclear means (obviously, these two classifications are not
independent of each other). Figure 9 shows the prefered hypothetical
system averaged over all individuals in the nation or nations that
have signed the NPT plotted against the time since the first electricity
generating nuclear reactor was placed into operation in that nation.[4]
The trend is quite clear: The longer the nation has been generating
peaceful nuclear energy the more stringent external controls the
nuclear elite of that nation prefer. In Figure 10, the hypothetical
system choice of the elite of those nations presently generating
electricity by nuclear means is displayed as a function of the capacity
that nation will have to generate nuclear energy by the end of 1972.[5]
Again, the same trend is quite apparent: When a nation has a large
nuclear energy capacity, the nuclear elite of that nation prefer more
stringent external controls over the nuclear material.

A similar result is seen in the elites' perception of the final
system to be established under the terms of the NPT. For example,
the second entry in Table 9 shows that the elites of the nation with by
far the greatest nuclear generating capacity (the United States) expect
a system considerably more stringent than other nations with nuclear
power stations. Further, the nations with no present nuclear capacity
expect a system much less stringent than either of the other groups.

Interestingly, the same pattern is reflected by the respondents
in the IAEA Department of Safeguards and Inspection. The mean
values for the preferred system of the sample of staff members from
nations with power reactors was 3.4 while the mean for the sample
of those staff members from nations with no power reactors was 2.7.
Since every respondent on the IAEA staff equated his preference with
his view of the model agreement, the same mean values hold for the
staff members' perception of the actual safeguards system to be
established under the NPT.

To investigate more completely the interaction between the
nuclear experience of a nation and the preferences of the nuclear
experts toward safeguards, consider the responses to the twelve
specific questions. The mean responses for three categories of nuclear
power generating capabilities are shown in Table 9. The variables for

TABLE 9

The Components of Parts of the Safeguards System with Preferences by Amount of Nuclear Power Generated

		United States	Countries with Power Reactors (except United States)	Countries with No Power Reactors
System choice	$\bar{x} =$	3.50	2.50	2.00
Perceived system	$\bar{x} =$	2.92	2.35	2.00
Design control	$\bar{x} =$	2.54	2.13	2.44
Plant change	$\bar{x} =$	1.84	1.68	1.91
Measurements (where)	$\bar{x} =$	3.13	2.65	2.32
Measurements (type)	$\bar{x} =$	3.36	2.63	2.06
Access	$\bar{x} =$	3.17	2.39	2.65
Diversions report	$\bar{x} =$	3.41	2.68	3.02
Reaction to report	$\bar{x} =$	1.58	1.65	1.85
Funds for IAEA	$\bar{x} =$	2.41	2.25	2.20
Funds for facility	$\bar{x} =$	2.20	2.24	2.26
Licensing	$\bar{x} =$	2.21	2.32	2.38
Settle disputes	$\bar{x} =$	2.52	1.80	2.29
Records report	$\bar{x} =$	1.71	1.90	1.65
Inventories	$\bar{x} =$	1.39	1.51	1.71
Detect or deter*		Detect and deter	Detect and deter	Detect

*Majority of respondents favored the response listed.

FIGURE 9

Hypothetical System Choice as a Function
of Years of Nuclear Energy Generation Experience

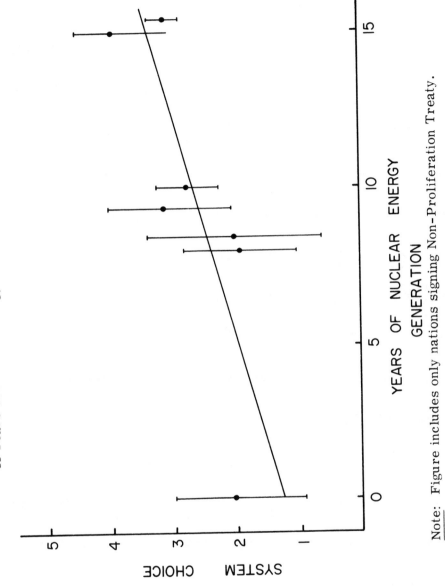

Note: Figure includes only nations signing Non-Proliferation Treaty.

139

FIGURE 10

Hypothetical System Choice
as a Function of Nuclear Energy Capacity

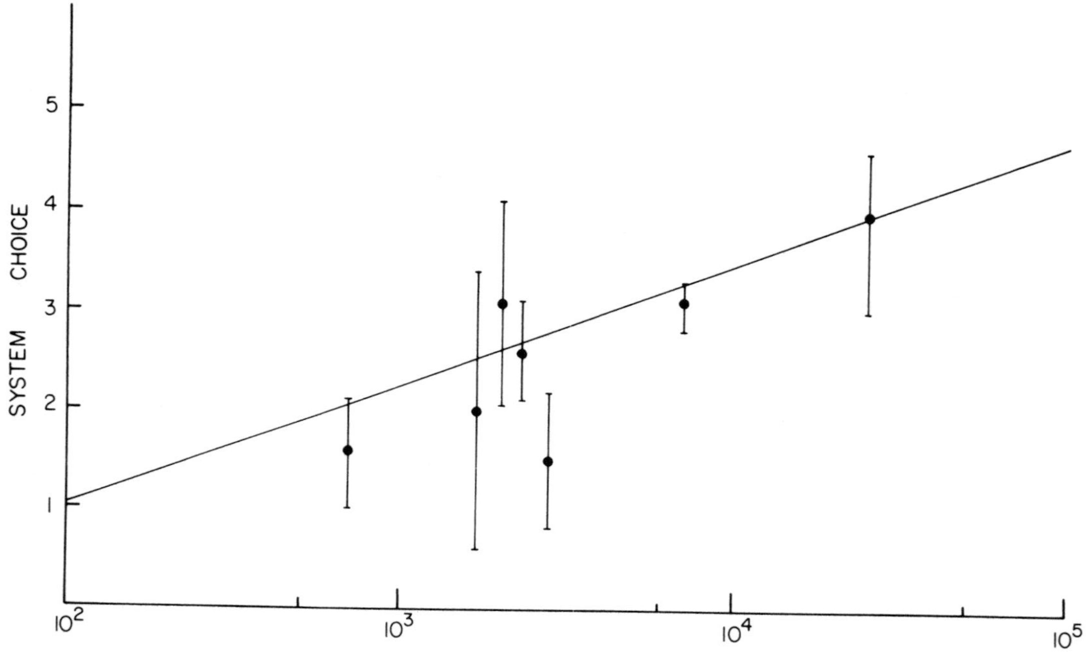

Note: Figure includes all nations in which interviews were conducted.

which disagreement exists between at least two of the three groups
are the following:

1. The extent to which the IAEA should be involved in the process
of designing the safeguard procedures of the nuclear facility

2. Where independent measurements should be performed by
IAEA

3. The type of independent measurements that should be made
by the IAEA

4. The denial of access due to the loss of proprietory information that should be allowed

5. How suspected diversions are reported to IAEA

6. How disputes between nations and IAEA are settled.

In each of these six cases, the nuclear experts from the United
States chose, on the average, the most stringent response of the three
groups. However, the lowest mean response is distributed between
the other two groups. Thus, an investigation into the variables on
which each group cued is necessary.

An extremely powerful method of determining which of the
variables are related is the smallest space analysis developed by
Guttmann and Lingoes.[6] Using this technique, the variables of interest
are plotted in the smallest number of dimensions such that the distance
between any two variables is inversely proportional to the correlation
coefficient between those variables. Thus, a two- or three-dimensional
profile of the relation between the various variables is obtained.
Such a device allows the investigator to "see" the relations between
the variables on a relatively simple graph rather than in a large (in
this case 12 x 12) matrix. Figures 11, 12, and 13 display the results
of this analysis for each of the three groups discussed above.

The sample of nuclear elites from the United States displays
a clear clustering of variables (see Figure 11). All of the variables
in the large cluster marked group I are preceived by the members
of the U. S. sample as related to one another (1.e., these variables
are highly correlated) and most closely related to the choice of a
hypothetical system. Each of the aspects of safeguards in this group
is closely related to the control of nuclear material. Groups II and
III consist of variables that are more closely related to administrative

FIGURE 11

Spatial Clustering for U. S. Respondents

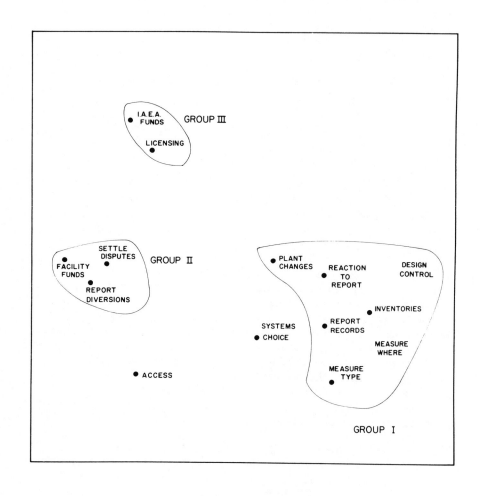

FIGURE 12

Spatial Clustering for Respondents in States
Other Than the United States with Power Reactors

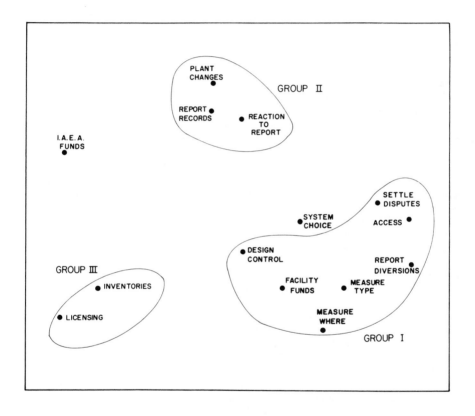

FIGURE 13

Spatial Clustering for Respondents
in States with No Power Reactors

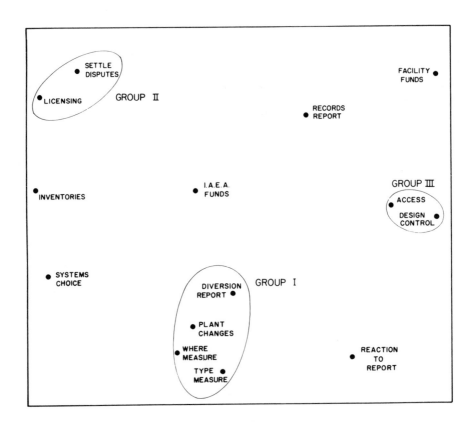

and funding details than to problems of materials control. Thus, individuals in the U.S. elite tend to cue on issues that are closely related to the methods needed to control the material and choose a hypothetical system accordingly.

Three clusters of variables also appear in the smallest space analysis of the responses from nuclear experts in countries other than the United States presently generating nuclear energy (see Figure 12). The cluster most closely related to the choice of a hypothetical system, group I, contains three of the same variables as group I in the U.S. sample (type and place of measurements and design control). However, some very important differences also appear. Four variables in group I in the U.S. sample that do not fall in the same group for other nuclear generating countries all require intrusions into the plant (i.e., inventories, reporting and reviewing records, reaction to a loss, and changing plant design), whereas the remaining variables in group I of the other nuclear generating nations are all related to relief from intrusions. That is, the most important variables include reporting suspected diversions to IAEA, denying access to IAEA inspectors, settling disputes with IAEA, and obtaining funds from IAEA for their own safeguards operations. Thus, this group of variables constitutes elements of a verification system rather than a control system.

The clustering of variables for the responses from nations with no nuclear power capability is much less pronounced (see Figure 13). Again, however, the group most closely related to the choice of a hypothetical system contains elements that require some intrusion into the facility (i.e., measurements and changing plant practices).

Table 10 summarizes the three figures by indicating which variables cued each of the groups. The underlying dimension of these variables is the amount of intrusion into a plant necessary to obtain the proper level of either verification or control of the nuclear materials within that plant. The degree of intrusion necessary is in turn strongly related to the previous experience the group of nations has had in generating nuclear power. Further, the variables over which the greatest disagreement occurs are the variables that are most important in choosing a hypothetical safeguards system.

CONCLUSIONS

The data of this study support the conclusion that the desire for stringent control over nuclear materials is related closely to a vast experience in nuclear technology. Since only fifteen of the

TABLE 10

Components of Safeguards System Most Closely
Related to System Choice

	United States	Countries with Power Reactors (except United States)	Countries with No Power Reactors
Design control	X	X	
Plant changes	X		X
Measurements (where)	X	X	X
Measurements (type)	X	X	X
Access		X	
Diversions report		X	X
Settle disputes		X	
Records report	X		
Inventories	X		
Funds for IAEA			
Funds for facility			
Licensing			
Detect-deter			

approximately fifty nations that participated in the model agreement discussions have nuclear power stations,[7] the influence of those nations that have a desire for less stringent control cannot be overlooked.

The actual stringency of the system imposed on any nation may differ from the model agreement in several ways. For example, Paragraph 71 of the model agreement provides that the IAEA may make ad hoc inspections to "verify the information contained in the initial report on the nuclear material." While later paragraphs present more information, the understanding of what constitutes verification is not completely clear. Thus, the inspections can be more or less intrusive than anticipated by the nation depending on the IAEA's, or possibly even an individual inspector's, concept of verification. Since many IAEA staff members come from nations with little or no nuclear power capacity, they might be expected to require less stringent controls than if all inspectors were citizens of, for example, the United States and the United Kingdom.

Since no international agreement is immutable, the present study can indicate the direction safeguards may take in the future. As the amount of energy generated by nuclear means increases, nations generating this power may prefer more stringent safeguards systems. However, other nations will be just starting a nuclear program. Thus, disagreements concerning the implementation of the points mentioned above might be expected. On the other hand, the population studied here has agreed on many of the components of the safeguards program. Therefore, these aspects can be expected to cause very little friction during the coming years when safeguards are being applied under the NPT.

Finally, not all of the data collected during this study have yet been analyzed, and thus many questions have not been answered. For example, no clear evidence indicates any strong dependence of the preference of safeguards systems on the national interest of a state. However, further investigation will be necessary on this particular aspect. Further, no analysis of the investigation concerning the relation between career perception and safeguards attitudes has been completed. The data for these and other topics have been collected and such analyses lie in the future.

NOTES

1. Allan McKnight, Atomic Safeguards: A Study in Verification (New York: UNITAR, 1971), p 46.

2. IAEA Document INFCIRC/26, (Vienna, 1965); IAEA Document INFCIRC/66(Rev 2), (Vienna, 1968).

3. IAEA Document INFCIRC/153, (Vienna, 1970).

4. The source of appropriate dates is "Power Reactors '71" in Nuclear Engineering International, 16 (January-February 1971), 91-99.

5. Ibid.

6. L. Guttman, "A General Nonmetric Technique for Finding the Smallest Coordinate Space for a Configuration of Points," Psychometrika, 33 (1968), 469-506: J. C. Lingoes, "An IBM-7090 Program for Guttman-Lingoes Smallest Space Analysis—I," Behavioral Science, 10 (April 1965), 183-84; J. C. Lingoes, "New Computer Developments in Pattern Analysis and Nonmetric Techniques," in Uses of Computers in Psychological Research (Paris: Gauthier-Villars, 1966), pp. 1-22; J. C. Lingoes, "An IBM-7090 Program for Guttman-Lingoes Multi-dimensional Scalogram Analysis—II," Behavioral Science, 12 (July 1967), 268-70; J. C. Lingoes, "The Multivariate Analysis of Qualitative Data," Multivariant Behavioral Research, 3 (1968), 61-94; J. C. Lingoes, "Some Boundary Conditions for a Monotone Analysis of Symmetric Matrices," Psychometrika (forthcoming, 1972); J. C. Lingoes and E. Roskam, "A Mathematical and Empirical Study of Two Multi-dimensional Scaling Algorithms," Multivariant Behavioral Research (forthcoming, 1972); E. Roskam and J. C. Lingoes, "Minissa-I: A Fortran IV (G) Program for the Smallest Space Analysis of Square Symmetric Matrices," Behavioral Science, 15 (July 1970), 204-5.

7. IAEA, Power and Research Reactors in Member States (Vienna, 1971).

While noting that U.S. respondents always preferred a strong system, <u>Ralph J. Jones</u> (Nuclear Fuel Service, Incorporated) asked what portion of the sample upon which Dean Zollman's paper was based was drawn from the U.S. nuclear industry which would be subject to IAEA control. Zollman replied that none of the respondents in the international sample were from U.S. industry. However, in the national sample, which included representatives of the U.S. nuclear industry, questions were asked concerning the IAEA's relationship to the U.S. safeguards system and a relevant analysis of the data from this sample is forthcoming.

<u>Charles Van Doren</u> (Arms Control and Disarmament Agency) suggested that semantic confusion exists over the words detect and deter. Since it is generally accepted that the international safeguards system is going to do no more than detect, he pointed out that a question of perception exists as to whether the art of detection has a deterrent value. Zollman said that he feels many people would like to see the evolution of a system that would provide for more deterrence than that entailed in detection. Upon a request for an example, he mentioned frequent security checks on people working in plants as one example.

<u>C. D. W. Thornton</u> (Director, Division of Nuclear Materials Safeguards, AEC) referred to Zollman's statement that safeguards would indicate that a country has not diverted and asked whether this does not assume that the material balances are closing. Zollman replied that he thought that, if it can be verified that the material balances are closing, one should be able to state that a country is performing its duties under the IAEA or the NPT. However, Thornton pointed out, and Zollman agreed, that there is no experience to indicate that material balances of countries are closing.

11

REMARKS OF J. H. JENNEKENS

For many years Canadian safeguards officials have advocated what we have called a balanced approach to safeguards implementation. By this is meant a combination of all of the elements in the set of resources available to a safeguards agency, be it national, regional, or international. These include, in addition to procedural elements, measurement equipment and such other safeguards measures as containment and surveillance.

We believe that attention must continue to be directed toward insuring the optimum use of the human element. In our eyes this human element is the single most important member of the set of resources available to a safeguards agency. Unfortunately, in recent years, at least in our eyes, a very large fraction of the safeguards community has directed its efforts toward the more technically attractive elements of the set. Now I do not suggest for one minute that there should be any reduction in the research and development efforts that are currently under way, but I do believe that more attention should be focused on the recruitment and training of competent, well-motivated inspectors. Moreover, we should continuously ask ourselves questions regarding what we expect inspectors to do, why they should be carrying out certain functions, and how these functions should be carried out.

Perhaps the next most important consideration, insofar as safeguards implementation is concerned, is what we term the threshold

151

concept. We have applied this concept to a joint program that we have between ourselves, the U.S. Arms Control Disarmament Agency, and the U.S. Atomic Energy Commission (AEC). That program is the Tamper Resistant Unattended Safeguards Techniques (TRUST) program. By the threshold concept we mean that, in light of the many demands that are placed on society today, the unlimited allocation of resources to international safeguards in an attempt to achieve absolute assurance against the diversion of nuclear material is clearly impractical if not unjustified. However, by insuring that the level of effort to which a would-be diverter must go is so high or is sufficiently high that he is deterred or discouraged, we can achieve a sufficient degree of assurance that, in conjunction with the other efforts of society, the membership of the nuclear weapons club will not be expanded.

This leads me to a final point. I would like to say that to a very large extent I am in agreement with the position that C. D. W. Thornton has adopted in that an effective international safeguards system is an important prerequisite to world security; of this I am convinced. Such a system is necessary to protect against those for whom there exist an incentive to divert. However, we must continue to investigate the ways and means that would insure that we could remove or at least reduce the incentive to divert nuclear materials. These ways and means fall within the totality of international measures to insure the peaceful solution of disputes.

There is no single panacea; it is a very difficult problem, but I believe that there must be expertise available in a wide spectrum of disciplines which would insure that at least a reasonable attempt is made to remove or reduce the incentive to divert.

REMARKS OF R. W. BUTLER

Any rational and clear understanding of international safeguard procedures must be informed by an understanding of the international political context within which safeguards are to be applied. The obvious reason for this assertion is that nuclear proliferation is not confined within national boundaries. In addition, it is historically true that, after the U.S. government took the world's first initiative in controlling atomic energy, it has been commonly accepted that the control of atomic energy demands international cooperation. Nevertheless, the need for a special and perhaps unique international effort to develop controls on atomic energy has not altered the fundamental nature of international relations. The participants in international relations remain in sovereign states. The governments of sovereign states are obliged to make their policy decisions on the basis of their national interest.

Their assessment of their freedom for maneuver or policy judgment is, of course, partly determined by the interests and power of other states. In addition, in most cases governments are not inevitably short-sighted and therefore attempt to adjust their policy decision to the long term effects of such external phenomena as atomic energy. But it seems quite wrong, and indeed fundamentally wrong, to understand the policy decisions of sovereign states in any other way than as an attempt to materialize the national interest. This is not necessarily a somber view, nor is it something for which an apology is necessary. Indeed, it is not difficult to envisage chaotic or even disastrous effects for the world community as a whole if nation-states could not be relied on to express their own best interests.

Equally clear as a fact of life in the modern world is the almost unimaginable growth in the nuclear industry and the concomitant need for measures to regulate that industry. This should be, and is, an activity in which nation-states recognize a mutuality of interest. Nowadays, the problem is not to establish that fact but to develop procedures, techniques, and agreements that give expression to that mutuality of interest.

At the risk of moving too quickly and perhaps too crudely to a definition, I think that the relationship between an international safeguards system and the expression of that mutuality of interest is derived from the essential function of a safeguards system: that is, to create a climate of confidence in support of the jointly pursued objective—the control of atomic energy.

This view of safeguards is based primarily on an assumption that sovereign states have been prepared to reach agreements on certain fundamental propositions—in this case the key proposition is non-proliferation. The creation and signature of the Non-Proliferation Treaty (NPT) is a concrete sign that most sovereign states have reached just such an agreement. I should also mention that even though the measurements involved in any safeguards system may lack the desired degree of precision, this does not necessarily prevent safeguards from contributing to a climate of confidence.

I would now like to refer to one serious dilemma of the safeguards system from the standpoint of international politics. This is its relationship to the concept of nuclear deterrence. Fundamental to the concept of non-proliferation is the rejection of the idea that

the possession of nuclear weapons will serve to deter others from
the use of those weapons. Thus, the concept of deterrence is disposed
of. On the other hand, the concept of deterrence is fundamental to
the international safeguards system. After all, the purpose of safeguards as defined by IAEA document INFCIRC/153 is "deterrence of
[such] diversion by the risk of early detection." Is the risk of early
detection an effective deterrent? To what extent is it possible, even
under a conceivably perfect safeguards system, to prevent a sovereign
state from diverting? The NPT recognizes the possibility of high
national interest leading a government to decide to abrogate its treaty
obligations. On the other hand, perhaps the concept of deterrence is
not indivisible and thus its operation in the context of the so-called
balance of terror between nuclear weapons states differs from the
deterrent effects of safeguards on non-nuclear weapons states. These
are difficult issues and clearly require further study. However, I
have already suggested that a safeguards system may in fact have
another and more real function: the provision of a climate of confidence
that will assist states in keeping the real undertakings they have
entered into internationally, the undertakings that are the only ones
that count.

Similarly, I should like to underline that it seems clear that
there is a direct relationship between the intrinsic efficiency and
effectiveness of a safeguards system and its ability to create that
climate. For this reason, national work in this field, together with
the extension of the techniques and the diplomatic activity of the IAEA,
is of crucial importance and must continue. Finally, it is a matter
of the greatest importance that governments prepared to accept the
international obligations of non-proliferation should continue to work
as vigorously as possible to insure that their national systems of
safeguards will be able to relate to and be integrated with the international standards agreed between governments.

Whatever is done, however, and it is a matter of real human
significance that so many intelligent and dedicated men are working
in the field of safeguards, it is important that we do what we are doing
for the right reasons and on the basis of a real understanding of the
forces operating in the international community.

As I said earlier, it is less important today for us to agree that
the world is better off with safeguards than it is for us to recognize
their real nature, including their limitations, and to design them in
a way that makes them capable of acceptance and will permit them
to play their role in support of the fundamental political decisions
of governments.

REMARKS OF G. BILLY*

My purpose is to consider the experience acquired in the control of source and special nuclear materials at the Commissariat à l'Energie Atomique (CEA) during the past several years.

Before specifying the principal aspects of this control, it appears necessary to emphasize the differences between controls within a nation and what might be called the procedures of international security as regards safeguards. It is possible to make a distinction among the following:

1. The internal control within a utility or industry over the conditions involved in the utilization or the unlawful possession of nuclear materials for various purposes. This internal control is similar to that exercised in an enterprise holding great quantities of gold or manufacturing bank notes so that objects of value will not be improperly used or misappropriated. For atomic energy, allowances must be made for certain political aspects, e.g., the conditions of usage imposed by the suppliers of special materials. Such situations were recognized by the CEA from the beginning; they are in large part codified in its "Administrative Code of Source and Special Nuclear Materials."

2. The national control by each government of activities concerning production, utilization, or trading of nuclear materials on its territory or outside its territory. Since the jurisdiction over such activities is either by state controlled agencies or by para-state controlled agencies, national control is blended with internal control in almost every state. With the development of private nuclear industry, national control has tended to diverge from internal control. For the states that ratified the NPT, the act of taking measures in order to avoid the possibilities of misappropriation or clandestine exportation is a juridical obligation. France, which has not signed this treaty, assumed a political obligation the day it declared that it intended to respect the principles of the NPT.

3. The international control by which a state or an international organization is given the means to ascertain that the political commitments taken by a state concerning the utilization of all or a part of

---

*Translated by C. Ruth.

the nuclear materials situated on its territory are respected. This control differs from the preceding in that it involves diplomatic rather than policing techniques. In reality, it has as its objective to verify the upholding of commitments taken by states but neither to prevent nor to restrain the unlawful or irresponsible diversions on the part of individuals.

In fact, in France, as in the United States and other nations having an appreciable nuclear program, the development of all these measures of control has followed a very pragmatic course. It has gradually adapted to the evolution of the situation, combining concepts and procedures from different sources in order to achieve the desired objective that alone is important, i.e., the effective prevention of all misappropriations of nuclear material. It is appropriate to emphasize that, as it has been said, this objective is different from the one assigned to various international organizations as regards safeguards.

The principal measures of control are adopted as much from the internal plan of the CEA as from the national plan, whose administration is entrusted to the same authorities. These measures of control do not constitute, on a national scale, a comprehensive body of codified rules but an ensemble of interrelated measures that are not all subject to the same system of administration. One could mention, for example, the rules concerning basic nuclear installations which are not officially a part of the measures in question but contribute largely to insure the effectiveness of controls.

Certainly, the CEA does not claim to serve as a model for other countries. The best procedure is for the authorities of each nation to face their responsibilities, which necessarily vary from one country to another as a function of the structures and customs of each.

The measures taken by the CEA are designed to avoid diversions and to detect diversions rather rapidly. Most of these measures have already been presented in the course of hearings held by the International Atomic Energy Agency. They apply as well to private industry, either as a result of the fact that the nuclear materials involved belong to the CEA or are subject to governmental control.

Thus, the internal and external inspections of the CEA thus far have never discovered grave anomalies in the administration and utilization of nuclear materials, therefore confirming the validity of the system presently in force. However, this is not a sufficient reason against improving the methods of administration and inspection in view of the increase in the stock of fertile and fissile materials and the rapid development of a number of enterprises possessing nuclear materials for private purposes. Everyone can profit by the experience of others and adapt, if possible, new methods to their own needs.

However, it is necessary to emphasize in concluding that if such exchanges of information on the procedures of control in force at the national level can be useful, it does not necessarily follow that the procedures of safeguards to be put into action at the international level must be an extrapolation or synthesis of these national procedures. Indeed, as was indicated earlier, the problems of international safeguards are by nature different from the problems of national control, and this is the reason I have not considered them in detail here.

At the onset of the discussion, Herbert Scoville (Carnegie Endowment for International Peace) emphasized that, since France was a nuclear weapons nation but not a signatory to the NPT, Gerard Billy's statement that France would abide by the objectives of the treaty was very significant and encouraging.

Joerg Menzel (Los Alamos Scientific Laboratory) asked what effect the admission of China to the United Nations would have on the IAEA and the NPT. Richard Butler replied that, as far as China and the IAEA are concerned, China will have to make a direct application to the IAEA for membership and that, as far as China and the NPT are concerned, the NPT is a question about which China will have to make an independent decision. Butler concluded that he felt a "wait and see" attitude would have to be taken on both points.

Ralph Lumb (Nuclear Surveillance and Auditing Corporation), attempting to precipitate a discussion of the possibility of minimizing or removing incentives for diversion, referred to a statement by Lawrence Scheinman (University of Michigan) on the possibility of transferring, in some fashion or another, separation technology to a multinational group. Lumb asked for comments on how this action might influence the incentive to go to a nuclear capability either independently or through diversion.

Jon Jennekens commented that, although no panacea exists in this area, if the technologically advanced nations attempt to deny a nation access to technological improvements, a sense of frustration will develop in that nation and it will decide to go it alone. This applies throughout the entire fabric of international relations. Thus, Jennekens pointed out that in the nuclear area, if there is no sharing of technology and given a sufficient amount of time and resources, non-nuclear nations will eventually decide to develop their own capabilities.

Butler underlined the difficulties in meeting requests from less well-developed countries for the provision of advanced technology. He emphasized that the consequences of such action may be precisely what safeguarders wish to avoid since a nation not having a nuclear capacity might have its ability to develop one on its own enhanced by the provision of foreign aid. However, Butler wondered to what extent the nuclear powers are willing to relinquish some of their control over nuclear facilities to a multinational body.

Lumb pointed out that he was not privileged to that kind of information and therefore could not answer the question. However, Lumb stated that one must recognize that, if certain kinds of technological information are distributed, the way to weapon capability is lubricated. He added that he did not accept the position that denying a developing nation a specific kind of technology was denying technology per se to that nation.

Scoville stated that, while he could not speak officially, he was of the opinion that the U.S. government has given an indication that in principle it is willing to enter into cooperative licensing arrangements concerning gaseous diffusion technology. He added that he did not visualize any nation having the capital and power to build a gaseous diffusion plant; thus, he felt that making the relevant technology available on a licensed basis was not a terrible risk. He concluded that he favored licensing arrangements as a basis for sharing nuclear technology where this sharing is multilateral, where the probability of diversion is not high, and particularly where in most cases low enriched rather than high enriched material is being produced.

Butler pointed out that he considered an urgent need of Western governments to be closer cooperation between the foreign aid authorities and the national agencies concerned with nuclear affairs. Developing nations often request aid they do not really need, e.g., a nuclear reactor instead of shovels. Cooperation between the foreign aid authorities and the national agencies concerned with nuclear affairs is important as a means of ensuring the transfer of nuclear technology under appropriate controls and in justifiable circumstances. However, if a developing nation requests nuclear technology and can demonstrate some basis for that request, the risk due to avoiding that request is great. The appropriate response is to insure the transfer of nuclear technology through licensing agreements that provide for adequate safeguards.

Scheinman commented that he felt a strong argument could be made on behalf of the proposition that mid-twentieth century technology, including nuclear technology, has as much prestige value as did industrialization a century ago. Thus, while Scheinman stated that he did not feel the nuclear powers had to give everything requested, they must somehow come to terms with the whole issue of technological transfer including the conditions under which such transfers are made. He contended that these transfers can be made under controlled conditions, that is, under conditions that would minimize the dangers inherent in the unilateral acquisition of technology.

These comments led to a general discussion of gaseous diffusion technology. Utilization of gaseous diffusion technology can contribute to nuclear weapons capability and so safeguards are a significant problem. On the other hand, it was emphasized that with gaseous diffusion technology a chance exists for multinational, but not international, cooperation. Samuel Edlow (Edlow International) suggested that, even if the United States offered to share gaseous diffusion technology, other nations might not anxiously accept the offer and might not accept the U.S. terms if they wanted to accept the offer; thus, the entire discussion might be a bit academic. Enrico Jacchia (Euratom Safeguards) highlighted Edlow's suggestions by pointing out that discussions about the transferring of gaseous diffusion technology had to be considered in the context of the fact that an ultra-centrifuge system is almost in operation. He stated that his office is regularly sending inspectors to visit the centrifuge plant at Almelo in the Netherlands.

In concluding the discussion, Eli Roth (Arms Control and Disarmament Agency) asked about the effectiveness, acceptability, and nature of safeguards in Eastern Europe. Inspector General Rudolf Rometsch (International Atomic Energy Agency) responded that many Eastern European nations have signed the NPT and made safeguards agreements but that the U.S.S.R. has not made an offer equal to that of the United States and the United Kingdom concerning the inspection of facilities in the U.S.S.R. However, a research and development contract has been concluded between the U.S.S.R. and the IAEA for developing and testing of safeguards procedures at the Novo-Voronezh power station for the reactors in use there.

12

INTERNATIONAL
INSPECTION
OF U.S. INDUSTRY

David J. Haymon

Under the terms of the Non-Proliferation Treaty (NPT), the safeguarding of nuclear material is required only in non-nuclear weapon states. However, two nuclear weapon countries, the United States and Great Britain, have offered to place their civilian nuclear industry, subject to national security restrictions, under international safeguards when the NPT is effectively enforced. To indicate U.S. support for the NPT, President Lyndon B. Johnson in 1967 offered to permit the IAEA to apply its safeguards to these nuclear activities within the United States. This offer was later reaffirmed by President Richard Nixon. The objective of the offer as stated by the President was to demonstrate that the United States was not asking other countries to accept safeguards that it was unwilling to accept itself.

To date, from our somewhat limited encounter with the concept of international safeguards under NPT, it does appear that the IAEA is taking a generally pragmatic view. In April 1970 the IAEA Board of Governors established a committee to advise it on the content of the agreements that the non-nuclear weapon states are expected to conclude with the Agency. This committee finished its work in March 1971, and in setting forth the general principles, technical procedures, and so forth that are to be employed it has done a reasonable job of defining the limitations of the systems and spelling out what was to be accomplished.

Domestically, we have been struggling with the concept of "safeguards," regardless of the nomenclature of the time, for a number of years, and we are still faced with a substantial number of

163

problems in the implementation of safeguards within the United States. For example, concerning the relatively straightforward problem of what constitutes a "significant quantity," "prompt detection," and so forth, American industry has been asking for definitions and guidance for a number of years but has yet to receive it. We have been told that a conceptual basis for these particular items of terminology would be developed in 1971, but as of this point of time there have been no precise, or for that matter, general definitions.

Obviously, in the area of international safeguards, which are still in the earlier stages of development, these same problems require solutions. However, they are complemented by numerous additional concerns. I would like to mention some of these briefly and then delve into some of them in more detail. One of the obvious problems is how to avoid infringing on the sovereignty of the various states. Another is how to handle relations between governments that signed the NPT and those that did not. Finances are a vital concern, of course. So is the preservation of national security information. Language barriers and discrepancies among the relative incomes of different nationals militate against uniformity in the ranks of the inspectors. The imbalance in the maturity of various national nuclear programs tends to produce a corresponding imbalance in the national origins of individuals available to act as inspectors. Another very basic problem is the question of enforcement proceedings and how minor and perhaps unknowing items of noncompliance would be treated. Deliberate and overt diversion would, of course, present even more serious problems.

Along with the many policy level problems just mentioned there exists literally a myriad of specific practice problems, and it is in this area of day-to-day operational practicality that industry will first feel the effects of the NPT safeguards agreement: who to inspect, when, how often, how, what data to require, how to protect proprietary information, what record forms to use, what analytical techniques to use, how to relate the various results, and whether resident inspectors should be considered. Any decision dealing with any one of these problems will have a direct effect on each U.S. fuel processor and fabricator. Both the policy level problems and the day-to-day operational problems must be considered in the light of two basic concepts of safeguards. First, safeguards are a means of promptly detecting diversion of special nuclear materials (SNM) to unauthorized uses, not of preventing diversion or of controlling the use of material. Second, it is technically impossible to achieve a practical foolproof system of safeguards. We do not now have, and probably never will have, the capability to devise practical systems that will give 100 percent assurance of prompt detection of any diversion no matter how small.

In May 1971 the AEC arranged a series of meetings with U.S. industry to discuss the application of international safeguards within the United States. Industry representatives were understandably cautious and concerned. The meetings pointed up that the IAEA safeguards program is still in its formative stages and emphasized the many uncertainties distributed throughout. However, there are perhaps some reasonably definitive statements that can be made regarding potential Agency requirements. First, the AEC stated that it expects that the first international safeguards under the President's offer will come about in early 1973. There is no money available within the IAEA for the program prior to that date, and in addition to this fact it is estimated that it will take from six to nine months to complete preliminary discussion on the subsidiary arrangements and perhaps an additional six months to finalize them.

Selection of facilities to be inspected has become a significant problem. Apparently, there will not be sufficient funds available to inspect all U.S. facilities; therefore, some selection process will be necessary. The AEC representatives have mentioned two possible approaches. One would be to select a particular case in point and follow the material through the fuel cycle: conversion to UF_6, enrichment, fabrication, through the reactor, through reprocessing. Another approach might be to select facilities by lottery initially and then rotate among all facilities with particular attention paid to those engaged in international commerce and/or new technology. The AEC has tacitly supported the Australian proposal which is essentially along the lines of the second approach.

One cheering factor is that there apparently will be no significant change in reporting requirements. There may be some changes in the format of the current forms used to report to the AEC, but there apparently will be no additional forms or reports. It will be the responsibility of the AEC to transcribe information as reported by industry on the existing or revised form 741 into a format suitable for IAEA use.

Another item of interest to U.S. operators is that the IAEA essentially considers three fundamental material balance areas as both applicable and necessary. These areas are receipt and storage, in-process, and shipment. It has been generally stated by both the AEC and IAEA representatives that this concept should not require a change in or addition to the material balance areas established within fuel processing facilities for domestic purposes.

An additional encouraging fact is that the safeguards agreement provides that the manner in which the procedures set forth are to be applied should be specified in detail in subsidiary arrangements made between the IAEA and the individual government. These subsidiary arrangements, by necessity, must be handled on a facility-by-facility basis. Therefore, it would appear that there will be some consideration given, on the international level at least, to the differences between facilities engaged in essentially the same type of work.

One area that continues to give cause for concern is the problems faced in the safeguarding of material in transit. From all indications, the IAEA is no closer to a solution of this very significant problem than we are domestically. Of course, the problem in the area of international safeguards is compounded by the fact of the long distances involved in the transport of international shipments and further by the fact that the nuclear material is in transit on or over the territory or territorial waters of a number of individual states during its transport.

As an aside, I would like to point out that if a non-weapons state seriously wanted to obtain either weapons-grade material or material that could be relatively easily upgraded to weapons grade, it would certainly seem to be more practical, and certainly more economical, to divert a shipment of plutonium or for that matter, any highly enriched fissile material, than it would be to take a handful of 3 percent enriched uranium dioxide out of a fabricator's plant each day over an extended period to be upgraded in some clandestine facility. Certainly if a state has the technical and financial wherewithal to construct a facility to take the material from 3 percent enriched to weapons grade, it has the capability to start from source grade as well rather than depend upon continuous "snitching" of handfuls of low-enriched material from an American fabrication plant for its raw material supply. Of course, as plutonium becomes more abundant it does indeed present additional cause for concern. I submit that it is in this area of safeguards that we should be concentrating the bulk of our resources, both internationally and domestically, rather than in the questionable area of source grade and low enriched material.

I have been using the term international safeguards frequently, and it is perhaps long past the time that an over-simplified definition of this term be given. Essentially, international safeguards is predicated on the fact that the individual state should have set up its own system to account for and control nuclear materials. Then, in practice, international safeguards consists of informing the IAEA of the general design of the individual facility so as to provide for the best application of safeguards; sending reports on movements and inventory of nuclear material to the IAEA; and permitting international inspectors to visit the nuclear facility, or at least defined parts of it, so as to provide reasonable assurance that no material has been diverted to the manufacture of nuclear weapons or other nuclear explosives.

The IAEA has stated that the actual frequency, duration, and so forth of inspections should be determined on the basis of a number of criteria including the effectiveness of the state's own accounting and control system, the characteristics of the fuel cycle, and the amount and form of material. Although the Agency has worked out a rather practical and simplified formula for determining the frequency of routine inspections, as mentioned earlier, it seems apparent that, at least at the outset, the financial means for such inspection are not available and some other method of making a selection of facilities to be inspected with the formula framework will have to be worked out.

In 1971 Westinghouse hosted at its fuel fabrication facility in Columbia, South Carolina, an IAEA inspection team that carried out an integral test with the specific objective of making a quantitative statement on the plant's material balance; the test accordingly was aimed at investigating an Agency inspection team's capability to attain this objective. For the purpose of the test, four meetings were held of IAEA inspectors and Westinghouse management and in addition there was an initial test inspection early in 1971. These four meetings and the test inspection served the purpose of defining the subsidiary arrangement for the facility and the review and verification of the information on the plant and its material accountability system. The actual physical inventory verification test was performed at the end of April 1971. In all cases, as under projected actual conditions, the IAEA personnel were accompanied by AEC personnel. All information was channeled from Westinghouse through the AEC to the IAEA and vice versa. All procedures that would precede application of safeguards under an NPT-type agreement were followed for the test and in every case they were found to be less than burdensome. Key measurement points were defined for material flow and the definitions were found to be consistent with Westinghouse measurement practices and reporting requirements to the AEC. It had originally been planned that the IAEA team would carry out the inventory verification on its own. However, the AEC Division of Nuclear Materials Safeguards (DNMS) notified Westinghouse that they wished to carry out an inventory verification at the same time as the scheduled IAEA verification. Inasmuch as Westinghouse was not overly enthused with two periods of interference with normal plant operations, we suggested rather strongly that the efforts be carried out at the same time and fully in parallel. This was done, and of course the AEC inspection, being based on regulatory requirements, took precedence over the IAEA verification. However, I would like to note that there was a complete interchange of information between the IAEA and the AEC and apparently both purposes were served.

At the conclusion of the test activity, it appeared that it was the consensus of all three major parties that the objective of the test was achieved and that the provisions and constraints laid down in the NPT-type safeguards agreements are for the most part realistic. We feel that the Agency requests made during the test were quite realistic. However, it might be noted that the test objective for this one inventory of one plant was achieved at the cost of some 32 man-days of IAEA effort alone on site, excluding any in-plant familiarization tours, and so forth. The amount of additional effort required of Westinghouse personnel during the actual inventory verification was considerable, but not beyond reason. Of course, Westinghouse operating management had devoted significant time and effort to the initial phases of the test program, but considered as a one-time effort this too can be considered as reasonable. The test apparently did establish that the requirements of the IAEA and the AEC are not mutually exclusive and can in fact be met without additional burdens on the U.S. processor. If we can maintain this approach to the non-proliferation of safeguards requirements, we probably will not be unduly burdened by the implementation of international safeguards requirements. As I have related, the limited encounter that we have had with international safeguards under the NPT has led us to at least be hopeful that there is some basis in reasonableness and logic in the implementation of international safeguards in the United States.

However, I must admit that there still remains an underlying uneasiness, perhaps based on the fear of the proliferation of safeguards requirements. To this point at least, all indications have led us to believe that the IAEA, in implementing international safeguards within the United States under the President's offer, will in fact take a reasonable approach and attempt to build its system on the firm foundation of our domestic safeguards program. If this approach, which has been stated and restated on a number of occasions by IAEA personnel, is in fact maintained and if in addition our domestic safeguards program is predicated on a sound approach to the basic principles of safeguards, then perhaps our unease is not well founded. I would like to reiterate the two basic concepts of safeguards I mentioned earlier. Safeguards are a means of promptly detecting diversion, not of preventing the diversion or controlling the use of the material. Second, it is technically impossible to achieve a practical, foolproof system of safeguards. We do not now have and probably never will have the capability to devise practical systems that will give us 100 percent assurance of prompt detection of any diversion no matter how small.

There have been scenarios developed both on an international and a domestic basis regarding ways of diverting nuclear material, such as tunneling through a concrete wall of a reactor containment or perhaps in real desperation carrying several million curies of irradiated fuel without any shielding, which have led industrialists from a Member State to be quoted as saying. "This certainly demonstrates that there is no shortage of imaginative thinking within the Agency Secretariat but possibly a shortage of appreciation of practical plant operations." When applied to safeguards, this kind of imaginative thinking does indeed give one cause to reflect.

A continuing dialogue is under way between the nuclear industry and the AEC on what is a reasonable amount of safeguards to be applied. The important word here is "reasonable," as was underscored by Marc Kramer (University of Michigan) while inquiring how the word was used in reference to the economic cost or the probability of theft. The response by David Haymon noted the extremes encountered in the nuclear industry, namely between uranium ore in the ground and plutonium. Obviously, considerable time, effort, and money need to be spent in handling plutonium. Somewhere between these two extremes a reasonable level has to be established through this industry-AEC dialogue.

The financial limitation of the IAEA in monitoring U. S. nuclear activities was clarified by Charles Van Doren (Arms Control and Disarmament Agency). The limited financing of IAEA safeguards activities must cover nuclear activities in all non-weapons NPT parties as well as in the United States and United Kingdom. The nuclear facilities in the United States potentially amount to about half of those in the world. Thus, he thought the financial considerations would constitute a practical limitation on the extent to which the IAEA would be willing to implement the U. S. offer to safeguard U. S. facilities.

As was noted in the presentation by Haymon, the IAEA inspection of the Westinghouse facility at Columbia, South Carolina, was conducted concurrently with an AEC safeguards inspection. Manuel Kanter (Argonne National Laboratory) inquired whether the presence of both groups in any way simplified the work of either group. In response, Haymon stated that he believed simplification did result. An example was the avoidance of repeated samples by the two groups. He did note that the initial joint inspections involved a large total number of inspectors and, in retrospect, the main problem seemed to be traffic control of inspectors.

The increasingly important question of personnel selection for nuclear industries was raised by Curtis Colvin (Atlantic Richfield Hartford Company) while noting that employees in a nuclear facility might gradually divert by repeatedly taking small amounts.

In the extensive discussion of personnel screening that followed, Leonard Brenner (Office of Safeguards and Materials Management, AEC) noted that specific statutory authority for a government personnel screening program applicable to the nuclear industry does not exist.

If such statutory authority is obtained, the details of how a personnel screening program might be implemented have not been developed. However, preliminary thinking is that criteria identical to those applicable to screening for access to classified information would not be applied to the nuclear industry, whose activities are unclassified. He noted that in a personnel screening program for the industry the final decision to grant access will involve a value judgment that related to assessment of the extent of risk that a particular employee is likely to divert nuclear material.

Some present problems about personnel selection were cited by Haymon. Certainly, the civil rights of the persons being screened limit the screening. Such companies as Westinghouse have a strong commitment to hiring the hardcore unemployed for whom screening for positions with access to fissionable materials poses problems. For the single case of hiring for fuel fabrication facilities, the question of what criteria are proper and suitable to be used by industry was faced. Possible criteria, but ones for which no decisions have been made, include the following: citizenship, membership in a subversive organization, conviction of a felony, or even conviction of a misdemeanor.

A desire for some improvements in the selection of employees was expressed by C. D. W. Thornton (Director, Division of Nuclear Materials Safeguards, AEC), but he was uncertain as to whether any possible legislation will be a guarantee against having criminal elements involved in the operations of the nuclear industry. He cautioned that personnel screening might be effective but can be unjust. A humorous example of this was the case of a seemingly very honest man who ran a laboratory at Oak Ridge during World War II. He was having polygraph troubles with the question of whether he had ever taken government-owned material. Investigation revealed that, during the war-time shortages in hastily-built Oak Ridge, he had indeed taken a large rubber stopper out of the laboratory to plug his bathtub.

CHAPTER

13

SOCIAL
PSYCHOLOGICAL STUDIES
OF THE
SAFEGUARDS PROBLEM

Leon Rappoport
J. D. Pettinelli

During the past quarter century an increasing majority of
scientists, businessmen, and politicians have recognized that activities
in the field of science and technology are matters of general public
interest. Thanks to the writings of C. P. Snow, Vannevar Bush,
Jerome Weisner, and others,[1] the linkage between science and society
is now very clear: research generates new possibilities for action by
industry and government and, depending upon which possibilities are
pursued, the quality of life available in society may be profoundly
changed. It also should be acknowledged that recent analyses of the
relation between industry, science, and government indicate that prevalent social values and allocations of financial support dictate the
orientation of much basic research.

But while gross causal sequences relating science to society
are pretty well understood, the fine grain processes by which scientific
or technical issues may give rise to social and psychological problems
are not understood. Worse yet, the very idea that one may legitimately
examine the social-psychological implications of technology questions
is often rejected. We have encountered such rejection in our work
on diversion safeguards, and we will have more to say about it later.
However, let us first consider the basis for this work.

––––––––––

Research for this chapter was supported under the Research
Applied to National Needs (RANN) Program of the National Science
Foundation.

From the very beginning of our interdisciplinary discussions about safeguards, it became clear that such technical problems as precise measurement and convenient accounting procedures were not only matters requiring further research by experts but also sources of psychological tension and uncertainty. This point should be emphasized very strongly: insofar as technical problems remain unresolved to the degree that honest error variance is large enough to conceal diversion of weapon-quality materials, the consequent uncertainty defines a problem area for social psychological research.

Thus, we have reasons to believe that, as it becomes necessary for responsible decision-makers in industry and government to formulate programs insuring a high degree of safety from diversion, the uncertainties they face may easily lead to conflict and confusion. Recent social-psychological studies of decision-making have in fact suggested that when persons try to reach consensus agreements under such conditions, conflict and confusion is the rule rather than the exception.[2] And this occurs because even honest men of good will often will not be aware of the underlying ambiguities causing their disagreement. Instead, they react to disagreement by becoming distrustful of one another, thereby increasing the potential for conflict.

If the foregoing analysis is approximately correct, it follows that one major contribution social scientists can make with respect to safeguards is to establish the patterns of uncertainty characterizing this problem area. Consequently, we have pursued three broad lines of inquiry.

First among these is the hazards survey. In order to identify particular sources of uncertainty in the safeguards environment, knowledgeable persons were asked for their opinions about risks and hazards at various points in the nuclear fuel cycle. They also were asked about the vulnerability of different forms of material to diversion, the criteria they would use to decide whether or not diversion had occurred, and the types of persons and situations likely to be associated with diversion efforts.

This last question developed into a second general study in the area of criminology: namely, an investigation designed to determine whether experiences with theft in other industries was in any way relevant to the nuclear power industry.

Finally, in the third and most complex part of our work we have begun to examine the way uncertainties about safeguards can influence the behavior of persons charged with such specific decision-making tasks as the following: (1) judging whether or not a diversion has occurred; (2) evaluating the merits of particular safeguard systems; and (3) negotiating agreements about these systems. Short of getting into the heads of real people, who would probably not even let us into their offices let alone their heads, the only way to conduct this sort of work is through laboratory simulations. And so we have developed several simulation tasks, complete with plausible scenarios, in which previously selected and trained graduate students are required to act out the roles of decision-makers.

Altogether then, starting with an analysis of how safeguards may be understood as a problem from the standpoint of social psychology and applying knowledge gained from basic studies of decision-making and conflict in conditions of uncertainty, we have embarked upon three general lines of work. The balance of this paper will be devoted to a discussion of the salient results.

RESULTS

The Hazards Survey

Developed in consultation with physical science project personnel and tested with locally available nuclear engineers and physicists, the hazards survey questionnaire solicited statements of opinion concerning the following six topics: (1) the risk of loss of fissionable material at different points in the fuel cycle; (2) the risk of diversion at these points; (3) the vulnerability of different materials to diversion; (4) the criteria for judging whether diversion has occurred; (5) the probable causes of input-output discrepancies; and (6) the persons and motives likely to be associated with diversion efforts.

Beginning in June 1971 questionnaires were mailed to people drawn from a list of over 1,100 "knowledgable persons" collected by other project personnel. This population was stratified according to whether the people were primarily associated with private industry, government, or government-supported laboratories, and names were selected randomly within each of these groups. Out of 488 questionnaires mailed, some never reached their destination because of address changes; others were not answered because the persons felt that they were unqualified, that the questions were unclear, that the answers were too complicated, or that the survey results might create bad public relations, and so forth. However, based on the 128 completed questionnaires that were returned, considerably more than the typical 15 or 20 percent returned in most commercial mail surveys, we have the results described below, calculated for 33 persons in government laboratories, 36 in other branches of government, and 59 in industry.

On questions concerning any sort of loss of fissionable material at 13 different points in the fuel cycle, the largest majority of all respondents, 56 percent, indicated that a substantial risk existed in fabrication plants during the fabrication process. But a further breakdown shows that this majority consists mainly of government and laboratory people: 62 and 60 percent of these groups, respectively. Only 46 percent of the industry respondents see the risk of loss in fabrication to be substantial.

The difference between these three groups is even sharper with respect to the point in the fuel cycle identified as a substantial risk of loss by the next highest majority of respondents. Transportation of material away from the fabrication plant is specified here by 55 percent of the government respondents, 39 percent of the lab respondents, and 22 percent of the industry respondents.

Turning now to questions concerning the deliberate diversion of fissionable material, the largest majority of all respondents perceive the risk to be substantial during transportation away from the fabrication plant: 70 percent of those in government, 53 percent of those in laboratories, and 42 percent of those in industry. A similarly high risk of diversion also is indicated for transportation away from the reprocessing plant, with this point mentioned by 69 percent of the government group, 62 percent of the laboratory group, and 56 percent of the industry group.

Thus, although it is not possible to present all the relevant data here in detail, it seems clear that certain points in the fuel cycle are thought to be particularly sensitive to loss or diversion by a majority of those responding. And while there is quite general agreement about which points in the cycle are involved, there is a strong tendency for government respondents to set the level of risk higher than industry respondents.

The next general question studied concerns a different form of uncertainty. Aside from risks of loss or diversion at points in the fuel cycle, different types of fissionable material are used in the fuel cycle and these materials may cause varying degrees of concern because of their vulnerability to diversion. Figure 14 shows how

FIGURE 14

Perceived Vulnerability of Materials to Diversion

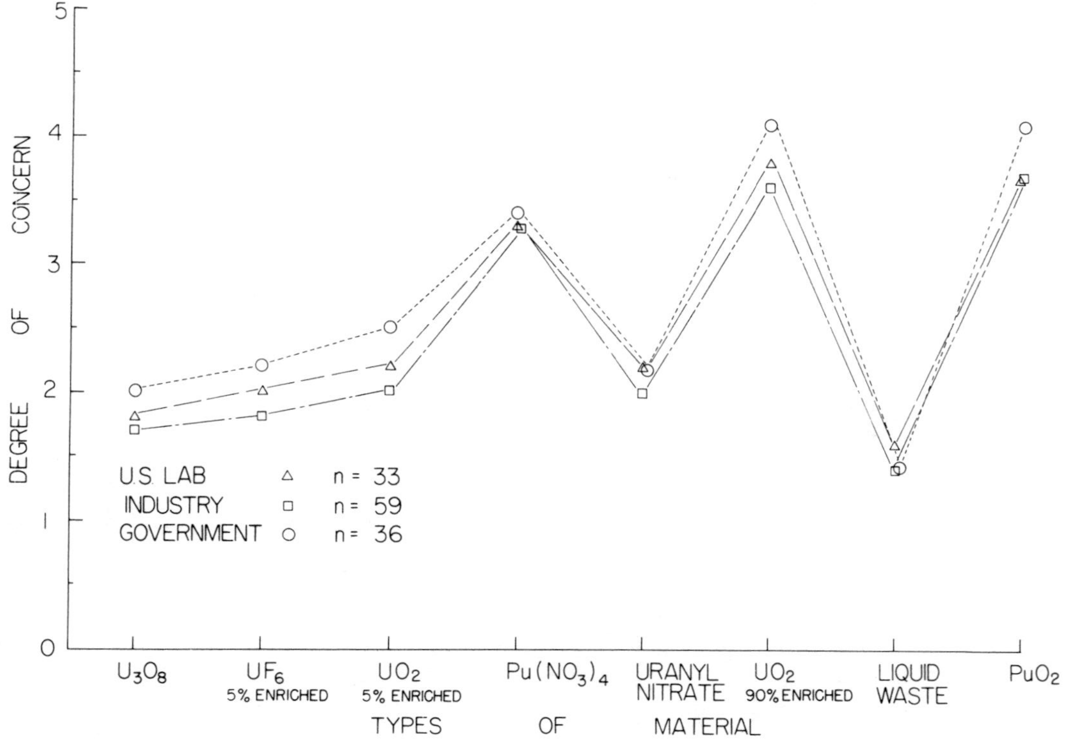

eight types of fissionable materials were rated on a five-point scale indicating concern over their vulnerability to diversion. The eight points marked on the horizontal axis of Figure 14 show the different materials involved. Five points on the vertical axis mark degrees of concern and the three functions plotted show the mean degrees of concern expressed by respondents in government, laboratories, and industry. The regularity of these data is noteworthy, and the general similarity between all three groups is impressive. One can see, for example, that liquid waste and U_3O_8 provoke the least concern and that 90 percent enriched uranium oxide and plutonium oxide provoke the greatest concern. One also can see that the function plotted for the industry group is consistently lower, with one exception, than the function for the government group. Just as the industry respondents tended to set lower risks of loss and diversion in the prior questions, they now generally indicate lower degrees of concern for vulnerability to diversion.

Another question presented two hypothetical situations in which plants responsible for different quantities and qualities of fissionable material showed varying levels of input-output differences. Respondents were asked to write in the probable cause of each input-output difference.

The results for the first hypothetical case, a plant with a throughput of 100 metric tons of uranium at a low power reactor enrichment, are given in Figure 15. The data plotted here indicate the percentage of respondents in the government, industry, and laboratory groups who specified abnormal error and/or diversion as the probable cause for each quantity of missing uranium fuel. As might be expected, these data show that statements of abnormal error and diversions grow more frequent as the quantities increase. And it is interesting to note that even when the quantities are very high, less than 50 percent of those responding are willing to judge the cause to be abnormal error or diversion. Furthermore, while the differences between the three groups are very small and infrequent, such differences as do exist show the government group judging abnormal error and diversion more frequently than the industry or laboratory groups.

The same general pattern of results occurs for the second hypothetical case, involving a plant with a through-put of 1 metric ton of plutonium. Figure 16 shows the input-output difference quantities of plutonium and the percentages in each group stating abnormal error or diversion for each missing quantity. While it can be seen here again that larger quantities lead to more frequent judgments of

FIGURE 15

Probable Cause of Input-Output Differences for Low Enriched Uranium
(throughput = 100 metric tons)

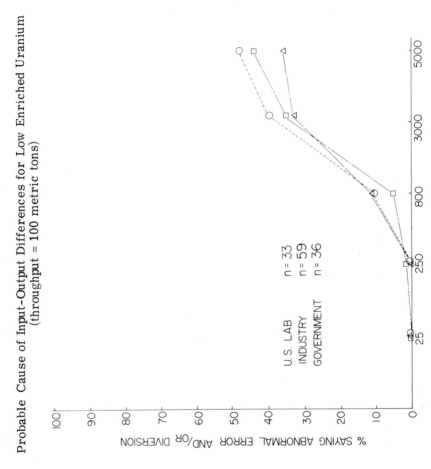

179

FIGURE 16

Probable Cause of Input-Output Differences for Plutonium
(throughput = 1 metric ton)

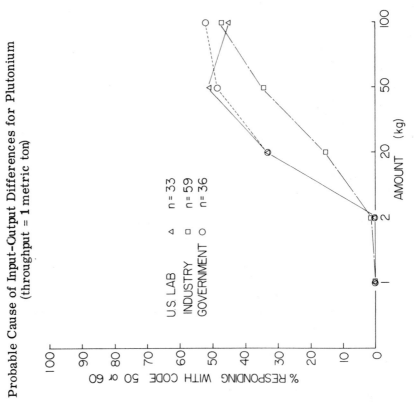

abnormal error or diversion, one difference to the previous case is
that the discrepancy between the industry and government groups is
now somewhat larger.

All of the data we have mentioned so far are descriptive, and
the trends in these data might be questioned because of the small
sample sizes and the possibility that those responding were not really
representative of the populations sampled. Moreover, it might be said
that even if the data are acceptable they do not provide any ideas that
could not have been obtained by simply sitting down and talking with
a few highly placed experts. The latter critique can be answered
directly with the argument that it is one thing to know about the ideas
people use in thinking about safeguards and quite another to try to
discover how many people hold these ideas and where these people are
placed in the groups that ultimately will be involved in important
decisions about safeguards.

Furthermore, despite all other possible criticisms, the data seem
valuable for the following three reasons: First, our results are consistent with other findings reported by Brady and Zollman concerning
the types of safeguard systems preferred by people in government
and industry (see Chapters 4 and 10). Second, by pinpointing the
location of uncertainties about the fuel cycle, materials in the fuel
cycle, and probable causes of input-output discrepancies, these results may aid decision-makers who will have to cope with honest
differences of opinion in the future. The basic research mentioned
at the outset of this paper suggests that to be forewarned about uncertainty is in some degree to be forearmed against conflict and confusion. Third, the data can provide at least rough parameters for
prevalent thinking about safeguards which can be used to guide efforts
to simulate relevant situations of decision-making and negotiation.

Before going on to describe two additional lines of research, it
should be mentioned that the hazards survey yielded some further
results of comparatively little value. In response to questions asking
what criteria could be used to judge whether diversion had occurred
at various points in the fuel cycle, approximately 20 percent chose
to give no answer at all while most of those who did answer emphasized
checking bookkeeping records and repeating physical measurements.
There were no notable differences here among government, industry,
and laboratory people. Similarly, there were no substantial differences
among these groups concerning the persons and motives likely to
characterize deliberate attempts at diversion. The most frequent
general response identified domestic militant political groups as
most likely to attempt diversion, followed by organized crime and

foreign powers. Most respondents also felt that present personnel
selection methods were quite effective in screening out unreliable
persons and that the motives for diversion might equally involve
either politics or personal profit.

The Criminology Research

Since it was plain enough from some of the hazards survey
results that persons in the nuclear fuel industry had little to say about
potential thefts, a special task group organized by Robert Leachman
began interviews with law enforcement authorities. This led to preparation of a questionnaire subsequently mailed to many persons in
law enforcement and industrial security positions. The work is still
in progress but the research plan and some of the preliminary results deserve mention.

It should first be noted that no substantial body of knowledge about
criminal diversion of fissionable materials exists because the problem
has no past history. But since there is knowledge available about
other forms of theft in industries, the Leachman group proceeded by
analogy, setting up interview guides and a questionnaire designed
to elicit relevant information from organizations handling such commodities as narcotics, precious metals and gems, and weapons. All
such organizations run the risk of diversion and they have considerable
experience in security systems. Moreover, government regulatory
agencies also are involved, thus strengthening the analogy to nuclear
fuel industries. To strengthen the analogy still further, questions
were arranged to stipulate thefts of approximately $70,000, the same
dollar value estimated to be associated with a quantity of fissionable
material sufficient to make a weapon.

The results obtained so far are relatively disappointing. For
one thing, it was discovered through interviews and questionnaires
that most law enforcement people have little experience with crimes
in the $70,000 bracket. Another difficulty is that enforcement
authorities frequently suggest that inquiries be made to the Federal
Bureau of Investigation, (FBI), which presumably keeps records on
relevant forms of industrial crime. Thus far, however, the FBI has
refused to provide any information.

Despite all the difficulties, responses obtained to date from 63
persons in law enforcement and industrial security suggest that from
among the various industrial situations examined, the narcotics or
dangerous drug industry offers the closest security parallel to the

nuclear fuel industry. And the record of security maintained in the narcotics area is outstanding. Very briefly, protective arrangements here are based on close cooperation between representatives of government, industry, and labor. These arrangements include a stringent system of accountability and inspection, careful screening of employees working in sensitive positions, strict physical checks of ingoing and outgoing workers, and great care in shipping procedures. Sizable quantities of opium, for example, are accompanied by armed guards traveling in special vehicles. In general, it may be noted that the level of security in the narcotics industry seems much higher than that presently existing in the nuclear fuel industry.

Further work on these matters, including more detailed descriptions of security conditions in other industries as well as profiles describing the types of persons typically apprehended for theft, will be presented in the future when sufficient data are available. We turn now to our final line of investigation involving the simulation of decision-making situations relevant to safeguards.

Simulation Studies

This work is in a very preliminary stage of development but pilot studies suggest that three types of simulation are both feasible and interesting.

The first type concerns what we refer to as an evaluative judgment model. Here it was assumed on the basis of interviews and published statements by authorities in the field that safeguards systems ultimately could be evaluated according to the following common sense criteria:

1. The dollar cost of the system: some systems obviously will be more costly than others.

2. The industrial secrecy or freedom from intervention provided by the system: some systems will allow inspectors to gain a greater knowledge of industrial processes than other systems and also give outsiders greater authority to intervene in plant operations.

3. The security against diversion provided by the system.

Working according to these three criteria, our subjects (graduate students in chemical and nuclear engineering previously given extensive information about the safeguards problem) were required

to make evaluative ratings of hypothetical safeguards systems. The
hypothetical systems were based on those constructed by Brady and
Zollman in another phase of our project (see Chapters 4 and 10), and
the systems varied in their general stringency.

The graduate students could perform this task without much
difficulty. They rated the most stringent systems as the most costly,
providing the best security against diversion, and providing the lowest
degree of industrial secrecy. Our pilot data therefore indicate a very
high negative correlation between the industrial secrecy criterion and
the criteria of dollar cost and security. In further work, the task was
reversed. Now students who were given patterns of information involving various levels of industrial secrecy, dollar cost, and security
were asked to identify the type of safeguards systems generating
each pattern. Results indicate the same negative correlations mentioned previously. An additional noteworthy result obtained in both
versions of the task was that certain safeguards systems of intermediate stringency are associated with very similar evaluation ratings
on all three criteria. In other words, certain systems seem optimum
with respect to minimizing discrepancies between secrecy, cost, and
security.

Very briefly, then, it appears that we have a rudimentary but
workable judgment model that may be used to explore how persons
translate the technical characteristics of safeguards systems into
the common sense language of evaluation.

The second general type of simulation involved negotiation. In
this connection, our student subjects were divided into two groups and
instructed to think of themselves as persons representing the interests
of government and industry, respectively. The scenario employed
here included several stages. First, each group was given time to
discuss its interests, which were, according to instruction, maximum
independence and flexibility for industry, and maximum security
against diversion for government. Second, the groups chose delegates
to negotiate a safeguards system. Third, the groups were given a
utility function stipulating a scale of money payments they would receive
depending upon the degree to which their delegates could protect
their interests in the negotiation. The negotiation session between
delegates came next, followed by having the delegates report back to
their groups where they sought further instruction or ratification of
tentative agreements. The final stage occurred when instructed
delegates returned to further negotiation.

This simulation, which is in principle similar to Kriegspiele* training exercises employed in the military, is fairly complex to organize and requires several days to complete. But although we have only given it a single test run the results are encouraging. Our student subjects took it seriously enough to have severe arguments, both within the groups and between the delegates. The industrialist group experienced much less trouble among itself than the government group. In fact, the government group actually voted to replace their delegate after hearing what he had to say following the initial negotiation. All of the verbal material was tape recorded and is now being analyzed for content. However, our initial impression is that the content is quite realistic because the uncertainties provoking arguments are similar to those identified in the hazards survey. It also seems that the government group was at a disadvantage because it tended to work from a more complex policy position than the industrial group.

The third simulation concerned how judgments of diversion may be made by a chief safeguards inspector. For this purpose, a series of hypothetical plant situations are presented in the form of test booklets. The first page of each booklet describes the nature of the plant and the quantity of fissionable material it handles. Then, on succeeding pages, four increments of variable information are given. First, the amount of material unaccounted for (MUF) and the presence or absence of physical security anomalies. Second, a statement of bookkeeping errors. Third, a statement indicating whether normal operating losses (NOL) are unusual. And fourth, the results of a physical inventory check of materials on hand.

To the best of our present knowledge, these dimensions of information represent the manifold of evidence available to a real chief inspector. In the simulation, student subjects are given the information in a variety of configurations, such as high or low MUF, large or small bookkeeping errors, usual or unusual NOL reports, and so forth, and the subjects are required to judge the probability of diversion associated with each configuration. The information can be presented either sequentially, as mentioned, or simultaneously, but our purpose is to determine the relative importance of each dimension of information as a predictor of diversion judgments.

This simulation also has been given preliminary tests and seems to be workable. As further data are accumulated, we plan to fit a

_____

*War game.

prediction equation to the data and then we will run the simulation
under different payoff and accuracy feedback conditions in order to
determine how these factors influence the judgment process.

SUMMARY AND CONCLUSIONS

Taken together, all of the work described in this chapter should
be understood as an effort to investigate social-psychological processes related to the safeguards problem. In the hazards survey
research, we have tried to identify the sources of uncertainty likely
to cause difficulties for decision-makers. In the criminology study,
past experience in other regulated industries is being scrutinized
for its relevance to security arrangements in the nuclear fuel industry.
In the simulation studies, we are trying to find out how decision-makers
may behave when they are faced with realistic problems caused by
technical and practical uncertainties.

In conclusion, it may be said that all of this work is unusual
and virtually without precedent because it represents an attempt to
anticipate social-psychological factors liable to influence public policies
concerning a complex technical problem. Some of the social science
methods employed in this connection may not be clear to those trained
in the physical sciences; indeed, we have encountered difficulties
because of this and because of our own failures to understand physical
science perspectives. Nevertheless, when engaging an issue of such
magnitude as nuclear safeguards, it behooves all of us to contribute
whatever we possibly can.

NOTES

1. See C. P. Snow, The Two Cultures: And a Second Look (New
York: Modern American Library, 1963); Vannevar Bush, Modern
Arms and Free Men: A Discussion of the Role of Science in Preserving
Democracy (Cambridge: MIT Press, 1968); A. Chayes and J. B. Weis-
ner, eds., ABM: An Evaluation of the Decision to Deploy an Antibal-
listic Missle System (New York: Harper and Row, 1969).

2. See K. R. Hammond, "New Directions in Research on Con-
flict Resolution," The Journal of Social Issues, 21 (April 1965), 44-66.
A number of relevant studies also appear in L. Rappoport and D. A.
Summers, eds., Human Judgment and Social Interaction (New York:
Holt, Rinehart and Winston, 1972).

Considerable interest was evidenced about the criminology studies mentioned by Leon Rappoport. The availability of drugs in the United States was reason for <u>Ralph Lumb</u> (Nuclear Surveillance and Auditing Corporation) to inquire how the narcotics industry could be cited as exemplary. Rappoport noted that the criminology study being reported was for thefts or diversions analogous to possible losses of nuclear materials; in this analogy the narcotics cases of interest concerned thefts rather than the illicit supply of narcotics from clandestine laboratories. Furthermore, he pointed out that these criminology studies were conducted by Robert Leachman of Kansas State University and were made for five different industries, each with a similarity to the nuclear industry insofar as they involved such factors as regulated materials, high unit cost, material generally guarded, and a specialized market. Rappoport thought that the narcotics industry not only offered the closest parallel but seemed to have the best record against diversions.

Concerning this criminology comparison of different industries, <u>Ray Heinisch</u> (Nuclear Assurance Corporation) introduced the sensitive matter of transportation with all its ramifications, including mode and frequency of shipment, distance involved, and physical security during shipment. Noting that a detailed analysis would be difficult, Rappoport said that the Kansas State University study initially sought instead the general parallels in transportation for the industries studied in order to see whether detailed studies are warranted. Comparison between transportation for narcotics and nuclear materials is particularly interesting. The armored cars and armed guards used in the former are in contrast to methods used in the latter.

The long-standing precautions of the narcotics industry were recounted by <u>C. D. W. Thornton</u> (Director, Division of Nuclear Materials Safeguards, AEC). In a survey of 28 valuable-material industries conducted about 20 years ago, the narcotics industry also was found to be thorough. Checks included auditing the affluence of employees by such measures as automobile purchases, and vacations taken.[3] Evaluating the care by the narcotics industry as a social scientist, Rappoport believed that the tremendous publicity about drugs has created a strong public opinion image about narcotics. This has consequently forced extremely stringent security arrangements. With narcotics available as they are without diversion from legal sources, he wondered whether these security arrangements for the narcotics industry are even more stringent than necessary.

The discussion turned to inspector decisions, with Thornton introducing the topic of false alarms in inspections. These alarms are irregularities that, once discovered, would warrant serious investigations to assure that real events are not overlooked. The question then follows as to how frequently investigations need to follow false alarms to assure that the system is highly sensitive. Ralph Jones (Nuclear Fuel Service, Incorporated) implied that industry investigates many irregularities that are not reported to the governmental authorities, the implication being that this avoids undue consternation on the part of the authorities over false alarms. In an elaboration on his preliminary studies in simulation, Rappoport reported that subjects were tested on false alarm situations. Different financial (payoff) conditions were tested; of particular interest was the case in which the subject simulating the inspector would lose more money by raising a false alarm than by going to the end of the test sequence which involved destructive inspection techniques. Further work in this area is planned by Rappoport.

Identification of criminal typologies as they might apply to the nuclear industry was a significant part of the discussion. Eli Roth (Arms Control and Disarmament Agency) noted the distortion in criminal typologies that results from using criminals who are caught when the worry should be instead about the criminals who are smart enough not to be caught. Rappoport confirmed that this was a known limitation in criminology and that criminals who are caught are well known to have a general profile of such troubles as drinking too much, using drugs, or making bad investments.

Possible distinctions between the profiles of a good inspector and a good diverter were sought by Richard Butler (Australian Mission to the United Nations). He noted that the potential diverter of nuclear materials must be skilled and intelligent to know and handle the material and that these are some of the same characteristics desired in an inspector. The difficulty in distinguishing a criminal from outward characteristics was confirmed by Rappoport. For example, the outward characteristics of young people on the verge of becoming revolutionists are not easy to distinguish from those of other young people. However, Rappoport cited some gross and commonplace characteristics. For example, those who commit crimes have records of instabilities in their backgrounds. On the other hand, colleagues have reported to Rappoport that inspectors of nuclear materials are generally somewhere in transition through their professional lives, generally being somewhere at the beginning or in the middle of their professions.

Further experience on selection of employees for nuclear facilities was provided by Frederick Forscher (Consulting Engineer). In addition to the safeguards aspect, other hazards including the criticality hazard increase the need for hiring emotionally stable people. Otherwise, they are a danger not only to themselves but also to the facility. Faced recently with the responsibility of staffing a plutonium facility, he sought professional assistance. An industrial psychologist, unable to help him, advised him to ask a consultant. After talking to several consultants about techniques to screen out emotionally imbalanced people, he came to the conclusion that none could provide meaningful advice, a conclusion that Rappoport did not find surprising.

14

JUDGMENT
IN SAFEGUARDS
ACTIVITIES

Frank Morgan

The signing of the Non-Proliferation Treaty (NPT) and the safe-guards flowing from it are a great historical event in arms control. The NPT itself did not say very much about safeguards as a principal component of that Treaty and one of the subsequent tasks has been to put flesh on this skeleton, flesh comprising technical, legal, and political considerations in very considerable detail; this is now embodied in the International Atomic Energy Agency (IAEA) Draft Model Agreement.[1] It seems to me important that the logic, the logical difficulties, and the practical limitations of the process be clearly understood insofar as they are relevant to future comparable situations. In particular, as the NPT comes to be implemented technically throughout the world we shall need to establish, for the first time, a system for international inspection and surveillance over materials management and control as recorded by national governments; this is a complex and challenging task and there is much yet to be learned about the correct technical and managerial approach to the problem and, in particular, about how disputed technical conclusions are to be resolved. I do not want to set myself up as an expert in any particular field but rather to suggest some of the questions to which we might reasonably expect answers from the real experts.

THE NATION AS THE UNIT OF CONTROL

The possibilities of acquiring military material would seem to be fourfold:

1. Straightforward abrogation of the treaty when a country wishes to use its civil material for weapons purposes. This contingency we shall not consider.

2. The government arranges to divert an amount of material sufficient for several weapons against a future military need. This diversion may take place in small amounts over a long interval of time or in one large amount. The second of these contingencies is much more easily detected and therefore we shall consider principally the first.

3. An individual or small group of individuals may divert material from a plant in country A either for domestic use or in order to pass it on to country B without the knowledge of country A. This might be done over a period of time in small amounts or the individuals concerned might make off with a quantity of fissile material in a convenient form and seek asylum in country B.

4. The final possibility is that the government might pretend (as a mechanism for possibility 2) that possibility 3 above has occurred when in reality it has kept the material for itself and hidden the criminals.

This led to the conclusion that it is the responsibility of the nation to frame its procedures so that the likelihood of possibility 3 happening is reduced to a minimum, which will largely eliminate possibility 4 as an excuse. How do we detect possibility 2? The problem of inspection in such a context raises several issues, notably (1) the assessment of benefits, costs, and financing and (2) the detection of trends in a complex manufacturing situation. These issues do not seem particularly novel, but there are several possible approaches that I want to discuss. I start from the assumption that the majority, whether plant operators or countries, will be acting in good faith and not seeking to divert material for weapons purposes. Analysis must be done in terms of "an adversary," but this is liable to give a distorted picture of the real world. Incidentally, as most will be acting in good faith, their initial data to the IAEA will provide a comparatively secure base of calculation.

THE DIFFICULTIES OF THE THEORETICAL APPROACH

There are attractions in assessing the problem of control by a "games theory" approach, but these seem to me to raise some pretty fundamental difficulties such as the following:

1. The rules of the particular game we are playing appear to create a built-in tendency to a draw: any nation may at any time take out any amount of material for a defined military (but nonexplosive) purpose, and the NPT provides no mechanism for verifying that it is not in fact being used for the manufacture of bombs, a problem to which we shall revert.

2. Can we apply such techniques to a multilateral situation? When essentially only two countries are involved, the tougher and more immediate the results following from any decision, the less weight is put on the views of their partners and the matter tends to become polarized. But in a multilateral situation, particularly where the issue is not stark and there is much more time, discussion and political negotiations are usual. To be specific, suppose country A suspects country B of diverting material: the initial decision A can make is whether or not to refer the matter to the competent international body; a second is whether to withdraw from the agreement. The means A chooses to make these decisions are its own affair, but I doubt that any realistic politician would resort to statistical arguments.

3. The game has a referee—the IAEA—which in any situation giving rise to the suspicion of diversion must assess the evidence at its disposal and decide on appropriate action. In my own experience of boards of enquiry, a great deal of additional information and subsidiary investigation generally is required before an acceptable verdict is reached. The totality of evidence must be adequate and convincing in the sense that it cannot be argued away. But the IAEA is not well-placed to obtain all this evidence: it has no powers of compulsion and must convince the nation that there is a prima facie case for examination. Nationally, one can take administrative action; internationally, someone has to end up with a red face. How does the IAEA marshal the evidence while maintaining its reputation for objective and impartial examination?

4. We are dealing not with a broad picture in mathematical symbols but with complex industrial processes; we are interested not in the good behavior of 99 percent of the fissile material but in small variations of 1 percent or so due to factors we may not understand too well. Some processes may be statistically in control; others are subject to minor changes in operating practice that may affect the material balance, not always in a predictable way.

5. There are problems of time and timing. We must appreciate how to handle some of these theoretically; for example, how quickly do we want the system to respond? How is the sequence of material unaccounted for (MUF) affected by events in plant operation?

6. Even if this approach were feasible, what is the proper
equation of gains and losses (or penalties and rewards)? One can
assess the cost of inspecting railroad tickets against the savings in
unpaid fares; experimentation to establish the parameters is straightforward and the sides of the equation are expressed only in terms of
money. But how does one equate a kilogram of diverted plutonium to
x dollars or y years in jail? Cheating on railroad fares is a common
phenomenon, but any serious diversion of fissile material must be
exceedingly rare if the system is not to fall into disrepute. Not only
will the events be rare but their incidence and nature are likely to
vary; the choice of constants in a mathematical formulation of strategy,
even if it is not entirely arbitrary, must reflect the social conditions
of the time.

These factors reinforce the importance of treating the nation
as a unit. I am not saying that these factors necessarily damn the
theoretical approach but that we cannot avoid serious difficulties in
associating quantitative and qualitative factors, common in many other
situations. Linking the whole matter together is the problem of cost,
so we start with "value for money."

COSTS, BENEFITS, AND EFFECTIVENESS

In financial appraisals, we generally are comparing alternative
courses to the same end and, provided our accountancy conventions
are sound, the analysis is straightforward. The correct balance of
cost and effectiveness is more difficult to determine; the balance of
costs and benefits can hardly ever be struck precisely, particularly
in "social" matters. Indeed, the costs often are the only item identifiable with certainty. Here they include not only the direct cost of
the inspection system but also the direct costs of counterpart activities
in data recording and national control as well as the indirect penalties
to the operator.

As an example in an entirely different area, consider the recent
extension of the London Underground: a scheme that will save a com-
muter an hour a day is "better" than one that will save him only ten
minutes, but how is this benefit quantified and translated into money?
Similarly, the benefits of reducing traffic congestion in central London
were included in the appraisal even though the beneficiaries might not
contribute to the revenue of the undertaking. Conversely, if a person
never intends to travel on the Underground it may be difficult to
persuade him that he should contribute to the installation cost even
though, as a taxpayer, he may have to contribute willy-nilly.

Therefore, it is not surprising that financial contributions to safeguards costs are a thorny problem. As Walsh and Williams point out, "if people were asked 'how much would you be willing to pay for so much extra defence?" it is likely that there would be systematic understatement, since people would suspect that they might actually be called upon to pay the amount they 'offer', and they will hope that other people's bids will lead to an amount of defence being provided which they regard as acceptable, knowing that once it is provided no one can exclude them from enjoying it too. Thus in the case of 'collective' goods and services it will be necessary for some valuation to be made via political processes of one kind or another."[2]

This leads to the conclusion that such things are not necessarily intractable to the decision theorist but they do require value judgments from sociologists and the political masters. To make such judgments, the technical man must assume a range of variables. It is generally recognized that a close degree of control is more expensive in manpower than a lesser degree of control, but the absolute value of cost or the likely effectiveness have not yet been defined with any degree of clarity. They depend, of course, on the nature of the facility and the scale of operations. To this extent, the technical job is not complete. The difficulty of obtaining such information was and is compounded by the fact that the level of practical experience of the fuel cycle is very variable in different countries, with the consequential difficulty of balancing an idealized and over-theoretical approach with the practicalities of operation. The problem of economy, of course, also falls on the plant operator. If the safety of his operations are not at risk, he normally will make a balance of practices, operation, and rejection of discarded material such as will satisfy his economic criteria. The shortage of funds also means that verification has to be partial (in a sampling sense) and therefore probabilistic, leading to the desire to rationalize the system and make it objective (we return later to discuss how far this desire can be fulfilled). What the technical man can do in these circumstances is to propose ways in which a given outlay can be used to the best advantage. We cannot hope to create the perfect system and so we seek one that will provide reasonable assurance on the detection of diversion giving the controller best value for money and the plant operator a tolerable level of inconvenience. This calls for some sort of "systems analysis."

SYSTEMS ANALYSIS

The practicalities of life necessarily introduce some uncertainty. For example, it is necessary to have some provision for de minimis

quantities, i.e., those below which no administrative action is taken
to control or internationally inspect the amount and location. We
have noted that non-explosive military activities are not prohibited
under the NPT, and these obviously could introduce appreciable uncertainties in the whereabouts and utilization of high-grade nuclear
material. From a logical point of view, when uncertainties of a given
magnitude exist in a system it is profitless to seek to make the uncertainties elsewhere in the system very much lower than these. This
was a wholly political question that has now been resolved in the NPT.
It seems to me likely that the right will be exercised only infrequently
and that the amounts will be only a small proportion of the national
inventory. Accordingly, the analysis of the system should identify
the critical points in the fuel cycle and demonstrate whether further
inspection or research and development is needed to reduce the overall uncertainty in amount. Thus, analysis of the situation in the United
Kingdom has shown that the analysis of residues moving between
accounting units and the determination of fissile material in large
"ever-safe" tanks, are topics well deserving further study.

THE TIME ELEMENT

It is possible to define technically in a quite straightforward
way where safeguards should begin, but the numerical factor converting natural uranium to effective kilograms is so small that the
choice of starting point does not particularly affect the subsequent
analysis. A feature that does seem to be more relevant is the
accessibility of the material, as noted above. This is undoubtedly
important for an isolated facility where material could be taken and,
for example, sold on the black market. Where the nation is judged
as a unit, the relevance is rather to the effective deployment by the
IAEA of its manpower. One can argue that the time of the reporting
and observation is so long that any material can in practice be used
and that classification in terms of the speed with which it might be
converted to military use is not important. However, it seems that
most people accept the idea that nuclear materials can be ranked in
some order of "critical time"; thus, irradiated material could in
theory be reprocessed immediately on removal from a reactor, given
suitable technology, but it is nevertheless a more difficult and tedious
operation to remove it illicitly compared with unirradiated fissile
material. Of course, the emphasis one places on such factors as
this is a matter of arbitrary judgment but such conventions are the
heart of any administrative system.

THE ANALYSIS OF PERFORMANCE

The central problem is accounting for material: What is the magnitude of the MUF? Since we are starting with a fixed amount of material, the inevitable small losses that may not be measurable mean that we must always tend to have less than we expect but never more. The errors of measurement compound the problem, which depends on the nature of the process and the experience of the operator. How is MUF kept under control? Evaluation of the MUF of a single facility is a difficult task. As noted above, a positive MUF can arise simply from the inadequacies of measurement or little-understood factors and indeed is likely to do so, but it need not necessarily mean that material is diverted. In the case of a "jobbing shop," such as a fabrication line producing a range of different fuels, there may be little historical data for the particular process and it is essential for each statement of MUF to be accompanied by a statement of the precisions of the constituent measurements. Similarly, research and development facilities, normally with little throughput, will have to be judged on this basis also, coupled with the historical record of the inventory. A batch-operated plant using a constant process is the easiest situation; not only is there the possibility of a material balance on each run but the number of data points rises quickly so as to readily provide an historic basis for decision. The economics of large-scale production may lead to continuous flow processes; the problems of calibration are more severe and a material balance can be struck with confidence only when the plant is cleaned out; as this is done at infrequent intervals, the historic data for decision accumulates only slowly. Plants of the latter type are currently fairly rare and, by close attention in the design stage to providing adequate accuracy in materials accountancy, the problem may be minimized in future plants, although it is not likely to vanish.

Large plants pose an additional problem of "serial correlation" arising from the estimation of the process inventory. This is not peculiar to the nuclear industry but is found in other chemical plants. It can affect the material balance in a funny way: an apparent loss can be created in one period if the inventory is underestimated, but if in the next period the inventory is correctly estimated the amount for that period will show an apparent gain. Such sequential behavior has been reported for plants of a very diverse nature.[3] The MUFs are no longer random, and uncritical application of probability laws can be quite misleading. The use of cumulative-sum techniques overcomes this problem, and various ways of making decisions based on them are described in the literature.[4] All such decisions, of course, require the arbitrary definition of "how much over how long"— the reaction time to a new trend.

Kouts and others, in the study of "procedural safeguards," state that materials accounting by a facility should be sensitive to the possibility of diversion of nuclear material exceeding a threshold value, this "strategic quantity" being small compared with the amount that can serve as the fundamental part of a nuclear device.[5] Although such concepts as this are of value in the study and analysis of a system, for wholly practical reasons they may be difficult to implement. In fact, I believe the considerations just advanced show that we must start with experience, not theory. This points up a central difficulty: the performance of the plant may introduce swings in accounts that will worry any inspector if they are greater than a predetirmined "strategic quantity." Possible courses of action lie between two extremes: (1) to implement the "strategic quantity" in ful rigor, including formal inquiries and/or closing down the facility as necessary or (2) to define an "action level" from the performance of the plant. Remedial measures would be taken only if the action level were exceeded or when it is consistently much worse than the "strategic quantity." The greater the compromise between theory and the realities of plant life, the less the value of the analytic approach.

From the rules of the game as laid down in the draft Model Safeguards Agreement, the inspectors cannot themselves operate a plant or close it down. This necessarily leads to the confirmation of normal plant data by observing and checking the calibration of vessels and through independent analysis of samples taken on request. We need not here dwell on the statistical aspects of this comparison (verification), but there are a couple of unusual features in the nuclear industry. The cylic nature of the process—from fuel to reactors to reprocessing to fuel fabrication—necessarily permits a good deal of cross-correlation. Further, the nuclear processes are pretty well understood theoretically and the various average reaction cross-sections are known for the particular reactor; the wide range of nuclear processes necessarily produces abundant supporting evidence in each sample taken for analysis. Thus, a sample from a reprocessing plant tells not only the concentration of plutonium per unit volume but also the Pu/U ratio, the isotopic composition of Pu and U, and the fissions induced in the original fuel. If measurements are made, what emphasis is to be put on each item of the data? Obviously, having decided on the type of information to be collected, the scope and validity of each class of measurement will need to be evaluated independently. Methods for combining these independent strands will need to be agreed.

LONG-TERM CONSEQUENCES

Hitherto, we have been discussing the rate at which MUF accrues, for example the amount per year, but if we consider the cumulative MUF over a period of years different considerations emerge. The cumulative MUF may continue to increase with time and we may be quite satisfied that this does not represent a real diversion of material but reflects factors that are not fully understood. Hopefully, we might end up with a situation where the cumulative MUF turns out to be zero as the uncertainties in one sense are compensated by subsequent uncertainties in the other sense and the average turns out to approximate zero. However, in both these cases it may readily be shown that the variability of MUF necessarily introduces an uncertainty that increases with time (actually as something near the square root of time). When the national inventory of special fissionable material attains its limiting equilibrium value, the uncertainty will tend to improve. But this situation is not likely to emerge for many decades.

OBJECTIVITY AND JUDGMENT

Part of the difficulty in applying an objective approach is that the people to be convinced usually are not skilled in the statistical art: they recollect such slogans as "lies, damned lies, and statistics" and indeed may not know exactly what the word means. It has a specific meaning in beauty contests; it is used loosely to mean the compilation of data that may or may not be used subsequently; and here it is the description of the process by which conclusions can be drawn from a mass of data to achieve a certain acceptable degree of confidence. At the risk of meandering, it seems worthwhile to expose some of the problems of selling and using statistical methodology. I can think of at least four:

1. What risks of being wrong are acceptable? The inspector will not wish to commit errors of the first type—to let faults go undetected—but will with at least equal emphasis wish to avoid errors of the second type—finding a fault where none exists. He therefore will wish to be more sure of his ground than the usual "5 percent limit of significance." But it is common experience that measurements

contain small unsuspected effects and 3- or 4-sigma assertions from
a single type of measurement are dangerous; it is much more desirable
to use 95 percent limits observed in two or three independent types
of measurement that lead to the same conclusion.

2. Life is full of meaningless statistical associations and it is
vital to have a valid explanation for such as may be observed. Thus,
if the death rate from tuberculosis in some desert resort were found
to be the highest in the United States, this could equally mean that the
climate is unhealthy or that it is so healthy that tuberculosis patients
tend to congregate there.

3. Another problem in dealing with events is that remarkable
coincidences exist simply because people remark on them. Thus, if
I toss a coin twenty times each morning for many years, sooner or
later I am going to remember the occasion when I got twenty heads
or twenty tails, not the many occasions when I did not. A similar
point occurs in the common superstition that unlucky events go in
threes. This appears to be true of, for example, airline crashes and
similar random and noteworthy events. I think there is some basis
for the belief: it is that random events of this nature follow what is
called a Poisson distribution, one characteristic of which in this
particular case is that shorter intervals between successive events
are more probable than long intervals. We can see this demonstrated
clearly if we watch a radioactive source emitting at very slow rates
(see Figure 17) or lightning flashes. In these circumstances, it is
not surprising that people tend to recollect two or three remarkable
circumstances occurring in close succession but, because of the
frailties of memory, do not recollect those not so closely associated
in time.

4. Lastly, people tend to assess the relative probabilities by
reference to their own experience. It would be interesting to know
how far and in what detail the average man regards the occurrence of
different contingencies. Thus, if he is a racing man, he is probably
accustomed to the idea of odds of 100-1 or in that range, but even
here, apart from small numbers like 7-4, the numbers chosen in
practice tend to be recurrent, 25, 33, 50, and so on, implying that the
bookmaker at least does not think it justifiable to go into any finer
degree of scrutiny. For example, I have never yet heard of a bookmaker quoting odds of 76.5-1 (or even 153-2). Similarly, although
people might read that their chance of being killed in a motor accident
is perhaps a few thousand to one against during the course of life,
they do not seem to let this fact get them down unduly; on the other
hand, they are quite prepared to wager considerable sums of money

FIGURE 17

Intervals of Time Between Emissions
from a Radioactive Source

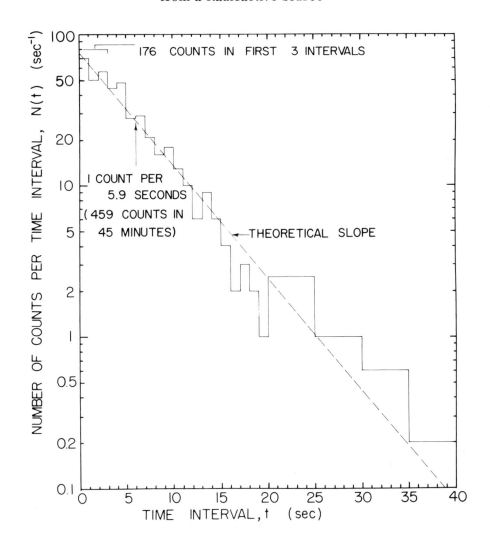

on lotteries and football pools where the odds against winning a fortune are comparable. The point I am seeking to get at here is that I suspect judgments tend to be made on the basis of everyday experience, generally in round numbers and even those stratified to a considerable degree, e.g., 10-1, 100-1, 1,000-1, 1,000,000-1, but with few other numbers ever quoted.

In the safeguards field, numerical data are readily available and the imponderable factors are fewer; this suggests a danger that an approach based on probability may be pursued too far. Perhaps a comparable area exists in courts of law. There has been sporadic debate over the last few years on the applicability of mathematical probability to legal evidence; this seems due partly to the present growth of the physical and social sciences and the growing acceptance that probability concepts underlie most judgments, e.g., "beyond reasonable doubt."

When a man is faced with a collection of evidence, the decision he comes to is a balance of all his past experience and prejudices, which he does not stop to analyze. In the English criminal system, such facets are averaged over a jury of twelve and the result has been pretty effective for many centuries. But this "accusatorial" system is, of course, inappropriate to the present situation which is more nearly akin to the "inquisitorial" procedure or a judicial inquiry in which the "facts" are assembled and assessed with expert assistance. Nevertheless, in each case and for quite different reasons we must assume at the outset that, although there is a case to answer, the "defendant" is no more likely to have offended than anyone else. The preceding arguments suggest that a wholly statistical approach is fallible, particularly when one is dealing with a material balance and it is necessary to associate the numerical factors with other evidence.

Finklestein and Fairley draw attention to the need in criminal cases for evidence that allows one to assess the prior probability of guilt before one introduces numerical data: Despite this Bayesian approach, they conclude that "the mathematical method ought to reflect the standards of probative value by which evidence would be judged if it were not statistical but merely descriptive."[6] Even given the circumstances of a formal inquiry, the value of expert evidence turns very much on the caliber of the individual expert who will base his appraisal on a lot of background detail that is difficult to catalogue but who also has prejudices and deficiencies of memory and, although he is experienced, whose experience may be insufficiently direct. For this reason, in legal proceedings in the United Kingdom, it is common

for the competence of the expert witness to be open to question by the
court, a method not likely to be followed in international proceedings.
So at the end of the day the choice is between expert judgment which
cannot be completely explicable or unanimous and numerical study
which can be formalized and objective but may be inadequate or
misleading.

You may fairly say that I have put up my own straw man merely
to demolish it. Perhaps so, but I am trying to make the point that we
ought to clear our minds now if we wish to debate the standards and
procedures needed when, if ever, we have the disagreeable task of
assessing the likelihood of diversion of nuclear material. Perhaps
it will never come to a formal confrontation; perhaps all that will
happen is that the nation is encouraged to use its own powers of compulsion over the factory concerned—but, if so, it seems to me that
"decision theory," "games theory," and so on are then largely irrele-
vant.

CONCLUSION

Such considerations have led me to the conclusion that, in this
new area of technological arms control, there is a proper place for
systems analysis to force one to think through the problem and
allocate priorities; this must be compared with, and consistent with,
the realities of factory life. There is an obvious place for statistical
analysis of observations to show up trends and occurences demanding
further investigation. But, for reasons deriving from the inescapable
fact of national control, the value of broader theoretical treatments
of decision-taking is dubious. We all would like to think that decisions
can be formalized and objective, but it seems more likely that each
investigation will, from the circumstances of the time, be sui generis.

NOTES

1. IAEA Document GOV/1444 (Vienna, 1971).

2. CAS Occasional Paper 11 (London: HMSO, 1969).

3. Frank Morgan, "The Usefulness of Systems Analysis," in
Safeguards Techniques (Vienna: IAEA, 1970), Vol. II, pp. 265-83.

4. R. H. Woodward and D. L. Goldsmith, "Cumulative Sum
Techniques," ICI Monograph No. 3 (London: Oliver & Boyd, 1964).

5. Kouts, et al., paper number 098 presented at the Fourth International UN Conference on the Peaceful Uses of Nuclear Energy, Geneva, 1971.

6. M. O. Finkelstein and W. B. Fairley, "A Bayesian Approach to Identification Evidence," Harvard Law Review, 83 (January 1970), 489-517.

A strong plea was made by Herbert Scoville (Carnegie Endowment for International Peace) not to downgrade the NPT and safeguards procedures only because they do not solve all the problems. A particular subject of the discussion was the provision in the NPT whereby a country can take fissile material out of the nuclear fuel cycle and apply it to non-explosive military purposes, without safeguards, by providing advance notice. Scoville contended that the required declaration is like the waving of a "red flag." All the nations are then alerted. Furthermore, Charles Van Doren (Arms Control and Disarmament Agency) noted that, in practice, the likelihood of such transfers to military uses is lessened by the fact that the arrangements under which one country provides the material to another commonly prohibit such uses.

Herbert Scoville spoke further about his contention that the NPT should not be expected to solve every problem of proliferation nor should IAEA safeguards be expected to solve every problem about violations. Instead, he viewed the importance of IAEA procedures to be in forcing any potential violation to the surface. Thereby, other countries that are party to the Treaty will have better evidence that violations are perhaps taking place.

In this argument by Scoville, such disclosures on military use or possible violations make political decisions very much easier. Decisions are customarily based on information from all sources. Difficulties are encountered in making political decisions when the data are "fuzzy" and when information is "under the table" and thereby difficult to view. The NPT and IAEA activities lessen these difficulties.

The dangers and limitations of the use of models and theories in safeguards decisions and actions were emphasized by Carl Bennett (Battelle Seattle). In this connection, he contended that decision theory is properly used to understand the nature of and basis for a decision but not necessarily to make decisions. Similarly, the value of decisions based on statistical analysis are dependent upon the knowledge possessed about the process.

While agreeing with these points, Frank Morgan summarized his points by saying that he believed safeguards should follow a heuristic approach based on experience. He expressed caution about reliance on the more mathematical tests which do not involve value judgments. These judgments are in the province of the politicians and administrators, guided by the physical scientists.

15

WHO ARE
THE ENEMY?

James E. Lovett

HISTORICAL BACKGROUND

In the months following the end of World War II when the awe-some terror of the atomic bomb was still being digested, scientists and politicians alike turned their minds to the question of how best to ensure that that terror did not strike again. There were those who argued that the terror of the atomic bomb was so great as to justify an international treaty outlawing all uses of nuclear energy. Others noted the tremendous potential benefits to mankind from the peaceful applications of nuclear energy. In the end, the prevailing opinion was that the potential benefits justified some risk. What was needed, it was argued, was a system of effective safeguards to ensure that nuclear materials were used only for peaceful purposes.

Perhaps the most famous plan for accomplishing these safeguards was presented by Bernard Baruch. He advocated international owner-ship not only of all nuclear materials but also of the facilities that would produce and use them. Others were less daring. Some sug-gested that nuclear materials could be poisoned by the deliberate ad-dition of U-236 or Pu-240, isotopes that rendered the materials unfit for nuclear weapons use but did not affect peaceful utilization in any unacceptable manner. Still others offered no specific plan but still argued for a strict system of controls and inspections.

Unfortunately, the world in general was not then ready to accept the concept of international safeguards inspections and no international control system was adopted. Lacking an acceptable international

207

system, the U.S. Congress adopted the Atomic Energy Act of 1946, establishing the Atomic Energy Commission (AEC) and providing for both military and peaceful atomic programs. However, the Atomic Energy Act of 1946 did not provide for a nuclear industry such as exists today. Instead, it authorized the AEC to undertake its own program of research and development activities designed to foster the peaceful application of nuclear energy. All nuclear materials were to be owned by the AEC as an agent for the U.S. government and a strict system of accountability controls was to be established and maintained at all times.

It is significant to this discussion to note that the many political discussions that occurred in late 1945 and 1946 did not clearly define the enemy against whom nuclear materials were to be safeguarded. Two atomic bombs had been exploded for military purposes and the world was determined that there should not be a third. No attempt was made to define the identity of a nation or person who might attempt to obtain and detonate a third device.

In 1956 when the International Atomic Energy Agency (IAEA) was established, a strongly worded safeguards article was included in its charter. However, the IAEA was restricted to the safeguarding of materials and facilities made available pursuant to its charter or otherwise voluntarily subjected to its control. In theory, nations still were free to undertake a nuclear weapons program so long as they did not use material furnished through IAEA channels.

At the same time, the United States entered into a number of bilateral agreements with various nations. These provided in all cases that the nuclear material involved would be used for peaceful purposes. The agreements also provided for safeguards, including inspections, to assure that this peaceful commitment was not violated.

Thus during the late 1950s and early 1960s the only commonly accepted potential diversion threat was the possibility that a non-weapon state that had received material through an AEC bilateral agreement or through the IAEA for peaceful purposes might attempt to divert that material into the manufacture of nuclear weapons. There were some who recognized that the diversion might be organized on a lesser scale than a national government, but the assumed purpose of diversion was still the acquisition of a secret nuclear arsenal.

In 1965 and 1966 the AEC undertook a fairly comprehensive review of its own nuclear materials safeguards policies. Included in that review was the establishment of an ad hoc committee of outside experts to recommend to the AEC what its policies and practices for the safeguarding of special nuclear material should be. This advisory panel introduced a new concept into safeguards thinking by suggesting that diversion might be attempted by a terrorist organization or by organized criminals for financial profit.

However, the panel did not pursue these suggestions by considering motives, resources, constraints, and so forth. Indeed, members of the panel stated privately that such a precise definition of the potential threat was neither possible nor desirable. Attempting to predict the actions of criminal groups is at best very difficult. It also could lead, they suggested, to a safeguard system that protected against "logical" diversion schemes while leaving the back door completely open to a divertor who, deliberately or accidently, chose to operate in an "illogical" manner.

This broad, indefinite definition of the potential diversion threat established in 1966 has persisted to the present time. In some respects it might be said to have flourished as more diversion scenarios came to mind. The result has been the development, within the family of safeguards specialists, of a "diversion hysteria" in which a potential hijacker is seen hiding behind every billboard and a potential diverter is seen lurking behind every extraction column.

This chapter reexamines the basic question of who might rationally be expected to attempt the diversion of nuclear materials. For each potential diverter thus identified, a number of questions are asked and answered, including the following:

1. What motive would the potential divertor be likely to have?

2. How much nuclear material is needed?

3. What technical and financial resources may be assumed to be available?

4. Considering the probable motives, resources, and requirements, what constraints may be assumed to exist?

5. In general terms, what are the basic parameters of a safeguards system adequate to decrease the possibility of diversion in each case to some arbitrarily small limit?

Two potential diversion threats are thus identified. For ease of reference, these are referred to as the non-weapon state and the

terrorist, although as will be shown neither accomplishes anything
more than the assignment of an identifying label to a general class
of potential diverters. A third potential diverter, the organized crime
syndicate, is discussed and discounted. It is conceivable that such a
group might undertake diversion of nuclear materials, but only in response to an offer of financial gain from one of the other potential
diverter groups. In responding to such an offer, the organized crime
syndicate becomes only a means to an end subject to all the constraints
imposed by the original diverter group and supplying no resources
beyond those assumed to be available to the original diverter group.

POTENTIAL ENEMY NUMBER 1:
THE NON-WEAPON STATE

Historically, the first potential diversion threat that has been
reasonably defined is the possibility that country A, a non-weapon
state, might secretly use nuclear material obtained from country B
to manufacture nuclear weapons. It is not necessary that country B
possess nuclear weapons, but this is usually the situation.

There are several variations of this scenario, all of them perhaps about equally plausible. One is that the non-weapon state, instead
of using nuclear material already in its possession and subject to
safeguards, might elect to try to steal material from another country.
Logically but not necessarily, this second country would be one with
large stocks from which a relatively small quantity might not be missed.
Thus diversion from a U.S. facility, which could not rationally be
organized by the U.S. government itself, might still occur as the result
of an effort organized by some other nation.

Another plausible scenario suggests that it is not the non-weapon
state per se that might attempt to create a nuclear stockpile but a
secret military clique. Such a group might be so dissatisfied with the
country's peaceful policies in the face of hostile neighbors as to elect
to attempt nuclear armament. The goal might be purely defensive
or it might be part of a broader plan to take over the country's
government.

Regardless of the assumed diversion scenario, the implied
motive for diversion by a non-weapon state is the acquisition of a
secret nuclear arsenal. Lesser quantities are useless and overt
diversion is not a credible possibility.

It generally is assumed that the definition of a nuclear arsenal is one weapon. Indeed, there are some who suggest that less than one weapon would be enough to create a nuclear panic. The argument here presented suggests that the minimum requirement is at least two or three operational devices. This stems from a consideration of how the non-weapon state might use its nuclear capability. Its choices are as follows:

1. To allow the existence of the arsenal to "leak out," and attempt to use the implied threat to political advantage.

2. At the appropriate time, to publicly announce possession of the arsenal and threaten to use it if necessary to gain a political advantage.

3. At the appropriate time, to use a nuclear device, unannounced, for military purposes.

There are infinite variations, of course, and the author does not pretend to be either a politician or a military strategist. However, it seems reasonable to argue that world intelligence forces ought to be adequate, under each alternative, to establish the extent to which the nation in question was bluffing. If only one bomb existed, the threat would be categorized as a bluff and the objective would be lost. In order for a nation's nuclear arsenal to be taken seriously, it must consist of enough weapons to create the appearance of a willingness to use them. That number very likely is at least two. Certainly it is not smaller than one.

The assumption that a non-weapon state must act secretly also has been challenged and requires justification. First, most or even all of the potential political gain is lost if the diversion is discovered in its early stages. The discovery could conceivably precipitate a military attack from a hostile neighbor under circumstances in which the guilty state was ill-prepared to defend itself. This need for secrecy eliminates outright theft, especially via truck hijacking: the fact that a hijacking has occurred can be kept secret for at most one or two weeks. It also eliminates many of the more obvious diversion schemes, which usually have a significant chance of being detected. The need for secrecy also suggests that a non-weapon state might more logically choose a course of action that did not include diversion, if one were available. For example, why divert low-enrichment uranium as feed for a gas centrifuge? Natural uranium is not as useful

but it is available without the risks associated with a diversion effort.
A non-weapon state also might prefer to attempt diversion of its own
safeguarded material rather than incur the added risks of infiltrating
the nuclear industry of another nation and then having to smuggle
the diverted material past that nation's customs inspectors.

Second, if a non-weapon state is not constrained by secrecy, why
should it undertake diversion? Natural uranium is commercially
available. Most suppliers insist on guarantees of peaceful end use,
but uranium is available without this string attached. Certainly it is
available to a nation that has announced plans to build facilities to
utilize it. If a country builds a natural uranium fueled power reactor
and then a reprocessing plant, who is to say at the start that the
natural uranium is intended for a military purpose?

The non-weapon state, in any of the variant scenarios thus
categorized, must be assumed to possess the financial and technical
resources to accomplish its objective using at least many of the
diverse materials available in the nuclear industry. Hot fuel reprocessing, gas centrifuge uranium enrichment, and recovery of fissile
material from relatively low-level residues, all must be acknowledged
as both financially and technically possible. So too, subtle diversion
schemes in which losses are concealed by fictitious measurement
biases or by shuffling material between facilities also must be accepted
as not only possible but probable.

This ready availability of resources gives the non-weapon state
some potential diversion advantages. The material diverted is not
restricted to high-grade metal; any nuclear material will do if other
factors are right. There very likely is no pressing time factor in
that the nation has no immediate need for a nuclear arsenal. If the
material is already physically in the country and needs only be
switched from peaceful channels, the diversion team has no problem
in gaining reasonable access to it.

There is one situation in which a non-weapon state that did not
feel itself to be constrained by secrecy requirements could achieve
an economic gain through diversion. This is the case where the
material diverted is plutonium or highly enriched uranium either in
the form of metal or of some compound readily converted to metal.
The cost advantages from not having to construct complex enrichment
or separations facilities would be large and might easily justify the
effort.

How does one safeguard against diversion by a non-weapon state? Clearly personnel and physical security measures are of minimum importance. The diverter is forced to avoid diversion schemes that are likely to be detected; he is also assumed to have the wherewithal and the patience to devise and execute subtle schemes that would defeat the most careful security system. On the other hand, the quantities needed are sufficiently large—at least several thousand grams of fissile isotopes—that material balance systems should be capable of providing a satisfactory detection capability. These material balance systems would not need to be prompt, in the sense of daily, weekly, or even monthly, so long as they were reasonably prompt, defined as somewhere in the range of monthly to quarterly. They would not need to be extremely sensitive to one-time diversions but they would need to maintain their sensitivity under long-term conditions. The one case where plutonium or highly enriched uranium might be diverted more openly would have to be precluded by physical security measures.

POTENTIAL ENEMY NUMBER 2: THE TERRORIST

In recent years most U.S. safeguards thinking has been dominated by the possibility that the diversion or theft of nuclear materials might be attempted by subversive elements, crackpots, or others who may be loosely categorized under the label of terrorist. Such individuals or groups presumably would undertake diversion for purposes of blackmail or extortion or possibly as a means of dramatizing the importance of their organization. The terrorist also might wish to use nuclear material as a disruptive force.

A great many scenarios have been suggested. Since the terrorist, more or less by definition, is assumed to be irrational, it is not necessary that the suggested scenario be rational. However, most scenarios may be considered to be variations of the following general patterns:

1. Bombing a truck carrying nuclear material.

2. Hijacking a nuclear shipment, e.g., of plutonium nitrate solution, and threatening to disperse it in a populated area (or actually doing so).

3. Stealing a quantity of nuclear material from an AEC or a

licensee facility and threatening to disperse it in a populated area (or actually doing so).

4. Stealing a nuclear device itself for blackmail purposes.

5. Stealing a quantity of nuclear material, or hijacking a truck, and attempting to construct a nuclear device.

It is difficult to ascribe to the terrorist any significant financial or technical resources. "Significant" is a broad term and cannot imply that the terrorist is alone and broke. A terrorist organization may number in the hundreds or even thousands in terms of loosely controlled adherents. Its financial resources may extend into the tens or possibly hundreds of thousands of dollars. By comparison to the non-weapon state, however, as well as by comparison to the requirements for nuclear production work, the terrorist has no significant resources.

Thus, the terrorist is constrained to the theft of material that is already in the desired form or is at least very nearly in the desired form. The terrorist cannot be assumed to be capable, either financially or technically, of converting UO_2 into UF_6, enriching it to above 90 percent U-235, reconverting it to metal, and fabricating that metal into a sophisticated nuclear device. If a terrorist constructs a nuclear device, it must be by virtue of having stolen enriched uranium or plutonium in a pure metal form.

The terrorist is subject to other constraints. It is probably oversimplistic to suggest that he has no normal access to strategically useful nuclear material. However, with good personnel security it should be reasonable to suggest that his access is severely limited. With good physical security it also should be reasonable to suggest that the terrorist will have difficulty getting his nuclear material out.

Many of the terrorist scenarios do not require that a nuclear device be constructed. It is doubtful whether any of the scenarios require more than one device. The terrorist, accordingly, is not subject to a minimum quantity constraint. Ten grams might not accomplish much but a few hundred grams might very well be ample.

How does one safeguard against diversion by a terrorist? Here material balance accounting systems are of minimum importance. Material balance accounting is totally incapable of minute by minute, hour by hour control of gram quantities in multikilogram operations.

Security measures, on the other hand, are capable of keeping ter-
rorists out of nuclear plants and of detecting their attempted thefts
if they somehow gain access. Security to the ten gram level should
be easy; security to the one gram level should be feasible with some
effort. This same physical and personnel security system, it should
be noted, provides needed protection against the one non-weapon
state situation in which secrecy is not a vital concern.

POTENTIAL ENEMY NUMBER 3:
THE ORGANIZED CRIME SYNDICATE

Most safeguards experts recognize the existence of a third
potential enemy: the organized crime syndicate. The existence of a
highly organized criminal element in the United States, and probably
in the entire world, cannot be denied. It appears to be true, for
example, that there are organized groups in the United States that will
hijack trucks or even entire warehouses on consignment. There are
those who would go so far as to state that, if or when an organized
crime group desires to steal a quantity of nuclear material, there
may be very little that the safeguards effort can do to prevent it.

As with the other potential enemies, many scenarios have been
suggested to describe how an organized crime syndicate might attempt
to divert or steal nuclear material. These scenarios are not repeated
here because they largely duplicate those already listed. More
important, all scenarios commonly ascribed to organized crime syn-
dicates lack one essential component: motive. Organized crime syn-
dicates have only one real motive for all their actions: the acquisition
or retention of financial wealth. Organized crime will attempt nuclear
diversion under one and only one condition, that it bring more money.
Organized crime has no use for nuclear material either as a blackmail threat or as a potential defensive or offensive weapon system.
Nuclear material is of value to it only if it has a buyer.

If this is true, then the organized crime syndicate is not a potential enemy in itself; it is only a means to an end that might be employed
by some other potential enemy. It is credible to believe that a non-
weapon state or a terrorist might employ an organized crime syndicate
to divert nuclear materials in return for a financial payment. It is
not credible to believe that organized crime of itself constitutes a
diversion threat.

Viewed as a means to an end, the organized crime syndicate is
subject to all of the constraints that previously applied to the terrorist

or the non-weapon state. If a non-weapon state is constrained by an absolute need for secrecy, it cannot contract to purchase diverted nuclear material from an organized crime syndicate without including in that contract a requirement that the diversion effort be conducted in the utmost secrecy. If a terrorist organization does not have the financial resources to undertake a complex long-range diversion scheme on its own, it likewise does not have the financial resources to hire an organized crime syndicate to undertake such a scheme for it. The syndicate may have an access to nuclear material that the terrorist does not have, but lack of access on the part of a terrorist was not assumed. Rather, it was suggested that physical and personnel security should make access difficult. The better the security, the more limited this access will be.

SUMMARY AND CONCLUSIONS

In conclusion, this chapter faces up to a controversial topic and may be expected to arouse controversy. Therefore, it is important to summarize what the chapter does and does not say.

First, this study maintains that there are in fact two potential diversion threats, each of which is significantly different from the other in its implied motives, goals, and constraints. Understanding these two threats does not simplify the safeguards problem so much as place it in a better perspective. Both material balance accounting and physical and personnel security are necessary, but each has its assigned role. Where promptness is necessary, it is necessary in terms of minutes or hours, not day or weeks. It cannot be used to justify demands for constant remeasurement of static items or for more and more frequent material balance closings.

One threat, that of the terrorist, must be met by a system that offers extremely prompt protection of the attempted diversion of relatively small quantities (a few hundred grams or less). Such a detection capability can be provided only by physical and personnel security measures. The basic techniques of material balance accounting, even extended to the ultimate in computer data processing systems, cannot hope to provide the needed detection capability. On the other hand, in the case of the non-weapon state diverter where it must be assumed that physical security measures would be at best marginally adequate, an extremely prompt and sensitive detection capability is not required. Here a material balance system capable of detecting a diversion of a few kilograms within a time span of a few months provides all the promptness and sensitivity that is required. Moreover, in this situation the material balance accounting system, by showing that all material is physically present, eliminates the need for a physical security system that is so tight as to make routine production operations extremely difficult or impossible.

This study does not claim that it has necessarily recognized and defined all of the potential threats. However, it does suggest that those who think that other threats exist should be required to define these other threats and to explore applicable motives, resources, and constraints.

Finally, this study does not preclude the possibility that a potential diverter may act in an illogical manner. There are limits to this irrational behavior, however. A diverter who has no enrichment capability cannot steal low enrichment uranium just to fool the safeguards team. A non-weapon state that desires secrecy cannot hire a crime syndicate to hijack a truck just because the safeguards effort assumed it would not.

In short, many people will disagree with this study. They are entitled to disagree only if they define their threat, explore its constraints, and evaluate their safeguards system in terms of whether it is the optimum system for that threat. The mere existence of an undefined threat cannot be used as a blanket justification for any and all proposed safeguards procedures without regard to potential effectiveness.

The discussion centered on the question of a process by which a country previously without nuclear weapons would make a credible claim of having the possession and delivery capability of nuclear weapons for the first time.

Frank Morgan (United Kingdom Atomic Energy Authority) argued that for a nuclear weapon to be a deterrent it must be demonstrated. James Lovett added to this by claiming that at least two weapons are required for a country previously without weapons. One would be for demonstration and the other would be held in abeyance to use if the need arose. David Hall (Los Alamos Scientific Laboratory) suggested that not just a second weapon but a weapons system would be needed. This means that use of the second weapon would require a delivery system. The requirements were further extended by James Lovett who pointed out that a detonation system also would be required. Without a detonation system, he said, the newspaper version of a bomb made by "slapping" two hemispheres of fissile materials together would not kill anybody in the room by an explosion although the radiation might well be fatal.

To illustrate that safeguards do have their limitations in preventing proliferation, James Lovett repeated a possibility that was raised years ago. In this possibility, a non-weapons country would maintain an inventory of fissile material in metal form and in much larger quantity than is conceivably necessary for its power program. All this would be properly approved by safeguards inspectors because, in this story, it would be properly weighed, recorded, and stored, although the safeguards authorities would likely wonder about this large inventory. Then when the military of that country claimed a need for weapons the metal could be rushed to a fabrication process to be combined with a detonation and delivery system that had previously been developed, with perhaps only a 60-90 day lead time.

16

THE NEED FOR A SYSTEMS APPROACH TO PREVENTING THEFT OF SPECIAL NUCLEAR MATERIALS

Theodore B. Taylor

It has become a matter of extreme urgency that systems of safe-guards against the theft of nonmilitary special nuclear materials be designed and implemented in all nations that contain large quantities (dozens of kilograms or more) of highly enriched uranium, plutonium, or U^{233}. There are several reasons for this.

First, safeguards now applied to such materials would not prevent the theft of quantities sufficient for constructing nuclear explosives. The present and formally contemplated levels of physical security provided for these materials, not only in the United States but also in other countries, are considerably lower than those associated with the protection of bank vaults or large shipments of money and other valuables, which continue to be robbed. Between 1958 and 1968 there were more than ten successful thefts throughout the world of money or materials valued at $1 million or more and over fifty thefts involving $100,000 or more. Most of these robberies required overwhelming armed guards or penetrating massive physical barriers and intrusion alarms. We now use neither of these safeguards as a matter of course to protect all special nuclear materials that flow through civilian nuclear fuel cycles.

Second, present U.S. nonmilitary inventories of highly enriched uranium and plutonium that is sufficiently free of radioactive materials to be safely transportable without shielding are of the order of several thousand kilograms. This is sufficient for the construction of hundreds of nuclear explosives. Present total non-U.S. inventories are probably

of the same magnitude. Most of these materials are used in experimental and demonstration reactors and in experimental critical facilities. As recycling of plutonium in light water moderated nuclear
power plants begins on a large scale, perhaps within two years, the
total annual rates of production, transportation, processing, and
fabrication of plutonium for use in power plants will increase dramati-
cally, reaching worldwide rates of production approaching 100,000
kilograms per year by the early 1980s.

Third, the knowledge and experience required for making nuclear
explosives, given the necessary special nuclear materials, continue
to diffuse worldwide. This is due not only to a continuing turnover in
the people who work directly on the design and fabrication of military
nuclear explosives but also to the rapidly increasing numbers of
nuclear scientists and engineers who are acquiring detailed knowledge
of and experience with chain reacting systems and nuclear material
processing techniques. The basic physics and engineering principles
related to the design of fission explosives are described in authori-
tative publications in sufficient detail to guide moderately experienced
nuclear scientists and engineers in efforts to design easily transportable fission explosives with yields in at least the kiloton range. The
information required for the conversion of uranium or plutonium
nitrates, oxides, and so on to metallic form also is widely published.
It can be used to guide the construction of material conversion facilities that could be operated clandestinely by a small number of people.
Resources required to do this are comparable to those required for
clandestine conversion of morphine base to heroin, a currently flourish-
ing illegal activity largely concentrated in southern France. In short,
the knowledge, time, and resources required to make transportable
nuclear explosives with yields in the kiloton range, starting with
special nuclear materials in forms that are common in civilian nuclear
fuel cycles, could be well within the capabilities of small groups of
people organized specifically for that purpose outside the framework
of any national government activity. To put it another way, just about
any country in the world, as well as subnationally organized groups
of people, could now "go nuclear" by stealing special nuclear materials
and clandestinely designing and making nuclear explosives.

A fourth reason for discussing this subject with an extreme sense
of urgency comes from being able to visualize many circumstances in
which nuclear explosives could be used to threaten society without
fear of nuclear retaliation. Extremist groups, or perhaps even
nations, need not necessarily reveal their identity when using nuclear
explosives to serve their purposes, nor is it always feasible to retali-
ate with a nuclear attack even if the identity of the threatening

organization is known. There are historic examples of terrorist
bombings with high explosives, such as the one on Wall Street in the
mid-1920s that killed several dozen bystanders. The bombing was
unannounced and carried out by people who were never identified.
Even announced threats designed to coerce a government into certain
actions need not point directly to a specific organization. A variety
of domestic and foreign organizations want the United States to pull
its military forces out of Vietnam, for example.

Fifth, there are many highly vulnerable targets where a small
nuclear explosion—even a fizzle by standards associated with most
military nuclear weapons—could cause severe damage through the
loss of thousands of lives, destruction of especially valuable property,
or the killing of selected groups of important people. Examples would
be the bombing of the U.S. Capitol during a State of the Union address,
the financial district of New York during a working day, a large nuclear
power plant, or a summit meeting between various heads of state.

Finally, professional criminals may be motivated simply by
prospects of huge profits to steal special nuclear materials for sale
to high bidders. Virtually every highly valuable material has been
traded in illegal national and international markets. It is hard to see
why inadequately protected special nuclear materials should be an
exception.

So much for reasons to be concerned about the problem. What
can be done about it?

I would like to first consider briefly the problem in the United
States. I am convinced that nothing short of a complete systems
approach to the design, assessment, and implementation of an integrated physical security system for all special nuclear materials in
the United States or under U.S. authority will provide the needed level
of security while at the same time allowing the nuclear industry to
expand rapidly to meet increasing demands for energy. An alternative
of patchwork "fixes" of the many individual components of the U.S.
nuclear energy system not only would be less effective but also more
costly. Specific elements of physical security subsystems, as well
as the system as a whole, also should be designed and assessed in the
framework of detailed projections of the future demands for nuclear
power along with alternative ways to meet those demands.

Some links in fuel cycle chains will require greater and more
expensive modifications than others in order to assure high levels of
physical security for special nuclear materials. Stages in the transport

of fission-product-free plutonium, for example, are now especially vulnerable to overt theft. Major improvements, such as the use of continuously operating communications between transport vehicles and monitoring stations, extremely heavy fuel shipping containers, and armed couriers, are likely to increase the transportation costs considerably. However, these will not necessarily increase overall fuel cycle costs to an unacceptable degree. System designs should therefore include methods for allocating and recovering these added costs in ways that are fairly distributed among parts of the industry and ultimately passed on to the users of nuclear energy. Alternative system designs should be assessed in detail in order to select the best way to distribute these costs.

There are also likely to be many opportunities for modifying nuclear fuel cycle components in ways that not only increase the effectiveness of safeguards but also perhaps even benefit the industry as a whole. The colocation of fuel reprocessing and fuel fabrication plants, for example, would remove a troublesome transportation link. Perhaps it could also decrease overall fuel cycle costs by allowing detailed optimization of both types of processes for maximum throughput of fuel at lowest cost. As another example, massive shipping containers, as well as specially designed transport vehicles, might be used both for safe shipment of irradiated fuel assemblies and for secure shipment of new fuel assemblies from fuel fabrication plants to reactors.

Perhaps the most compelling reason for using a systems approach arises from the extreme complexity and interrelatedness of the components of the entire U.S. nuclear energy system. Systematic efforts by competent criminal groups to identify weak points in a security system have characterized many major historic thefts. The Brinks robbery, for example, was preceded by almost two years of detailed planning and analysis including several dozen covert entries of facilities, detailed analyses of alarm systems, and so on. Not only should protection be provided for all elements of the existing system that contain even occasional strategic amounts of special nuclear material but also appropriate security measures should be incorporated in anticipation of planned or likely changes in the system. This implies a continuing detailed analysis of the entire system and assessment of alternative ways to cope with anticipated changes.

I would now like to discuss briefly some possible guiding principles that I believe could help considerably in designing and implementing a national system of physical safeguards for special nuclear materials.

The first of these, which I call the "Principle of Containment," is actually a summary statement of the purposes of the system: that is, to restrict the flow and storage of all special nuclear materials within specified, authorized channels that can be physically identified. In contrast to the majority of present safeguards procedures, which are primarily designed to detect diversion or theft after it has happened, application of this principle strongly implies prevention of unauthorized removal of special nuclear materials from authorized places. As far as detection of losses of materials is concerned, detection systems operating under this principle should be designed to detect any penetrations of materials through unauthorized channels as they happen and transmit the information directly to control centers equipped to initiate action to prevent the successful completion of an attempted theft. Application of the principle also implies the use of physical barriers and other means, including armed guards if necessary, to obstruct the flow of materials through unauthorized channels. To put it another way, the idea is to concentrate attention on the presence and flows of special nuclear materials where they are not supposed to be rather than on precise measurements of flows and inventories of materials where they are supposed to be. This is not to imply that present use of the materials balance approach should be discarded but rather that it should not be the primary basis for safeguarding special nuclear materials. We are all familiar with the difficulties of achieving material balance accuracies in large fuel processing or fuel fabrication facilities sufficient to disclose losses of tens of kilograms per year. However, it is quite possible to achieve extremely high sensitivities for detecting small quantities, even grams or less, of special nuclear materials that flow through channels where there are supposed to be no special nuclear materials whatever.

We can illustrate this principle by imagining how it might be applied to plants that fabricate fuel containing plutonium. Imagine that all the plant operations in which plutonium is used are enclosed in a big box. Physical penetrations of the box for authorized input of plutonium (from, for example, a fuel reprocessing plant) and output of fuel elements are surrounded by a physical surface, the outside of which is visually or instrumentally continuously monitored to detect unauthorized removal of small quantities of plutonium through the barrier. All penetrations not to be used for the flow of plutonium—employee entrances and exits, channels for input and waste water, air, chemicals, equipment, and so forth—are also continuously monitored as are the sides, top, and bottom of the overall enclosure. In addition, heavy storage containers, metal walls, and obstructing fences are used inside the plant to impede the unauthorized transport of materials away from authorized channels. Automatic alarm systems to detect attempts to penetrate the barriers are used as signals for rapidly

deploying reserve forces of armed guards. Finally, a secondary
containment system of peripheral fences and movable barriers that
can be placed along vehicle routes surrounds the entire complex.

A second guiding principle, illustrated to some extent in the above
example, I call the "Principle of Security in Depth." In general terms,
its application is for the double purpose of impeding the progress of
attempted thefts while at the same time allowing the deployment of
successively more powerful reserve forces to the scene of the theft
as the various impediments are overwhelmed. Application of the
principle requires not only a number of successive physical impediments to theft but also a system of alarms, communications, and
transport methods that will allow greater restraining forces to be
brought to the scene before special nuclear materials can be removed
from places under surveillance and control. The "depth" and strength
of such restraining forces are determined by the level of intensity of
theft attempts that the system is designed to cope with. One possible
such level would be somewhat greater than that associated with any
historic nonmilitary theft operation, corresponding to several dozen
heavily armed individuals using several different types of vehicles for
forced entry and getaway as well as hundreds of pounds of high explosives. Obviously there is a level of attack that can overwhelm
practically any defensive system. Nevertheless, it would be no more
rational to abandon efforts to set up a security system that would successfully cope with theft attempts up to some rather large scale simply
because the system is not absolutely effective against all conceivable
threats than to abandon the use of city police forces because they do
not prevent all crime.

With these guiding principles in mind, various alternative physical
security systems could be designed and assessed for direct costs,
effectiveness, and side benefits or impediments to the development of
nuclear power systems. Although I am unaware of any major efforts
to do this, I can suggest a number of possible elements that might be
included in such a system. These include the following:

1. On-site armed guard forces to keep exposed SSNM (super-
special nuclear materials—highly enriched uranium, plutonium, or
U^{233} not mixed with hazardous quantities of radioactive fission products) storage facilities under direct surveillance

2. Protective structures around all places that contain strategic
quantities of SSNM

3. Intrusion alarms to detect unauthorized penetration of containment structures

4. Detection systems to discover the flow of SSNM through authorized penetrations of the containment structures that are not authorized channels for the flow of SSNM

5. Tamper-proof communications systems for transmittal of intrusion alarm signals, SSNM detection signals, and reports of on-site guards or couriers to one or more information monitoring stations

6. Tamper-proof systems for communications between information monitoring stations and places from which armed forces can be quickly deployed to the scene of an attempted theft

7. Devices and heavy containers designed to impede removal of SSNM from areas that have been successfully penetrated by unauthorized people

8. Reserve units of armed guards at a sufficient number of locations, in a sufficient state of readiness, and with appropriate vehicles so that they can be deployed to any area at which there are strategic quantities of SSNM or nuclear weapons before the material or weapons can be removed.

As I understand it, the primary purpose of the safeguards called for under Article 111 of the Non-Proliferation Treaty (NPT) is to inhibit or deter non-nuclear weapons states from making nuclear explosives for military purposes, not to prevent thefts of the type I have been discussing. I do not now suggest changing vent thefts to the type I have been discussing. I do not now suggest changing that purpose. Nevertheless, I must point out that the danger of theft of nuclear materials for use in nuclear explosives for non-nationally sanctioned destructive uses is worldwide and somehow must be drastically decreased. Elements of society in one country could be attacked by nuclear explosives made from nuclear materials stolen in another country. This is an international problem, whatever one may think about its near-term seriousness. In the long term, I find it very hard to imagine how anyone could feel comfortable living in a world in which hundreds of thousands and eventually millions of tons of plutonium or U^{233} are in storage and being transported hither and yon without more security precautions than are used for shipments of mail and ordinary manufactured products.

Realistically, the primary responsibility for seeing to it that special nuclear materials are adequately protected from overt theft probably should be left to each nation. I strongly urge that the United States design and implement a system for doing this within a sufficiently short time for it to be in operation before plutonium recycle

starts on a big scale. At the same time, it would seem prudent, to
say the least, for the other nations that have custody of large amounts
of special nuclear materials to do the same. One possible role for
the International Atomic Energy Agency (IAEA) in all this might be to
establish physical security standards along lines analogous to those
the Agency has developed for handling and shipment of radioactive
materials, to help guide nations in setting up their individual physical
security systems.

I recognize that this problem is fraught with large political and
possibly legal difficulties. The technical and economic problems, on
the other hand, are reasonably well defined and appear to be tractable.
In any case, I can think of few, if any, problems that need to be handled
with a greater sense of urgency. We have very little time. Two or
three years from now may be too late to start bringing the problem
under control. Talk of waiting until a major theft of special nuclear
material has actually taken place is, in my view, irresponsible. I can
leave it to you to imagine the kind of public outrage that would follow
the explosion in a city of just one nuclear device made from stolen
plutonium that was guarded inadequately.

Samuel Edlow (Edlow International) began the discussion with a strong reminder that a measure of physical protection is presently given to nuclear materials, at least while on site. He feared that some of the arguments presented might indicate otherwise. In the United States, Part 73 of the AEC Rules and Regulations prescribes for physical protection. Furthermore, he reported that the nuclear facilities he has seen in other countries have similar physical security. However, he admitted that discussion is certainly warranted on whether the existing physical security is adequate.

Edlow agreed that much more security can be used during the transportation phase of the nuclear fuel cycle. In meeting this need, he stated that he was encouraged by the numerous system analyses under way on methods to improve security during transportation.

Of interest to Edlow was the general agreement he felt existed in this part of the symposium about what materials should be covered by safeguards. Since at least a certain amount of physical security is being used today, the issue instead seemed to him to be one of reaching agreement on the degree of physical security needed.

The response of Theodore Taylor was that the present degree of physical security in nuclear facilities in the United States is demonstrably less than the level of protection used in storing money in banks. Yet banks are continually robbed successfully. The Brinks robbery in 'Boston was given as an example of a sophisticated robbery involving numerous people. Two years were spent in planning the Brinks robbery, including forty individual covert entries into the area finally robbed and a trip to the Patent Office in Washington to examine the details of the alarm system. The possibility of similar concerted attempts against nuclear facilities must be considered. Furthermore, in his response, Taylor stated that, in his evaluation, essentially no physical security is afforded nuclear materials while in transport.

Further information on the increased cost of nuclear power resulting from any increased costs for physical security was requested by R. B. Sewell (Consumers Power). Taylor estimated that by 1980 the desired improvements in physical security would increase the cost of power by 1 percent over an assumed six mills per kilowatt-hour. This increase would cover the large increases in cost for certain parts of the nuclear fuel cycle, e.g., in the area of transportation. In absolute terms this 1 percent is a significant amount of money, but nevertheless it is small compared to the maintenance costs of the U.S. strategic delivery systems, which are planned to maintain a state of stable deterrence.

PART

V

THE FUEL CYCLE
AND
MEASUREMENTS

17

Norman C. Rasmussen

INTRODUCTION

Nuclear detection methods as used here refer to methods that can be used for safeguards assay and that depend upon the measurement of nuclear radiations from the sample. These methods are commonly divided into two general types: active and passive. In passive methods, the detected radiations are emitted spontaneously from the sample as a result of radioactive processes. In the case of active methods, the detected radiation is stimulated by radiation from an external source. The nuclear methods have several characteristics that make them particularly useful for many safeguards applications. Most of them are nondestructive, have quick responses, and allow assay of fairly large samples thus often reducing sampling errors characteristic of many other assay methods.

It is the purpose of this chapter to discuss the principal nuclear methods proposed for safeguards assay and to identify generally where each may be applied in a safeguards system. To do this, it is necessary to discuss the principle of each method as well as its advantages and limitations. The following two sections discuss active and passive methods; the next section discusses their application to the nuclear fuel cycle; and in the final section some general comments are made on accuracies of the methods.

ACTIVE ASSAY METHODS

These methods all are characterized by the requirement of an external radiation source that can be either an accelerator or an appropriate radioactive material. Although the added complexity and expense of the external source is a disadvantage when compared to passive methods, it does allow for a great deal of flexibility in terms of speed of response (by varying the source intensity) and in the choice of the phenomena to be observed (by changing energy and type of interrogating radiation). The principal methods developed to date use either neutrons or γ rays as the interrogating radiation.

In safeguards work, neutron interrogation techniques are used to induce fission in the isotopes of interest. It is then necessary to determine the fission rate in the sample. This can be accomplished by a number of experimental techniques. The prompt fission neutrons or the prompt fission γ rays can be measured. In other applications the delayed neutrons or the delayed fission product γ rays can be measured. In addition to a choice in what radiation to detect, the experimenter also can vary the energy of the neutron source. If low energy neutrons (< 1.0 MeV) are used, fissions will only occur in the fissile species (^{235}U and ^{239}Pu). This is often called subthreshold interrogation. If neutrons with energies greater than 1 MeV are used, it is possible to induce fission in both the fissile and the other fissionable species. This is often called superthreshold interrogation. The three principal neutron sources and their characteristics are discussed below.

In the case of γ-ray interrogation, one induces photofission and measures the fission rate, usually by the prompt fission neutrons although both delayed γ rays and delayed neutrons can be used. In most applications, γ rays with energies high enough to cause fission in both fissile and fissionable species are used.

Neutron Interrogation Using a (d,n) Source

Description

The well known (d,n) reaction

$$_1^2\text{H} + {}_1^3\text{H} \rightarrow {}_2^4\text{He} + {}_0^1\text{n} + 17.6 \text{ MeV}$$

can be used to produce a 14-MeV neutron source of high yield. To produce the reaction, deuterons of 100 keV or greater are required. These are conveniently obtained with either a Cockcroft-Walton generator or sealed gas discharge tubes. The discharge tubes generally are limited in output to a few times 10^{10} n/sec while the Cockcroft-

Walton generators can be operated at a few times 10^{11} n/sec. Los Alamos Scientific Laboratory (LASL) has done considerable work using this reaction as a neutron source.[1]

The most satisfactory technique seems to be to pulse the neutron source and then count delayed fission neutrons during periods while the source is turned off. Typically, the source is operated at about a 50 percent duty cycle with pulse widths of 50 to 100 msec.

The neutron detector typically employed is a bank of ^{3}He tubes imbedded in CH_2 moderator usually covered with Cd to reduce thermal neutron efficiency. Such a detector system has a high efficiency for fast neutrons.

There are several inherent characteristics of this method that must be considered in assay applications.

Isotopic Sensitivity

As shown in Figures 18, 19, and 20, the delayed neutron yield decreases rapidly at about 5 MeV in the nuclides of interest.[2] For-tunately, however, the yield is quite constant below 5 MeV. The experimental solution to this yield variation employed by LASL has been to surround the (d,n) source with suitable materials to moderate the major fraction of the neutron spectrum so that it is below 5 MeV in energy. LASL has done considerable theoretical and experimental work in optimizing the so-called "beam tailoring assemblies" around the target. Table 11 is the result of some of this work. This problem now seems to be solved and the (d,n) source with tailoring can be used to produce a spectrum either dominant in the superthreshold, i.e., 1-5 MeV range, or the subthreshold, i.e., 0-1 MeV range.

When one multiplies the delayed neutron yield/fission and the fission cross-section to get the sensitivity per nuclide, one finds that above E_n of 1 MeV the method has roughly (within a factor of 2) the same sensitivity for all species of interest. Thus, when interrog-ating with high energy neutrons, the measurement gives a total fissile plus fertile content. A second measurement with lower energy neutrons can, of course, yield the fissile content. One can readily obtain a discrimination factor of 50 or more for fissile/fertile by this technique called the superthreshold-subthreshold method.

Matrix and Geometric Sensitivity

Considerable investigation has been carried out by LASL to understand the effect of matrix variations and the geometric effects

FIGURE 18

Absolute Total Delayed-Neutron Yield
from Neutron Induced Fission of 233U

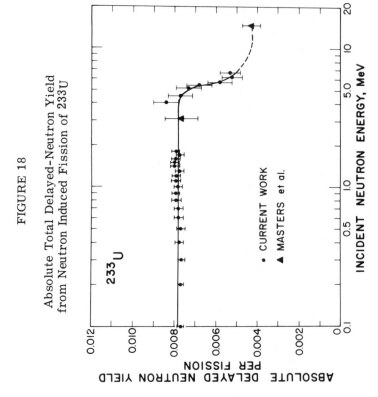

Source: Reprinted from M. S. Krick and A. E. Evans, "Delayed Neutron Yield Vs. Energy Measurements," in G. Robert Keepin, ed., Nuclear Safeguards Research and Development: LA-4523-MS (Los Alamos: LASL, 1970), p. 15 (with permission).

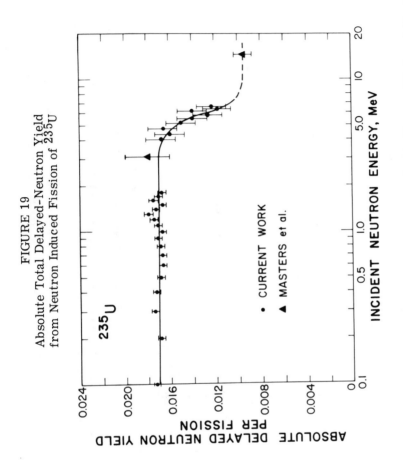

FIGURE 19

Absolute Total Delayed-Neutron Yield
from Neutron Induced Fission of 235U

Source: Reprinted with permission from M. S. Krick and A. E. Evans, "Delayed-Neutron Yield Vs. Energy Measurements," in G. Robert Keepin, ed., Nuclear Safeguards Research and Development: LA-4523-MS (Los Alamos: LASL, 1970), p. 16.

FIGURE 20

Absolute Total Delayed-Neutron Yield
from Neutron Induced Fission of ^{238}U

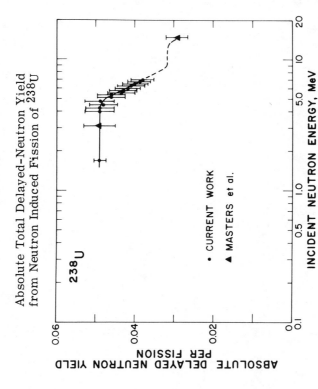

Note: The indicated extrapolation of the curve to 14 MeV takes into account a second inelastic scattering threshold level associated with the step rise in the ^{238}U fission cross section around 14 MeV.

Source: Reprinted with permission from M. S. Krick and A. E. Evans, "Delayed-Neutron Yield Vs. Energy Measurements," in G. Robert Keepin, ed., Nuclear Safeguards Research and Development: LA-4523-MS (Los Alamos: LASL, 1970), p. 16.

TABLE 11

Moderator Configurations with 14-MeV Primary Neutron Source

Moderator Configuration[a] (Thickness in centimeters)	Total Leakage (percentage)	Median Energy (MeV)	Percentage of Neutrons with $E_n < ^{238}U$ Threshold	Fission Ratios[b]			
				$^{235}U/^{238}U$		$^{237}Np/^{238}U$	
				Meas.	Calc.	Meas.	Calc.
Pb - 7.5 (Cd)	146	1.76	39	3.19	3.10	3.03	3.41
Pb - 10 (Cd)	154	1.76	45	3.56	3.52	3.36	3.74
W - 7.5 (Cd)	135	0.47	78	5.68	6.53	3.63	3.30
CH$_2$ - 10 (Cd)	85	13.0	11	4.08	3.17	2.37	2.40
W/C/ - 7.5/7.5 (Cd)	122	0.19	79	15.3	13.3	3.40	2.84
W/C/CH$_2$ - 7.5/7.5/2.5 (Cd)	73	0.056	69	55.7	50.1	3.06	2.61
W/C/CH$_2$ - 7.5/7.5/2.5 (no Cd)	109	0.002	80	600.	788.	–	–
Pb/C/CH$_2$ - 7.5/7.5/2.5 (Cd)	110	1.14	55	31.5	20.1	3.30	3.14
Pb/C/CH$_2$ - 7.5/7.5/2.5 (no Cd)	140	0.47	66	316.	312	–	–

[a] The moderators and detectors were covered with 0.76-mm-thick Cd where noted. DTF-IV calculations were used for the two moderators with no Cd (all others used the Monte Carlo code).

[b] Fission ratios are for equal weights of each fissionable isotope.

due to inhomogeneities in the sample. The neutron interrogation
method, especially with subthreshold neutrons, is very sensitive to
changes in hydrogen content of the matrix. In 55-gallon drums containing varying amounts of hydrogen, the neutron yield per gram of
fissile material has been observed to change by a factor of 50 due to
moderating effects of the matrix on the interrogating neutron spectrum.

A method has been devised to partially correct for this effect.
It consists of putting a fission chamber containing the same fissile
species as is being assayed for next to the sample. Any moderating
effects that the sample produces on the interrogating spectra also
will be seen as an increased counting rate in the fission detector.
When one normalizes the delayed neutron count to the fission chamber
counting rate, the variations due to matrix and geometry are reduced
from a factor of 50 to a factor of about 4. The factor of 4 can be
further reduced by using the ratio of the fission chamber count to the
beam monitor count combined with information from calibration runs
done on known standards. Using this technique on Rocky Flats 55-gallon
waste drums, LASL was able to reduce the error to $\pm$ 36 percent.
The 55-gallon drums containing various amounts of hydrogen are
probably the most difficult category for this method. However, it
does have a high sensitivity (< 0.1 gram) for fissile materials. Despite
its lack of high accuracy, the high sensitivity of the method is well
suited for deciding whether a given sample can be discarded or should
be reprocessed for recovery of the fissile material.

As an example of a case where the method works with considerably better accuracy, we consider the results on the series of
approximately one-gallon cans of U-Al$_x$ powder. This is clearly a
type of sample well suited to the neutron interrogation method. Using
the result of destructive chemical analysis on one can to provide the
standard, it was found that individual measurements on the other cans
varied from the chemical determination by less than one percent and
the discrepancy in the total amount of ^{235}U assayed in ninety cans
was less than 0.2 percent.

Effects due to nonuniform distribution can be rather large, but
they are considerably reduced by rotating the sample. Even so,
variations of a factor of 2 or more can be observed in extreme cases.
These variations can be large enough so that all but very homogeneous
or very small samples will require rotation. In the case of very large
samples (i.e., 55-gallon drums), both rotation and translation may be
required.

Neutron Interrogation Using the (p,n) Source

Description

This method is in principal similar to the (d,n) method described
above except that the neutrons are produced by the endoergic (p,n)
reaction. This allows the maximum energy of the neutrons produced
to be carefully controlled. The advantage of this is that no spectrum
tailoring is required and the discrimination ratio for fissile to fertile
can be very large. It also is possible to detect the prompt fission
neutrons by using special neutron detectors (e.g. ^{4}He counters) that
respond only to neutrons of energy greater than the interrogating
neutrons.

The most commonly used (p,n) reaction is

$$_3^7\text{Li} + _1^1\text{H} \rightarrow _4^7\text{Be} + _0^1\text{n} - 1.63 \text{ MeV}.$$

This reaction, therefore, requires protons greater than 1.90 MeV.
The accelerator most commonly used as a proton source is a Van
de Graaff generator capable of several MeV or greater. This method
is currently under investigation at LASL where it has been used to
assay small inventory samples and a mockup of a BWR fuel assembly.[3]

Isotopic Sensitivity

As noted above, the energy of the (p,n) neutrons can be carefully
controlled so both subthreshold assays for fissile material and superthreshold assays for fissile plus fertile are possible. There is the possibility of distinguishing between ^{239}Pu and ^{235}U on the basis of the
prompt to delayed neutron ratio.

Matrix and Geometric Sensitivity

Although this method has not been tried on as wide a range of
samples as the (d,n) method, it is safe to assume that roughly the
same type of matrix effects would be observed. The yield would be
expected to vary markedly with the hydrogen content of the sample
(in the case of large samples). The method should be fine for small
samples and for heterogeneous samples with nonmoderating matrixes.
Unknown or variable amounts of efficient neutron moderators will
strongly affect the accuracy of an assay.

The geometric sensitivity will be comparable to the (d,n) method. The principal experience to date has been on a mockup of a BWR fuel assembly where quite uniform spatial sensitivity (better than ± 5 percent) has been achieved with the aid of a two-inch steel reflector.[4] This is achieved without rotation.

Neutron Interrogation Using ^{252}Cf

Description

Recently ^{252}Cf has become available in reasonable quantities at a cost of $10/\mu$gm. This isotope decays by spontaneous fission at a rate of 1.2 x 10^9 fissions/curie and produces neutrons at a rate of 2.34 x 10^6 n/sec/μgm. Clearly, ^{252}Cf offers a reliable source of neutrons with little operation and maintenance costs. From this point of view, ^{252}Cf has a considerable advantage over accelerator produced neutrons.

The application of ^{252}Cf is in principal the same as the neutron methods discussed above. However, the ^{252}Cf neutron spectrum peaks at about 1 MeV and drops off rapidly with energy so its sensitivity is low for superthreshold interrogation. However, it works well for subthreshold interrogation.

One method developed has been to use fast neutron detectors for the fission neutrons from the sample while moderating the majority of the source neutrons below this energy. This method has been employed successfully by LASL on cold power reactor fuel rods and on spent UHTREX (Ultra-High Temperature Reactor Experiment) fuel rods.[5]

A different approach has been employed by Gulf Radiation Technology (GRT) where the sample is looked at by four high efficiency scintillation detectors.[6] The detectors are plastic scintillation counters sensitive to both fast neutrons and γ rays produced in fission. Since there are 2.5 neutrons and 5 or 6 γ rays per fission the chance of coincidence in the detectors is quite good when a fission event occurs in the sample. By requiring three detectors out of four to record a simultaneous event and by using a short coincidence resolving time ($\sim$60 nsec), the background and chance rates can be kept low.

Isotopic Sensitivity

The ^{252}Cf source can readily supply neutrons suitable for subthreshold interrogation and so is suitable for assay of fissile species. The fraction of the spectrum above 1 MeV combined with practical source intensity limits means that superthreshold interrogation will not be feasible in many applications. It is possible that superthreshold ^{252}Cf interrogation can be developed in certain special cases.

Matrix and Geometric Sensitivity

As noted above, neutron interrogation methods will be quite sensitive to moderators in the matrix, especially when samples are large. At this time the ^{252}Cf method has not been developed in a form suitable for large drum assay. The GRT method has been developed and successfully demonstrated for containers up to about one gallon in size. LASL has developed the method for the assay of fuel pins prior to assembly into bundles and for small spent fuel samples.

For reasons discussed earlier, the matrix will have important effects. GRT work with Pu showed that the sensitivity increased by a factor of more than 2 as the amount of moderator in the sample was increased. Thus, as with other neutron methods, some knowledge of the matrix composition will be needed so that a proper calibration can be applied in order to obtain accurate results.

Gamma-Ray Interrogation

Description

In this method, γ rays (5-10 MeV) are used to produce photofission in the sample. The fission events are detected by measuring the prompt fission neutrons. In principle it is also possible to detect the fission event by either the delayed neutrons or the delayed γ rays. However, in applications to date the much higher yield of the prompt neutrons has made them the preferable radiation to measure. The development of this method has been done by GRT.[7]

The intense pulsed γ-ray source required for the method is produced by an electron linear accelerator by allowing the electron beam to impinge on a high Z target. When electrons up to about 5 MeV are used, these γ rays all will be below the photofission threshold, but once the energy gets above about 6 MeV photofission is possible in all the fissile and fertile isotopes.

The neutron detectors are slab counters consisting of BF_3 detectors embedded in a hydrogenous matrix. These counters typically are turned on about 40 μsec after the γ burst and remain on for about 250 μsec. During this time, a majority of the prompt neutrons moderate in the detector and are counted. The average background rate (primarily due to delayed neutrons) is obtained by observing the detector counting rate after the prompt neutrons have died away and before the next γ pulse (i.e., t=1 msec to t=5 msec).

Isotopic Sensitivity

To understand the isotopic sensitivity of the method, see Figure 21 which shows the prompt yield as a function of energy for the nuclides of interest. Note that the response is similar for all elements of interest. Below 7 MeV—near the threshold of the (γ,f) reaction—the yield varies very rapidly with energy. This variation is roughly a factor of 10^3 for a 20 percent change in energy. Above 7 MeV the change in yield versus electron energy is much less and also the difference in yield for various isotopes is small. The result is that the observed yield above 7 MeV becomes a good measure of the total amount of fissile plus fertile material in the sample if isotopic content is known; otherwise there is a 10-20 percent error due to yield differences.

If measurements were made at two or more energies in the 5 to 8 MeV range, it would in principle be possible to discriminate the various species. This has been demonstrated only under laboratory conditions with a two-component system and is not yet developed for any practical assay. One way proposed to develop this as a practical method is to place fission chambers containing the isotopes in question next to the sample to measure the ratios of the fission rates directly during the run. This could automatically correct for variations in energy of the interrogating γ-ray spectrum.

Matrix and Geometric Sensitivity

The γ-ray interrogation method will be sensitive not only to photofission neutrons but also to any (γ,n) neutrons produced in the sample. Fortunately, below electron energies of 7.5 MeV only 3 elements give a significant (γ,n) response. These are hydrogen, beryllium, and carbon due to the low neutron separation energy in ^{2}H, ^{9}Be and ^{13}C. The response of H and Be can be corrected by making a run at 5.5 MeV or less (below the (γ,f) threshold). This result can be used to correct the second at 7.5 MeV for the response due to ^{2}H or ^{9}Be in the sample. This method is also accurate enough to correct for carbon in hydrocarbons but it was discovered that one cannot use this method to correct for large amounts of C in the sample because the

FIGURE 21

Prompt and Delayed Neutron Yields
in Fissile and Fertile Material Produced by Bremsstrahlung
from Electrons of Energy E_e

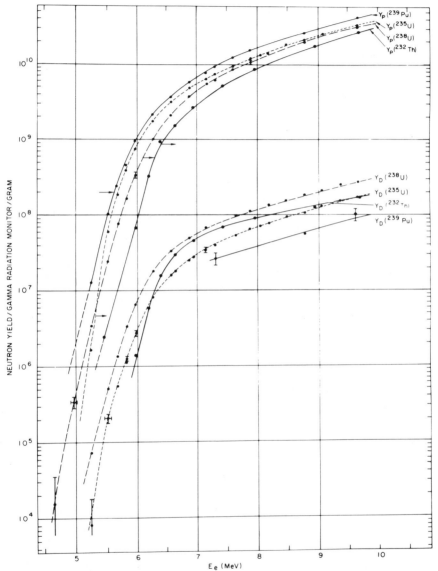

Source: Reprinted with permission from R. L. Bramblet et al., Application of Photoinduced Reactions to Nuclear Materials Safeguards Problems: GA-10272 (San Diego: Gulf Radiation Technology, 1970), p. 88.

C threshold is very close to the photofission threshold. In the case of a pure graphite matrix, the correction was based on the weight of the graphite. It should be noted that certain other high Z materials will be subject to photofission (e.g., Pb). Thus, the method can be fooled by the use of such materials.

In highly hydrogenous matrixes such as wet combustibles, the correction for the (γ,n) production in the matrix (in the case of 55-gallon drums) was found to be equivalent to the response of about 100 grams of Pu. Thus, 10 grams of Pu would increase the response by about 10 percent over a drum of wet combustibles containing no Pu. Wet combustibles and pure graphite produce the highest observed background and in other types of waste this background was less by a factor of 2 or 3.

One of the important advantages of this method is that over a wide range of matrixes the response per gram of Pu varied by less than 20 percent. It appears that possible corrections for neutron effects would reduce this error somewhat. This correction combined with matrix segregation and a good set of calibration standards should make it possible to apply this method to a variety of waste drums containing 50 grams of Pu or more with an accuracy in the 5 to 15 percent range.

As in the neutron interrogation method, both translation and rotation of large samples is required to average out geometric effects. The response as a function of radial position is about 30 percent greater than the volume average response for samples at the very center. However, by using off-center γ-ray interrogation this effect is reduced and variations due to heterogeneous effects should be less than $\pm$ 10 percent. Interpretation of the data makes possible a correction for this nonhomogeneity error.

PASSIVE ASSAY METHODS

Gamma Ray Methods

Description

In this method one simply measures the γ rays from the radioactive decay of the materials in the sample. Fortunately, both ^{239}Pu and ^{245}U give off γ rays of significant intensity.[8] The most useful line in ^{235}U is at 185 keV, while in ^{239}Pu several lines from 330 keV to 414 keV can be used. Unfortunately, ^{238}U gives no lines above 60 keV directly but it does have a decay product ($_{91}$Pa^{234}) that gives lines at 1001 keV and 767 keV. Since the longest half-life in the decay chain is 24 d (^{234}Th), it is almost always safe to assume secular equilibrium has been reached and to use the γ ray for assay purposes. This is not true in all cases, however, for some decay product γ rays change their intensity with time and so are not direct measures of the parent unless the time dependence is known. Because of the possibility of γ rays from the sample whose intensity varies with time of γ rays from extraneous sources, it is necessary in almost all cases to use an energy-sensitive γ-ray detector.

Two types of available spectrometers might be used: the NaI scintillation counter and the Ge(Li) solid state detector. The basic difference is that in the energy range of interest the Ge(Li) is capable of energy resolution of about 1 percent (FWHM $\simeq 1$ keV) while NaI has $\simeq 10$ percent (FWHM $\simeq 10$ keV). Currently, Ge(Li) detectors are limited in size to $\simeq 50$ cm.^{3} of active volume. NaI, on the other hand, can be obtained in sizes 10 to 100 times larger. The overall efficiency is roughly proportional to volume. The other principal difference is that Ge(Li) detectors must operate in a vacuum at liquid nitrogen temperature while NaI operates readily at room temperature. The basic electronics of both systems are about the same although a high quality amplifier and a larger pulse height analyzer would be required to realize the full energy resolution potential of the Ge(Li).

Isotopic Sensitivity

With the very high energy resolution of Ge(Li) detectors and under ideal conditions, it is possible to detect all the fissile and fertile isotopes of interest. The method has been demonstrated to be practical for ^{239}Pu, ^{235}U, ^{241}Pu, and ^{241}Am in field tests. In addition, the 1-MeV line from the decay of ^{238}U has been used for successful analysis in some cases and ^{233}U also looks promising.

Matrix and Geometric Sensitivity

One of the major problems encountered with the γ-ray method is determining the amount of absorption within the sample. The severity of this problem is indicated by the mean free path of the γ's in a PuO$_2$-UO mixture having a density of 10 gm./cm.^{3} At 385 keV the mfp is $\simeq 0.3$ cm., at 185 kev $\simeq 0.07$ cm. Since more than 90 percent of the γ's measured come from within 2 mfp of the surface, this means that in the case of ^{235}U the γ rays come from the outer 0.14 cm. while in ^{239}Pu they come from the outer 0.6 cm. The method can be used

for assaying fuel pins ($\sim$ 0.6 - 1.0 cm. diameter) with suitable corrections, but unless homogeneity can be assuemed the method will not
work on large samples of fuel material.

The absorption problem is not quite so severe in low Z materials
such as often appear in wastes where the mfp is 10 gm./cm.^{2} at 400
keV and 7 gm/cm^2 at 185 keV. Thus, if the average density of this
material were 0.5 gm./cm.^{3} (the value for many waste categories
is less than this), the mfp would be 20 and 14 cm., respectively. In
a 55-gallon drum this would require a correction factor of about 10 for
^{239}Pu and 25 for ^{235}U. Results on Pu assay indicate that attenuation
corrections can be made adequately for cases where the diametric
attenuation factor is 500 or less if the collimation angle of the detector
is optimized.

The normal method of determining this correction factor is to do
a transmission measurement through the sample to obtain an average
attenuation in the sample. An example of a way this can be done is
the LASL NaI barrel counter which has a row of 8 NaI detectors
parallel to the axis of the drum and a row of 8 shielded sources dia-
metrically opposite.[9] The source shield is mechanically activated
so that it can be opened for the transmission measurement and closed
while the barrel is being counted.

This method of correction is fairly good for waste barrels in
which the fissile material is distributed through the matrix; however,
if the fissile material should be in a small lump, assay errors could
be very large even with the correction. It is possible to discover
such a lump in ^{239}Pu by simultaneously doing a passive neutron
count as described above. In ^{235}U no passive backup method exists
and an active method would be needed for such a check of the passive
γ method.

The γ-ray information can be used in a slightly different way
when large (compared to the γ-ray mfp) homogeneous samples of
known composition, e.g. UO$_2$ or U metal, are measured. Consider
the case of a thick sample of U metal: it can easily be shown that the
number of 185-keV ^{235}U γ's emitted per cm.^{2} of surface is proportional
to the enrichment.[10] Thus, by collimating to look at a fixed surface
area and calibrating for the matrix, one can read directly the uranium
enrichment from the intensity of the 185-keV line. The LASL enrichment meter, employing this technique, has worked well on a variety
of samples.

The geometric sensitivity for nonuniform samples can be greatly
reduced by rotating the sample and optimizing the collimation of the
detector.

Neutron Methods

Description

Materials of interest in safeguards work produce neutrons by two processes, spontaneous fission and (α,n) reactions. The (α,n) neutrons are mainly the result of the (α,n) reaction with ^{18}O in oxide fuels and in the case of heterogeneous matrixes the yield of (α,n) reactions is particularly large with F and B. The spontaneous fission process which gives rise to two or more fast neutrons simultaneously is energetically allowed in all isotopes of interest. As can be seen in Table 12, it is a rare process in the isotopes of interest except for the cases of the even A isotopes of Pu. The rate of fission neutrons produced should give an accurate measure of ^{240}Pu content. In cases where the sample is homogeneous the (α,n) rate should be a good measure of the total α activity in the sample. Methods for distinguishing between the two processes are given below.

Normally, to detect fast neutrons with high efficiency, one uses a bank of BF_3 and/or ^3He detectors imbedded in a good moderator such as polyethylene. The most widely used method for distinguishing between fission and (α,n) neutrons is a coincidence method that will detect fission but not (α,n).[11] This neutron coincidence method has been developed and used at a number of laboratories for ^{240}Pu assay. The neutron detection systems range in size from small (one gallon or less) to one big enough to put a 55-gallon drum inside.

TABLE 12

Spontaneous Fission Rates

Isotope	Number of Fissions Per Gram-Second	Total Disintegration (percentage)
U^{233}	$\leq 1.9 \times 10^{-4}$	5.4×10^{-11}
U^{234}	3.5×10^{-3}	1.5×10^{-9}
U^{235}	3.1×10^{-4}	3.9×10^{-7}
U^{238}	7.0×10^{-3}	5.6×10^{-5}
Pu^{238}	1.1×10^{3}	1.7×10^{-13}
Pu^{239}	1.0×10^{-2}	4.4×10^{-10}
Pu^{240}	4.6×10^{2}	5.49×10^{-6}

Source: Data from H. Etherington, ed., Nuclear Engineering Handbook (New York: McGraw-Hill, 1958), pp. 2-5.

In the case of many homogeneous samples such as fuel rods
and other clean product forms, it has been found that the total neutron
count can be an accurate assay method. It has the advantage of producing a larger counting rate per gram of material, thus reducing
counting time for the same accuracy.

Isotopic Sensitivity

As pointed out above, the method is quite sensitive to ^{240}Pu.
In cases where the ^{239}Pu/^{240}Pu ratio is known, it becomes a good
measure of total Pu. Although the response is much less per gram,
the method also has been used to determine the amount of 238U present
in slightly enriched samples. The minimum sensitivity for 238U is
in the few tens of grams range.

Matrix and Geometric Sensitivity

There are several ways the method will be sensitive to the
matrix. In heterogeneous matrixes the (α,n) background may vary
tremendously (especially if they contain florine compounds). This
will mean that total neutron counts will be totally unreliable. This
background also will increase the chance rate in coincidence counting
and thus reduce the sensitivity and accuracy of the method.

In highly hydrogeneous matrixes the neutron absorption rate in
the sample can become important and affect the response. The correction for moderator effects has been made at LASL by taking a
second measurement with a small neutron source of known strength
added.[12] Studies to date have shown that in a 55-gallon drum this
correction could be as much as 25 percent. In high Z samples, however,
the neutron absorption correction usually is small. Thus the passive
neutron method has the biggest corrections for low Z matrixes while
the passive γ-ray method has its biggest corrections when the matrix
is high Z. For this reason the two methods complement each other
very well and a combination of the two makes a good Pu assay method.

The final effect is that, in samples containing considerable
fissile material, a multiplication effect can take place and change the
response per gram. This manifests itself as a nonlinear calibration
curve and rarely leads to serious error (usually less than 5 percent)
since for safety reasons the multiplication factor in any sample usually
is quite small.

Since most of the present neutron counters have essentially a
4π geometry, the method is not very sensitive to geometric effects
and barrel rotation and translation are not necessary.

Calorimetry

Description

The principle of the calorimetric method is simply to measure the power level in the sample. If the exact composition and decay energetics of the sample are known, this power level can be related to the quantity of material present. The greatest advantage of this method is that the power level in the sample can be measured with very high precision (better than 0.1 percent has been achieved).[13] However, the accuracy is limited by the measurements of sample isotopic composition. The method requires considerable time for the sample to equilibrate thermally. For example, reasonable samples may require from 2 to 4 hours for a measurement.

Isotopic Sensitivity

Table 13 gives the power per gram of a number of isotopes of interest. Because of the very low power output of the uranium isotopes, calorimetry is not considered a useful technique for U assay. The response to ^{239}Pu is a factor of 10^6 higher than ^{238}U, and the method is quite sensitive to Pu. However, the isotopic composition must be accurately known and corrections for the buildup of daughter products must be made. Calorimetry measurements are particularly sensitive to ^{238}Pu and ^{241}Am, the daughter of ^{241}Pu.

Matrix and Geometric Sensitivity

The method is sensitive only to heat sources in the matrix so it will respond to extraneous sources of radiation and any heat producing chemical activity in the sample. It is generally considered useful only for clean, uniform material such as process product or feed to the process. The method has been successfully employed in Germany on entire Pu containing fuel assemblies.[14]

If the matrix contains no extraneous heat sources, it may affect the equilibration time but not the final answer. However, the limit of sensitivity may be affected by the mass of material or the size of the sample.

APPLICATIONS TO SAFEGUARDS

The rate of growth of the nuclear power industry has clearly made control of strategic material in the commercial fuel cycle the

TABLE 13

Energetics of α Decay

Isotope	Half Life (years)	Q_α MeV	E_α (principal) MeV	Specific Activity Disintegrations $\overline{\text{(grams/second)}}$	Specific Heating Power (watts/gram)
^{233}U	1.62×10^5	4.90	4.816 (84%) 4.773 (15%)	3.50×10^8	2.74×10^{-4}
^{234}U	2.48×10^5	4.85	4.768 (72%) 4.717 (28%)	2.28×10^8	1.77×10^{-4}
^{235}U	7.13×10^8	4.66	4.58 (10%) 4.40 (83%)	7.89×10^4	5.88×10^{-8}
^{238}U	4.49×10^9	4.25	4.182 (77%) 4.135 (23%)	1.24×10^4	8.43×10^{-9}
^{238}Pu	8.96×10^1	5.59	5.495 (72%) 5.452 (28%)	6.2×10^{11}	5.54×10^{-1}
^{239}Pu	2.43×10^4	5.24	5.150 (72.5%) 5.137 (16.8%) 5.099 (10.7%)	2.27×10^9	1.9×10^{-3}
^{240}Pu	6.58×10^3	5.249	5.162 (75%) 5.118 (25%)	8.37×10^9	7.03×10^{-3}
^{241}Pu	13.2	5.121	4.893 (75%) 4.848 (25%)	4.16×10^{12}	1.3×10^{-2}*

*Approximate value mostly due to β decay.

Source: Data from I. Perlman and J. O. Rasmussen, "Alpha Radioactivity," in Handbuch der Physik, Vol. XLII (Berlin: Springer-Verlag, 1957), p. 124.

area of prime importance from a safeguards point of view. Of course, it is also essential to have excellent safeguards procedures in the production of nuclear explosives. Since much of this work is classified, this study will not consider this area of safeguards. The following discussion will be limited to the application of these techniques to the commercial fuel cycle.

Description of the Commercial Fuel Cycle

The commercial fuel cycle is about the same for all reactors independent of the type of fuel since at present almost all use the fuel in the oxide form. The overall fuel cycle is shown in Figure 22 where main operations are indicated in the blocks. The circled letters indicate points in the cycle where some accountability will be required if a material balance is to be maintained throughout the cycle.

Application of Nuclear Detection
Methods to the Fuel Cycle

The techniques described above can be used at a number of points in the fuel cycle. In some cases, they will be the method of choice; in other cases, more standard analytical methods are preferred. The following discussion is an analysis of the various points in the fuel cycle giving this author's opinion of where the various methods may have application. The reader is warned that there is not universal agreement with the opinions here expressed.

Spent Fuel Assemblies

Spent fuel assemblies are highly radioactive so the possibility of diversion seems very remote. They are difficult to assay by nuclear methods and the accuracy probably would be no better than ± 10 percent. Probably the best method of control is simply an item count with positive identification (serial number) required for each element.

Accountability Tank

Once in solution, a small sample should be carefully analyzed by chemical and mass spectrometry methods. This also will require an accurately known total volume or total weight of material in the tank. The above information will provide an accurate number for the total input to the reprocessing plant. This is one of the most critical measurements in the cycle from the accountability point of view. I

FIGURE 22

Commercial Fuel Cycles

Fuel Reprocessing Plant

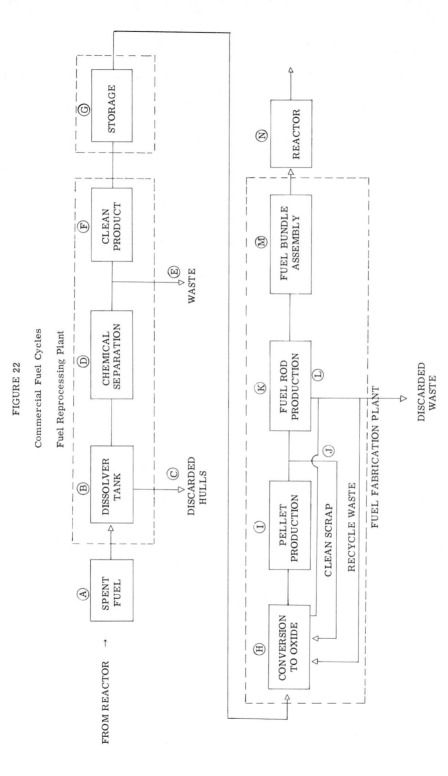

Note: Circled letters indicate assay or inventory points discussed in text.

252

feel that an independent check for errors in analysis is justified. A quick check by a nuclear method, probably active neutron, could be used.

Discarded Hulls

Discarded hulls represent a very unlikely source of divertible material. The fuel reprocessor will have to assure nearly complete dissolution for economic reasons. If an assay is considered necessary, a passive γ scan for fission products probably would be best but the active neutron method for total fissile content also could be used.

Chemical Separation

These processes are carried out on the highly radioactive solutions from the dissolver. Accurate assays will be hard to make by any method. Chemical analyses will be poor because the concentrations change from step to step. Nuclear detection methods will be equally hard to apply. The accountability control probably is best done by careful input-output measurements.

Waste Streams

All waste leaving the plant should be assayed for Pu and U. Since these wastes are almost entirely in solution form, sampling errors should be small and chemical analyses seem indicated. These waste streams will be mostly highly radioactive with low concentrations of Pu and U. Neutron interrogation is the only nuclear method that could be used.

Clean Product

This measurement plus "waste" should equal "accountability tank" (see above) to provide the material balance. It is important that it be done accurately. The clean product is homogeneous so the sampling error should be small and chemistry and mass spectroscopic methods seem best. The amount in the final product containers is very important from a safeguards standpoint and, once sealed, they should be checked by a nuclear method. For plutonium product, either passive neutron or passive γ or both should work well. For $235U$, the γ-ray attenuation would be very high so neutron interrogation probably is best.

Storage

Currently a considerable amount of the Pu product goes into storage because its market for recycle or fast reactors is not yet developed. It is important to keep track of this Pu both as it goes into and as it comes out of storage. There is a considerable advantage in not opening the sealed containers. This is a point where the passive neutron or passive gamma could be used to great advantage.

Oxide Conversion

The incoming material should be carefully assayed. There is considerable advantage to measuring the unopened package to immediately identify any shipper-receiver differences so that any questionable packages can be returned unopened. Once accepted, the contents should be assayed by chemical and mass spectroscopic techniques.

For incoming Pu material, either the passive neutron or γ-ray method would work well for as-received packages. Once the incoming liquid has been converted to a solid, the problem of obtaining a representative sample becomes more difficult and the nuclear methods become more valuable. The PuO_2 product has been assayed very successfully using calorimetric techniques as well as the passive neutron and γ-ray methods. Any of these methods properly calibrated should be accurate to ± 1 percent or better.

U usually arrives as UF_6 from the enrichment plant. It is difficult to measure in this form and the best measurement probably will be chemical and mass spectroscopic after careful mixing. The UO_2 product could be measured by the passive γ method if samples were relatively small, but with production-size containers the high γ-ray attenuation would probably make neutron interrogation a preferred method. Recent studies at United Nuclear Corporation have shown ^{252}Cf interrogation to work quite well.[15]

Pellet Production

The assay methods would be the same as described for oxide product above.

Clean Scrap

PuO_2 scrap could be assayed by passive neutron or passive γ. In the case of UO_2, active neutron probably would be required because of high gamma-ray attenuation.

Fuel Rod Production

Assay of fabricated fuel pins is possible by nuclear methods. For Pu rods, passive neutron or γ-ray methods would work and passive

γ-ray method would work for UO_2. In normal commercial production, however, the counting times required by these methods may be too long. This time can be shortened by using the active neutron method. Such a system using a ^{252}Cf has been developed at LASL and is performing well.[16]

Heterogeneous Waste

Probably the most difficult assay problem is that of heterogeneous waste. Normally such waste consists of a variety of discarded process materials (gloves, wipes, floor sweepings, and so forth). For Pu containing waste, passive neutron and γ methods will work only if packages are small and the waste is segregated by type so that reasonable calibrations can be made. If the waste is carefully segregated by type, it is possible to do assays of 55-gallon drums by passive γ and neutrons for Pu. Accuracies of 10 to 20 percent can be expected. For completely heterogeneous waste in large packages, γ-ray interrogation works well with a reasonable sensitivity for quantities of 50 grams of Pu or more with accuracies of 5 to 10 percent. For lower levels, the higher sensitivity of neutron interrogation methods is required.

The case of U waste is about the same except that the passive neutron method will not work and the passive γ-ray method will be less accurate because of more severe attenuation corrections.

Fuel Bundles

Fuel bundles will be difficult to measure. A careful assay of the pins prior to assembly probably is sufficient. If a measurement must be made, it will have to be by neutron or γ-ray interrogation.

Reactor

Identification of bundles by serial number should be adequate. This method combined with vessel head seals should be sufficient for adequate safeguards.

SUMMARY AND CONCLUSIONS

We have discussed above the principal nuclear detection methods and the places where each may have application to the nuclear fuel cycle. As indicated by the references, considerable developmental work has been done on these methods during the last five years. In many cases there is now enough information available to decide which will be the method of choice in a given assay situation. In particular, we know fairly well such parameters as overall sensitivity, effect of various matrixes, effect of sample inhomogeneity, the amount of expense and effort that the method will entail, and the approximate accuracy that can be expected.

A rough idea of the methods and their assay capability for materials of interest is given in Table 14. The clean homogeneous column represents the easiest assay situation while the dirty heterogeneous represents the most difficult. The accuracy numbers are only approximate and will vary considerably especially with sample size and shape. They cover most situations to within a factor of 2. In general, column A represents about the best that can be expected, and at many assay points somewhat poorer accuracy will be obtained. The poorest value in the B column is about what can be expected for 55-gallon drums. To achieve this, some information about the matrix usually will be required.

An important point to note is that only the neutron interrogation and the passive gamma-ray methods measure the fissile content of the sample directly. All other methods measure a quantity proportional to fissile content, but the proportionality constant must be known from other sources. This gives active neutron and passive γ a distinct advantage for safeguards measurements. They will be difficult to fool. Deliberate attempts to fool the other methods are in many cases relatively easy to accomplish.

In terms of practical usefulness, the passive methods are, in general, less expensive and complicated to use because they require no source. For this reason, I would expect them to be the methods of choice in many applications. The active methods employing a radioactive source will, in general, be somewhat more expensive but no more complicated to operate than passive methods. Neutron interrogation with a ^{252}Cf source can be expected to have many useful applications.

In the case of active methods using accelerators, both the initial expense and the complication and expense of operating the source will, in this author's opinion, restrict their use in industry to a limited number of specialized applications; for example, a facility that must handle large amounts of heterogeneous waste in large containers. Accelerators also may be used in some very high volume operations where a shorter analysis time can economically justify their higher expense.

As a result of active programs during the last five years, a number of systems suitable for on-line use in commercial facilities already have been built and tested. These include the following:

TABLE 14

Assay Techniques

Assay Technique	239Pu A	239Pu B	240Pu A	240Pu B	235U A	235U B	238U A	238U B
Subthreshold neutron interrogation (measures total fissile)	0.5%	10-30% 1-5 gms.	NR	NR	0.5%	10-30% 0.05-2.5 g	NR	NR
Superthreshold neutron interrogation (measures fissile plus fertile)	A 1-2%	——Measures sum of all—— B 10-30% (combined with subthreshold) (except for hydrogen matrix) 1-5 gms						
γ-ray interrogation (measures fissile plus fertile)	A 1-2%	——Measures sum of all—— B 5-10% (if isotopic known) 50-100 gms.						
Passive γ (measures individual isotopes)	0.2%	5-10% 1 gm.	Low sensitivity		0.2%	5-10% 1-10 gms.	25%	1 gm.
Passive n (spontaneous fission detection)	NR	NR	1%	5-10% 50 mg.	NR	NR	Sensitivity > 100 gms.	
Calorimetry (measures total power)	Precision > 0.1% accuracy Depends on isotope assay				Very low sensitivity Not practical for assay			

Notes. A = clean homogeneous materials such as food and product.
 B = dirty heterogeneous material such as waste and scrap in 55-gallon drums.
 NR = no response.
 Sensitivity values are for sample signal equal to background.

257

1. NaI scanners for container sizes up to 55 gallons

2. Neutron coincidence counters for container sizes up to 55 gallons

3. Neutron interrogation with ^{252}Cf source for 1 gallon containers

4. Neutron interrogation with ^{252}Cf source for fuel pins

5. Calorimeter for Pu product

6. Numerous NaI and Ge(Li) γ-ray spectrometers for passive γ assays

7. Uranium enrichment meter using the passive γ method.

One of the major tasks now before the safeguards program is to get these devices installed and operating in commercial facilities.

Another major problem that must be recognized is that the volume of strategic material being commercially processed is growing rapidly. In order to assure effective safeguards through the years ahead, assay methods will have to improve in sensitivity and accuracy. If these methods are to continue to improve, a reasonably steady level of research and development effort on methods development and improvement must continue.

In conclusion, it is the author's opinion that these nuclear assay methods will have an important and necessary role in any effective safeguards program. They currently are developed to the point where they can be effectively applied to many commercial operations. If they are to meet the demands of safeguards for an ever-growing nuclear industry, improvements in their accuracy and sensitivity will be required.

NOTES

1. R. H. Augustson and H. O. Menlove, "Accelerator I Neutron Generator," in G. Robert Keepin, ed., Nuclear Safeguards Research and Development: LA-4162-MS (Los Alamos: Los Alamos Scientific Laboratory, 1969), p. 26; A. E. Evans, M. S. Krick, and J. J. Malanify, "Improvements in Van de Graaff Accelerator Facility for Extensive Nondestructive Assay Application," in G. Robert Keepin, ed., Nuclear Safeguards Research and Development: LA-4605-MS (Los Alamos: LASL, 1971), p. 38.

2. M. S. Crick and A. E. Evans, "Delayed-Neutron Yield Vs. Energy Measurements," in G. Robert Keepin, ed., Nuclear Safeguards Research and Development: LA-4523-MS (Los Alamos: LASL, 1971), p. 15.

3. A. E. Evans and J. J. Malanify, "Delayed Neutron Assay of Pu Inventory Samples by Van de Graaff Neutron Interrogation," in Keepin, ed., Nuclear Safeguards Research and Development: LA-4605-MS, p. 5.

4. R. H. Augustson and A. E. Evans, "Non-Destructive Assay of Power Reactor Fuel Elements," in Keepin, ed., Nuclear Safeguards Research and Development: LA-4523-MS, p. 9.

5. H. O. Menlove, J. L. Parker, and H. A. Walter, "Assay of Hot UNTREX Fuel Rods Using ^{252}Cf," in Keepin, ed., Nuclear Safeguards Research and Development: LA-4523-MS, p. 14.

6. R. L. Bramblett et al., Application of Photoinduced Reactions to Nuclear Materials Safeguards Problems: RT-10511, (San Diego: Gulf Radiation Technology, 1971).

7. R. L. Bramblett et al., Application of Photoinduced Reactions to Nuclear Materials Safeguards Problems: GA-8812 (San Diego: Gulf General Atomic, 1968); R. L. Bramblett et al., Application of Photoinduced Reactions to Nuclear Materials Safeguards Problems: GA-10272 (San Diego: Gulf Radiation Technology, 1970).

8. Norman C. Rasmussen, "A Review of Passive Methods," in Proceedings of the AEC Symposium on Safeguards Research and Development (Washington, D. C.: Office of Safeguards and Materials Management, U.S. AEC, 1969), pp. 96-107.

9. G. R. Keepin et al., "Application Areas and Results of Non-Destructive Assay Measurements," in Safeguards Techniques, Vol. II (Vienna: IAEA, 1970), p. 101; J. L. Parker, T. D. Reilly, and R. B. Walton, "Gamma-Ray Assay of Fifty-Five-Gallon Barrels," in Keepin, ed., Nuclear Safeguards Research and Development: LA-4523-MS, p. 29.

10. T. D. Reilly, R. B. Walton, and J. L. Parker, "The 'Enrichment Meter'—A Simple Method for Measuring Isotopic Enrichment," in Keepin, ed., Nuclear Safeguards Research and Development: LA-4605-MS, p. 19.

11. R. J. Omohundro and F. A. Marchetti, A Prototype Coincidence Neutron Counter for International Safeguards and Arms Control Applications (Washington; D. C.: Naval Research Laboratory, 1969).

12. R. H. Augustson et al., "Development of Techniques for Active and Passive Assay of Fissionable Materials," in Safeguards Techniques Vol. II, p. 61.

13. K. C. Jordan, "Calorimetrium at Mound Laboratory," paper presented at the Sixth Tripartite Instrumentations Conference, 1959.

14. W. Gmelin, D. Nentwich, and H. E. Otto, Safeguard Exercise at the Fabrication Plant Alkem: KFK-901 (Karlsruhe: Institut für Angewandte Reaktorphysik, 1969).

15. W. J. Gallagher, Evaluation of Isotopic Source Assay System (ISAS) Under Commercial Operating Conditions, (New Haven: United Nuclear Corporation, 1971).

16. H. O. Menlove and R. A. Forster, "Design of a Reactor Fuel Rod Assay System," in Keepin, ed., Nuclear Safeguards Research and Development: LA-4605-MS, p. 10.

The dependence of the passive neutron technique (neutrons from spontaneous fission) upon the presence of other isotopes of plutonium was raised by G. F. Molen (Allied Gulf Nuclear Services). Noting that this technique measures ^{239}Pu by the ^{240}Pu content, he asked at what point difficulties would be encountered from the ^{238}Pu and ^{242}Pu content in high burnup plutonium. In reply, Norman Rasmussen expected that the method would become less and less useful as the material is progressively recycled, for then the isotopic ratios become increasingly different. The problem is then the possibility of mixing of materials of different isotopic ratios during the industrial processing. Of course, the higher spontaneous fission rates of the even-numbered plutonium isotopes mean that for passive neutron measurements the isotopic rations of ^{238}Pu and ^{242}Pu need to be known as well as that of ^{240}Pu.

A method for determining these isotopic ratios was mentioned by John Miskel (Lawrence Radiation Laboratory). With a Ge(Li) detector and passive gamma rays from a solution, which is an ideal sample, the method gives about one percent determinations of ^{240}Pu content. Isotopic rations of ^{238}Pu, ^{239}Pu, ^{240}Pu, and ^{241}Pu also are obtained.

An inquiry as to whether the ^{233}U-thorium fuel cycle should be considered since it may be inherently safer from diversion was made by George Nelson (University of Arizona). Rasmussen replied that he had not included this cycle because it was not yet an active part of the nuclear industry, although it appears that it will be soon. In principle the ^{233}U component is sensitive to the usual measurement techniques of other fissile components. The ^{232}Th can be measured by passive gamma-ray techniques, although William Higinbotham (Brookhaven National Laboratory), Lorenz Kull (Science Applications Corporation), and Rasmussen all recognized that allowance must be made for daughter product gamma rays building up with time after chemical separation of thorium.

Higinbotham questioned the 50- to 100 gram sensitivity that Rasmussen listed in Table 14 for gamma-ray interrogation and asked if the sensitivity is not instead 10 grams. Rasmussen conceded that 10 grams can be measured, but stated that Table 14 was for the criterion of the sample signal being equal to the background signal. Fifty grams were used because the data he had seen from Gulf General Atomic indicated that the signals from about 50 grams of plutonium were the same as from the matrix.

Inspector General Rudolf Rometsch (International Atomic
Energy Agency) asked whether bundles of spent fuel from reactors
could possibly be identified by their radiation characteristics. Rasmussen had worked this out six or seven years ago at the Massachusetts
Institute of Technology and confidently reported that spectroscopy of
passive gamma rays from the spent fuel could provide information.
However, the assay would be limited to providing information about
whether the identity of the fuel bundle was what it was believed to be,
about the kind of irradiation history the bundle had in the reactor,
and about how long it had been out of the reactor. Although this method
is successful, Rasmussen wondered whether a serial number on the fuel
bundle is instead sufficient.

Measurement problems associated with the reprocessing plants
were raised by Stephen Lawroski (Argonne National Laboratory) and
by Kull. Lawroski emphasized the desirability of devising some type
of dynamic inventory in order to continuously measure the fissile
material content in separation plants without requiring total plant
shutdown. This is particularly needed for the contactors (solvent
extraction equipment) which should be run continuously to avoid losing
production during the time required for restoration of equilibrium conditions after a shutdown. The goal is to develop a capability to inventory
fissile material in the contactors without shutdown by proper choice
of detection methods and types or designs of contactors.

Kull mentioned that the presence of curium isotopes in the
radiated fuel materials and particularly of the discarded hulls at the
reprocessing plants result in a problem only now being broached.
Neutron emission from spontaneous fission of curium will provide a
substantial background for any neutron methods of measurement.
Rasmussen concurred that this would then necessitate a very intense
neutron source to overwhelm the background.

While agreeing that the active neutron method developed by the
Los Alamos Scientific Laboratory is good for measuring individual fuel
pins, A. W. DeMerschman (Westinghouse Hanford) inquired about possible methods for measuring a full assembly, for example, of 217 pins.
With associated material involved in a large fuel element of a modern
power reactor, Rasmussen noted that the self-absorption of ingoing or
outgoing radiation presents a severe measurement problem. A practical but tedious alternative is to measure each of the component fuel
pins. However, some success in measuring bundles of fuel pins by the
active neutron method was reported by Munson Thorpe (Los Alamos
Scientific Laboratory). In their laboratory, the fissile content of a mockup element consisting of a six by six array of half-inch diameter pins

five feet long was measured with a 1-2 percent accuracy. Similar
accuracy can be expected for the measurement of full-length boiling
or pressurized water reactor fuel elements.

The problem of making allowance for wastes in attempting a
materials balance was raised by Frank Pittman (Director, Division
of Waste Management and Transportation, AEC) with particular
reference to the downward arrows labeled waste in Figure 22 presented
by Rasmussen. In amplifying this, Rasmussen noted the dependence
on two factors, one being the time scale of recycling the waste into the
cycle and the other depending on whether the waste was "clean" or
"dirty." If the recycle time is sufficiently short, Rasmussen believed
material balances could be made even without measurement of the
wastes. If the waste material is "clean," such as chipped pellets, the
0.5 percent or so of accuracy in columns A of Table 14 should be
achieved. On the other hand, if the waste is "dirty," then the accuracies
of 5 or 10 percent of columns B will result from the difficulty of
making accurate measurements.

The remaining comments involved strategy of measurements.
Carl Bennett (Battelle Seattle) suggested the desirability of multiple
methods of measurement on the same items for the purpose of increasing measurement validity. Although agreeing to the advantages,
Rasmussen cited the need first for getting just one system into all the
places that are needed. Frank Morgan (United Kingdom Atomic Energy
Authority) and Rasmussen emphasized the need to first determine
what is important in the measurements. Specifically, systems analysis
should be used to determine whether the accuracy of measurements
sought for wastes and for outputs are mutually commensurate.

18

THE INDUSTRIAL
SAFEGUARDS PROBLEMS
THROUGH
THE FUEL CYCLE

Ralph J. Jones

The title of this chapter implies that industry has a problem or problems with safeguards in the fuel cycle. Before one can solve a problem it is said that one must first recognize and define the problem. If we use the word objective instead of problem, we then ask: What is the objective of safeguards in the fuel cycle? Therein, I believe, lies one of the major problems industry has with safeguards in the fuel cycle. What are we trying to accomplish?

On the other hand, we also might ask: What is the objective of the nuclear industry in establishing a material control system? There is, of course, one objective directly related to the high monetary value of the materials and the financial aspects of using these materials in our plants. It has been stated that controls for financial purposes are not adequate for safeguards. I question this. I believe that adequate financial control of material, including adequate physical security measures, will provide adequate safeguards control for material in the U.S. nuclear industry. However, this is true only if the industry realizes the full impact of the financial aspects of using special nuclear material and provides controls accordingly. We have heard the industry criticized for poor control of these nuclear materials. We have been warned that we must be able to defend our safeguards system and disclose our failures to close material balances to the public. If we also were required to defend our imbalances to the stockholders and the company's auditors, as is the case in some companies, we would see material control systems that should satisfy any reasonable domestic safeguards requirements.

It has been suggested that there may be a highly organized, technically competent effort to divert special nuclear material to a secret operation to develop a nuclear weapons capability. I submit that, if this is the case, it becomes a matter for the FBI, the CIA, and such organizations rather than an industrial safeguards problem. It also has been suggested that diversion efforts may be carried out by dissident or terrorist groups not technically oriented and not particularly concerned with secrecy over any long period of time. Protection of nuclear material against these types of diversion efforts and the ability to assure that the material is protected appears to be the objective of the U.S. safeguards program. However, the objectives have been stated in terms of philosophical assumptions and threats of public dissatisfaction.

We are not in disagreement with the need to guard against special nuclear materials falling into unauthorized hands. A second major objective of the industry material control systems is to protect these materials from theft and diversion on the basis of their strategic importance as well as on the basis of their monetary value. The industry has developed material control systems employing the long accepted control mechanisms of material balance accounting and physical security or containment. The problems arise in determining the extent to which each type of control is to be employed and the standards and criteria that are to be used to measure the effectiveness of the control.

Regardless of the philosophy or purpose for a theft, diversion, or loss, it will take one of two forms: small amounts of material could be removed over a period of time or a large amount of material could be removed at one time. Without defining small or large just yet, let us consider the material control mechanism that will best guard against each of these types of theft, diversion, or loss.

No material balance accounting system will ever be sufficiently accurate to detect a small loss over a short period of time. However, material balance systems should be sufficiently accurate to detect a continual small loss over a longer period of time. Physical security and containment systems must be employed to detect or prevent small losses over the short term. Material balance accounting over a longer term will provide a measure of the effectiveness of the physical security systems.

No material balance system can be sufficiently in real time to prevent a large loss at a given time. Again, physical security and containment systems must be employed with relatively short term material balances as an effectiveness control.

Now all that remains is to define our terms: large or small loss, long or short time, and their interrelationships. This, of course, brings us back to the beginning: What are we trying to accomplish?

Perhaps some insight can be gained by looking not at the problems of the safeguards agency or the nuclear industry but at the problems faced by a potential diverter. First, of course, he must gain access to the material without arousing suspicion or setting off security alarms. The only logical way to accomplish this is as an employee who has access to the material in the normal course of his job. Security clearances or reliability checks on personnel having access to material will eliminate at least the most obvious potential diverters.

Assume our diverter has passed these checks in some way. Health and safety indoctrination will tell him, if he did not already know, of the hazards to himself as well as to others of handling these materials, especially plutonium. He also will know that in many cases if certain amounts of these materials are removed from their containment, such as glove boxes, radiation alarms will sound thus calling attention to the diversion attempt. Now he must work out some scheme for removing the material from its containment and the plant without setting off alarms or seriously contaminating himself. The diversion of very small amounts of material at any one time may be one way. The very small amount, however, may be too small in many cases to be practical for his purpose. In addition, the numerous small diversions tend to increase his risk of detection by fellow employees and others. The use of special devices and containers for larger quantities could be another way for him to solve his problem. However, he would now risk detection because such devices and containers are necessarily large and visible. Also, such devices or containers probably would be different from those normally found in the plant. If not actually different, they would be in a different from normal place in the plant so that suspicion would be aroused. Of course, collusion with other employees who might be suspicious could solve this problem but the number of employees whose cooperation would be required begins to make the scheme unbelievable.

We must conclude then that with a reasonable security and containment system the only diversion that could reasonably be expected to succeed in removing material from a plant site undetected would be that involving small amounts of material over an extended period of time. Accurate material balance systems over the extended period of time will detect such diversions or losses so that appropriate steps can be taken to stop them. We still must have a shorter term material

balance as a check on the security and containment system for larger
amounts of material. However, it does not need to be as sensitive
and probably could not be as sensitive as the longer term balance.
Certainly there is some minimum quantity that can be detected by
material balance.

We still need some quantitative definition of objectives. This
definition might be approached from the philosophical and political
standpoint. What risk of diversion is acceptable? Is an amount of
material sufficient for a single weapon the limit? Is this limit applicable to one plant at one time? More than one plant over what time?
It readily becomes apparent that these questions are either impossible
to answer or, if answered, impossible to accomplish. Other means of
defining terms and setting objectives must be found. We also must
have finite objectives that we can work toward with some hope of
attainment.

During 1971 we have been subjected to numerous new interpretations of existing safeguards regulations and license conditions. These
interpretations have had the effect of imposing added procedural
requirements on the material control systems with no clear definition
of the end result expected. Further, these regulations have been
imposed by edict and interpretation rather than by the prescribed
rulemaking procedure. During 1971 requirements and license conditions have been imposed on some licensees that are different from
and more strict than those imposed on other licensees. In fact, license
conditions on one part of a process were different from those already
in effect on another part of the same process. This mixed or nonuniform safeguards procedure can only lead to confusion and inequities
that in the long run will weaken the safeguards system. There must
be a statement of objectives in terms of well-defined standards and
criteria developed from logical and rational bases and applied uniformly to the U.S. nuclear industry.

I submit that a logical approach to defining safeguards objectives
is through the state of the art in combination with cost-benefit analyses
in terms of both financial and social considerations. The industry has
told that it must make more accurate and more precise measurements.
It has been told that the technology is available if it were but willing
to spend the money. I agree that the AEC has sponsored some excellent
research and development programs. These programs have advanced
the technology of nuclear materials measurements. This work has
been characterized as a "giant international side show" that has seldom
been customized by the industry for actual in-plant use. This is not

altogether true. From this "side show" have come some practical workable devices and techniques that are being customized for in-plant use. Many of us in the industry are participating in programs sponsored by the AEC for in-plant development. Others are proceeding on our own to apply the technology to our plants' problems.

The industry must keep in mind that much of the technology and equipment that has been the result of the government's program is quite sophisticated and complex. In-plant equipment cannot practically be such as to require for operation a team of Ph.D. nuclear physicists. It is not always a matter of cost but also a matter of elapsed time. The industry cannot practically operate a process where measurements of some of the materials require up to an hour or so to make. It now must examine the technology that has been and is being developed to establish how well it can possibly measure inventories, scrap, in-process materials, and shipments and receipts. The industry must select those methods and techniques that have been demonstrated to be reliable for in-plant routine operation. I believe many of us in industry are examining the technology for these applications to our plants.

Given a level of technology, we then must ask: Does industry need to measure our materials that accurately and that often? What benefit has it attained if it measures accurately enough on a monthly basis to detect the potential development of a clandestine weapons program that would take a year or more to come to fruition? What benefit has it attained if it takes monthly inventories that may be able to detect material unaccounted for of a few hundred grams in tens of hundreds of kilograms when the toxic properties of some of these materials are such that a dissident's purpose would be served by less than 100 grams? What benefit has it attained when we control low enriched uranium to within fractions of a percent on a monthly basis when the process from low enrichment to a weapon covers periods of several months or a year or more and requires extensive and sophisticated equipment?

I am not complacent enough to believe that the industry has perfected material control systems in our plants. I know from personal experience that our system leaves something to be desired. But neither do I believe that the industry has been as lackadaisical as it has been characterized. I submit that the industry is developing and applying more advanced nuclear material control technology. It is receptive to the needs of nuclear material safeguards. However, it does urge that these needs be defined in terms of logical, rational performance standards and criteria within which the industry can operate.

The presentation by Ralph Jones stimulated lively and far-ranging discussion. Most was on financing the cost of safeguards, with some discussion of parallel problems encountered in industry, instrumentation for safeguards in industry, and the objectives of the safeguards program.

At the heart of the cost discussion was the question of how to finance any safeguards cost resulting from government-imposed requirements beyond those that industry otherwise would undertake for cost-benefit reasons. To determine the magnitude of the financial problem, Theodore Taylor (International Research and Technology) asked what level of safeguards cost would be tolerable—1 percent, 10 percent, or 50 percent—as measured by the additional cost of electricity. He further asked whether the costs of safeguards can indeed be passed on to the ultimate consumer in the price of electricity. The discussion indicated that the problem was not so much the amount of the increase as the manner in which it is instituted. Jones pointed out that a key problem was the danger of new government-imposed regulations adding to safeguards costs after bids have been made or after contracts have been signed with the customer of the product in that particular part of the nuclear fuel cycle.

The importance of contract relationships in normal business activities was emphasized by Frederick Perella (National Bureau of Standards). He used the illustration of a contractor building a home for a private individual. Only if an increase in price is arranged can the contractor afford at the request of the owner to make additions or changes that add to the cost of the building. Otherwise, the contractor will suffer financially. An important point was made here by Jones. Although this is also true in the nuclear industry if the customer makes the change, he noted that, if the added cost resulted from a government imposed change, the manufacturer is unable to charge his customer for the added cost because the contract has already been signed. Furthermore, he feared that industry will be unable to get customers to sign a contract saying the customer will pay for any additional costs from regulations imposed by the government. Neither did he believe the government would pay for these added costs. However, Frank Pittman (Director, Division of waste Management and Transportation, AEC) had seen some wordings in contracts that take into account possible regulating impositions by the AEC or other regulatory agencies. These wordings suggest how this problem might be resolved. Nevertheless, this possibility has not yet been generally used.

In answer to a question on whether legislation might rectify this problem, Jones said that he did not know how to legislate between a seller and a customer. Industry has no particular problem, Jones emphasized, if it knows what the safeguards requirements, standards, and criteria are to be; the costs can then be passed on to the customer. However, this takes time to work out.

The time element in this problem was illustrated by R. B. Sewell, (Consumers Power). From the utility standpoint, nuclear fuel costs can be precisely determined only after cycling a complete batch of fuel through the reactor, having the fuel reprocessed, and determining the recovery amounts. Only after about six years following the signing of the contract for the nuclear fuel is all of this determined. After that, one or two years is required to go through the public service commission to obtain an adjustment in rates. Even then, the adjustment will not be retroactive to cover any previous underestimate in fuel costs. Therefore, this cost planning cannot be approached haphazardly. To help further in understanding these time leads, Charles Van Doren (Arms Control and Disarmament Agency) inquired concerning the duration of contracts in the nuclear fuel industry. The reply of from one to twenty years by Jones was confirmed by Ray Heinisch (Nuclear Assurance Corporation), who reported that some existing contracts for fuel service extend into the mid-1990s. Heinisch and Jones also explained that, to contend with inflation, these contracts have built into them escalation clauses which are based on such measures as the cost of labor and the cost of products.

The financial incentives for industry to undertake safeguards expenses also were discussed. Skepticism that the economics of materials management alone would provide adequate safeguards was expressed by Perella. For example, a fuel manufacturer might have a contract to supply fuel elements with a fissionable material content specified within a five percent accuracy. Would the objectives of the fuel manufacturer be to measure within a five percent accuracy or, for safeguards objectives, within a fraction of one percent? He believed that industry should propose to government an answer, which might be in between, rather than put the burden of proof on the government alone.

While recognizing that adequate safeguards are going to help industry make money, John Loeding (Argonne National Laboratory) asked whether the need for safeguards might not transcend the need for making money. The determining fact expressed by Jones in reply was that industry will not stay in business unless it makes money. Clarification of this point was attempted by Ralph Lumb (Nuclear

Surveillance and Auditing Corporation) who noted that management
of industry should provide a system adequate for safeguards simply
as a result of the process of providing a system for protecting its
valuable assets. He conceded that the regulatory people are faced
with a problem primarily when industrial management is not top-notch.

Ralph Page (Division of Nuclear Materials Safeguards, AEC)
addressed himself to this problem and contended that, concerning
materials management, the financial incentives alone are not enough
to assure adequate safeguards. Obviously, the performances of operation for different companies are not the same. Differences exist in
the yields of their products as well as in their material unaccounted
for (MUF) levels. Yet all are still in business. Earlier Lumb had
recognized that the worst managed industries do frequently go bankrupt
but sometimes are rescued financially by the government. Countering
these points, Jones contended that, if their management realized what
percentage of their profit the MUF represented, then industries would
change their systems radically.

Sewell cautioned that standards must be applied uniformly to
all plants so that some are not given competitive margins.

Parallel problems for industry were considered to see whether
lessons from these provided insights into the safeguards problem.
However, this exploration was inconclusive. Pittman recognized that,
although the safety aspects do not necessarily earn any money for the
nuclear industry, they are a necessary requirement. William Higinbotham (Brookhaven National Laboratory) cited other examples of
concern such as the reduction of pollution, the increasing requirements
of health and safety, and the desire for storm-proof buildings. These,
like safeguards, are of importance to the public, not just to a government regulator. He hoped that the way contracts have been written
would not hold back these needs.

Frank Morgan (United Kingdom Atomic Energy Authority)
inquired whether the United States had any methods for subsidizing
such public needs as safeguards without passing the costs on to the
customer. As another way of handling this type of problem, he cited
the tax on fuel oil used to generate power in the United Kingdom. The
tax insures that the coal industry is run in an orderly manner. An
example of this principle in the United States was believed by Samuel
Edlow (Edlow International) to be the gasoline tax that goes into a
special fund which may be used only for the building of freeways.

In regard to instrumentation, David Hall (Los Alamos Scientific
Laboratory) sought objectives from industry. James Lovett (Nuclear

Materials and Equipment Corporation) provided a detailed example
of his study of the ideal instrumentation fulfilling his industrial need.
It would be one instrument covering all the different types of material
needing measurement in the plant and providing results on a while-
you-wait basis in 15 to 30 minutes. It would be operated by two individuals, only one of whom possesses any physical science training.
Such an instrument would be worth a quarter of a million dollars to
his industry, but one with all these properties has not yet been developed. The goal for Jones was to have in-plant operations that can run
on-process. Both Jones and Lovett wished to avoid instruments
requiring Ph.D.'s for operators and to avoid the need to wait days or
a week for results.

Higinbotham continued this discussion with the claim that, in
the solution of instrumentation problems, there have been shortcomings
by both the potential users in industry and the government-sponsored
developers of the instrumentation. In his observations the nuclear
industry employs chemists and reactor designers but few physicists
or electronics specialists who could save money for the companies
by instrumented quality and quantity control. These instruments
also would serve safeguards purposes, but the alternative classical
methods of chemistry and sampling are becoming insufficient at the
present time. On the other hand, the developers of instruments for
nondestructive measurements have not had an adequate feeling for
such factors as exactly how fast and under what conditions the instrumentation will be useful to industry.

As for utilization, Higinbotham thought it wrong for industry to
wait for an ideal instrument. With the government demonstrating that
measurements can in fact be made by certain well-developed and
exhibited techniques, he felt that the task of industry is to make these
automatic for mass production. Jones countered by saying that industry
is indeed doing this by contracts with consulting firms. This statement
was supported by David Haymon (Westinghouse Electric Corporation)
who said that almost all the industry is doing independent research
supporting the AEC research and development program at a very
substantial cost. However, he contended that realistic assignments of
the needed sensitivity of measurements—whether it is to be one gram
or ten grams of plutonium and over what period—need to be made
before sensible installations of instrumentation are made in major
facilities. In his opinion, interdisciplinary investigations preferably
would be directed to determining these quantities rather than to
establishing the disagreements between the government agency and
industry.

Part of the discussion pertained to the objectives of the safeguards program. Frederick Forscher (Consulting Engineer) focused
upon the objectives of either prevention or deterrence of thefts in the
safeguards program. He wished for a good definition of deterrence.
Furthermore, he noted that to help deter it is necessary to define the
regulations involved and the punishments applicable. In the thinking
of Jones, prevention is when a theft or loss is never permitted to
occur but this requires an impossibly perfect security system. The
concept of deterrence extends only to where a diversion is difficult
or a person thinks twice before trying to divert. However, he feared
that an irrational person is not likely to be deterred.

Noting that even with sophisticated security systems there are
robberies like "the great train robbery," Marc Kramer (University
of Michigan) asked if studies were being made of an allowable rate
of thefts. Is it one theft a year or one every ten years? No knowledge
about such studies was made available.

THE ADAPTABILITY
OF FISSILE MATERIALS
TO NUCLEAR EXPLOSIVES

D. B. Hall

This chapter seeks to answer the question that has been posed as "The Adaptability of Fissile Materials to Nuclear Explosives." Several previous chapters have touched on this subject. There is little that can be said on this topic outside the confines of classified data. It is not my intent to embarrass the AEC nor to give assistance to the criminal with malice in mind. This chapter presents my own thoughts as developed in the framework of my responsibilities as manager of the safeguards program at the Los Alamos Scientific Laboratory (LASL).

For the present purposes, it is necessary to define a nuclear explosion as opposed to a radioactive mess. The mess, as defined here, is not trivial—it can be costly and embarrassing resulting in injuries or deaths—but is not the disaster associated with a nuclear weapon. The present discussion will be restricted to explosions equivalent to tons of high explosive (HE), realizing that the effects of lesser amounts are intolerable in the extreme and can cause extensive damage. However, damage from amounts up to approximately one ton of HE can be achieved by conventional explosives that are easier to acquire and to handle and are not excessive in size. The use of nuclear material will likely be contemplated only for very large effects, an order of magnitude above that attainable by conventional explosives. Whether or not the expectations are realized is a different consideration.

Work for this chapter was performed under the auspices of the U.S. Atomic Energy Commission.

It is necessary to consider the following aspects: (1) people and groups for insight as to capabilities and intent as they relate to materials and (2) weapon properties of materials that are subject to diversion. First, who is likely to be contemplating the use of illegal nuclear explosives? The answer could be: (1) one or a few individuals acting on their own in an irrational manner; (2) a group or organization dedicated to destruction of a country and its leaders; (3) organized criminal activity for money; (4) a minor, undefined nation in border dispute or internal rebellion; or (5) a major nation desiring to join "the club."

The order given is intended to be representative of increasing capability and decreasing probability or credibility. For any but the first or perhaps the second group, a theft of a significant quantity of ^{239}Pu or fully enriched ^{235}U would be required to attain objectives. One or two explosions would certainly cause panic but would be unlikely to achieve definitive military objectives.

The question has been raised many times as to what an intelligent person or group could contrive in the form of a weapon with no access to classified data. In one sense, asking the question is trying to assess the value of secrecy and classification, but in another it can serve to point out clearly the hazards confronting the world.

In 1947 a group at the Massachusetts Institute of Technology headed by Clark Goodman developed a two-volume text entitled The Science and Engineering of Nuclear Power which confounded the classification officers and was effective in demonstrating the futility of the then existing classification rules.[1] The rules are undeniably more rational now but some individuals still have a strong tendency to depreciate their enemy and not give him credit for equal or even superior intelligence. There have been controlled studies of the problem of designing a nuclear weapon without benefit of classified information. The fact that these studies were made is unclassified, but any information about them or their success remains restricted data. To the best of my knowledge, studies of this type have been limited to paper studies only. I am not aware of any attempt to actually fabricate a nuclear explosive under these simulated diversion conditions.

Indeed it is only necessary to reflect on the historical fact that Russia, France, and China have successively and successfully joined the nuclear bomb club, originally founded by the United States and United Kingdom partnership, albeit with an extended testing program.

It also is significant that each has gone from a fission weapon capability to a thermonuclear capability with shorter time development than the United States required. The knowledge that a result has been achieved is of overwhelming importance in a development of the sort discussed here. As Theodore Taylor and others have said, there is no secret.

Information in Glasstone's The Effects of Nuclear Weapons suggests two methods of achieving a nuclear explosion: (1) a gun-like assembly of two or more subcritical pieces that when brought together form a supercritical assembly and (2) compression by a symmetrical implosion to achieve increased density.[2] Of these two methods, the first is straightforward and might be approached with confidence. The second is perhaps more difficult but cannot be dismissed from present considerations.

It is recognized that since 1945 the number of individuals who have had exposure to weapon designs in varying degrees and in various countries and who no longer are in the trade is large and growing larger all the time. The same can be said for employment in uranium and plutonium processing facilities. Despite the clearance require- ments and internal compartmentalization, it would not be surprising if some of these individuals should belong to one or more of the groups categorized earlier. An even larger number of people have had univer- sity instruction in reactor physics with at least an introduction to fast reactor calculational techniques with virtually no control or knowl- edge of their social attitudes. This aspect increases the probability of the agent being successful but does not materially make his job easier in the practical sense of fabricating a device. It is true that experimentation of a highly developed technical quality would be required to adapt diverted nuclear materials to the creation of a predictable highly efficient military-type weapon. However, efficiency and predictability are not necessary to achieve some of the possible objectives, and a crude device of uncertain but large yield may be sufficient. It is not likely that many honest individuals have specula- ted seriously or care much about the details and problems of making a nuclear weapon. What follows may seem to be giving guidance to someone for his illegal bomb, which is certainly not the intent. One must assume the potential thief is intelligent and informed of the basic principles of physics. If he is not, what is said here will not help him, and if he is he will learn more than the present description from published works.

So, with that preamble, one can consider a nuclear bomb, choosing first a so-called gun type. It has been described as requiring the rapid

assembly of at least two pieces. When assembled, the fission chain
reaction will proceed with an exponentially increasing rate controlled
by the excess reactivity at a particular time. As energy is developed
in the assembled mass, it heats up, expanding the fuel. With reduced
density, the criticality is reduced and the reaction stops. A shock
wave—or explosion—develops only if the material motion due to the
release of energy exceeds the velocity of sound in the material. Hence,
there is a limit on the time in which the energy can be developed.
Characteristic times are measured in hundredths of a microsecond,
known as a "shake"; the whole reaction takes place in less than a μsec.
If the excess reactivity is not large, the nuclear energy will not be
developed rapidly enough to reach levels required for a nuclear
explosion. Hence, if the reaction time takes as long as a millisecond
the full energy will not develop. The energy developed in 30 to 40
generations (10^{17} fissions) will cause a disassembly without major
damage. The significance of this lies in the restrictions of the ratio
of the two masses to be used and the amount of neutron moderation
that can be permitted. Since speed of assembly is important, one
might choose a small projectile and a large massive target. But the
excess reactivity achievable by such a ratio may not result in an
explosion. Maximum rate of reactivity addition would indicate the
choice of two equal masses such as hemispheres divided on an equa-
torial plane. In this case, the physical momentum will make it difficult
to retain them together without separation while the nuclear reaction
initiates and develops.

In 1960 in Nuclear Science and Engineering, a collection of
papers dealt with fast neutron critical assemblies.[3] Godiva—a bare
critical assembly of ^{235}U—is described in detail in Figure 23. Two
of the figures in one of the articles have been redrawn with some
liberties, principally the unpardonable technical sin of extrapolating
the data as presented.

In the range of large reactivity insertions, the resulting yield
appears to increase proportional to the cube of the excess reactivity.
A reasonable fit to the curve can be obtained by the expression $Y = 2.2 \times 10^{14} R^3$ (fission/gram), where R is the maximum reactivity in
units of dollars.

So if one can change the reactivity of the system by $10, where
$1 is equal to a $\Delta k/k$ of 0.007, the reactivity would change from a safe
subcritical of -$5 to a supercritical state of +$5. The formula then
will predict a yield of 2.8×10^{16} fissions/gram. Godiva has a total
mass of 50 kilograms and, remembering 1.25×10^{20} fissions is
equivalent to a ton of HE, the total yield would be as follows:

FIGURE 23

Energy Developed in Supercritical ^{235}U Assembly
as a Function of Reactivity Added
Either Suddenly (Step) or Slowly (Ramp)

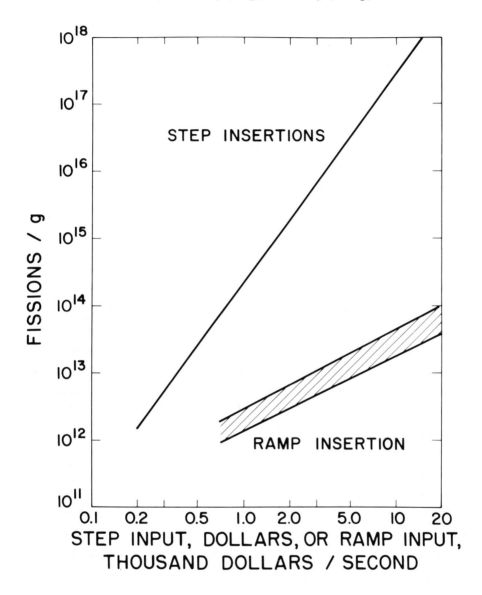

$$Y = \frac{2.8 \times 10^{16} \times 5 \times 10^4}{1.25 \times 10^{20}} = \text{tons of HE.}$$

If the $10 change in reactivity started at -$2 and went to +$8, the result would be 40 tons. Other examples can easily be worked out for different masses and reactivity changes. If one believes this extrapolation, $18 supercritical would result in a kiloton explosion. Obviously, this simple projection will break down at some point. The mass of fissile material chosen for this illustration is 50 kilograms of fully enriched uranium. Glasstone and Sesonske describe how to substitute reflector material for core mass so that the material requirements are lessened.[4] The total yield also will decrease.

Godiva-like systems are characterized by pure metal with very low neutron backgrounds. For a step insertion of 70¢ above delayed critical (-30¢ below prompt), an average waiting time of about 30 sec is required before a chance neutron starts a successful chain. This waiting time decreases in predictable manner for larger reactivity conditions as also described in the <u>Nuclear Science and Engineering</u> series.[5]

However, if too many neutrons are present, a successful chain will develop at delayed critical conditions in the assembly process and the yield is much reduced. This type of insertion is described as a "ramp" and is characterized by the reactivity insertion being compensated by the energy build-up. Disassembly therefore takes place at the earliest possible time. The more violent the assembly rate, the more violent the energy release, but it is almost linear with reactivity insertion rate (increasing to a 3/2 power dependence). Large masses or high velocities are required to achieve the same results for a ramp insertion as with a sudden step increase, but explosive conditions can be achieved.

One can summarize the discussion to this point as follows: It is relatively easy to make a truly formidable, even though crude, nuclear explosive starting with highly enriched ^{235}U metal. With more difficulty, a less potent device also can be constructed from fully enriched UO_2 or U_3O_8. The oxygen dilutes the uranium but it is a moderator, not a poison for neutrons. However, the moderation effect is not very strong and one can estimate large reactivity coefficients and short neutron life times for a UO_2 device, depending on the final state of the material at the time of explosion and other design assumptions.

For lower enrichment uranium, even that typical of a fast reactor fuel, for example 20 percent, explosions could be achieved but only by truly heroic efforts. If one calculates the result of the sudden reassembly of the fuel in a modern fast reactor into a perfect sphere, with its reflector intact, the answer is likely to be tens of kilotons yield. This result derives solely from the large mass of material involved. The motion required from a critical condition to a compacted sphere is too great to be practical. Restricting attention to manageable masses, the results, while expensive in the extreme, would not be what has been defined here as a nuclear weapon.

Turning next to plutonium, the situation is strikingly different. Since uranium and plutonium are different elements, a separation by chemical methods can in principle provide the enrichment capability not as readily available for uranium. The hazards of handling the highly toxic plutonium are perhaps forbidding to most of us, but perhaps not to the desperate or fanatic with whom we are concerned. Using simple methods for fast reactor criticality calculations as, for example, in Nuclear Reactor Engineering by Glasstone and Sesonske, one can calculate what mass of plutonium oxide would be certain to have explosive properties.[6] An examination of the fast neutron cross sections for the appropriate energies will quickly show that plutonium is at least 50 percent more reactive than ^{235}U. Thus it is evident that the reactivity for a plutonium device will be greater than for a uranium device under similar conditions. Commercial grade plutonium will have a large fraction of its content as ^{240}Pu with its high spontaneous fission rate. This constitutes a large neutron presence of more than 10^6 neutrons per second and complicates the design. One can imagine rapid assembly methods that will to some extent overcome this difficulty and result in an explosive yield. In general, it can be stated that the high ^{240}Pu content will make the explosive performance quite unpredictable but not impossible. The degree of sophistication required for a successful device with this material is greater than the types previously discussed. However, one should not assume that such sophistication does not exist in the criminal or fanatic world.

As a summary, I have tried to be more convincing in the statement that almost all forms of fully enriched uranium—greater than 90 percent—constitutes a real and not an imagined hazard as an explosive device. This statement includes oxides of uranium, in contrast to earlier remarks. The same statement can be made for plutonium, including commercial grades, with the added concern that its enrichment is obtained by chemical separative techniques fully described by the Atomic Energy Commission in its handbooks.

NOTES

1. Clark Goodman et al., The Science and Engineering of Nuclear Power (2nd ed.; Cambridge: Addison-Wesley Press, 1952).

2. Samuel Glasstone, The Effects of Nuclear Weapons (Washington: United States Atomic Energy Commission, 1962).

3. See Everitt P. Blzaid, ed., Nuclear Science and Engineering, Vol. 8 (New York: Academia Press, 1960).

4. See Samuel Glasstone and Alexander Sesonske, Nuclear Reactor Engineering (Princeton: Van Nostiand, 1963).

5. See Blzaid, ed., Nuclear Science and Engineering.

6. See Glasstone and Sesonske, Nuclear Reactor Engineering.

The presence of other plutonium isotopes in plutonium produced by power reactors was considered in the discussion. G. F. Molen (Allied Gulf Nuclear Services) inquired what content of ^{240}Pu this involved. Frank Pittman (Director, Division of Waste Management and Transportation, AEC) suggested it could be as high as 10 percent, or 15 percent, but David Hall cautioned against leaning on the crutch of ^{240}Pu to render the plutonium impotent for constructing a nuclear explosive. Molen noted that higher abundances of other plutonium isotopes are sometimes mentioned and included in this are all the non-fissile isotopes ^{238}Pu and ^{242}Pu.

The illicit industry for heroin production was used by Theodore Taylor (International Research and Technology) as an example to illustrate that the toxicity of plutonium might not be a practical deterrent against handling of plutonium in a clandestine laboratory. Heroin suspended in air is dangerous to workers, and so the equivalent of dry boxes are consistently used in part of the production cycle in all heroin laboratories thus far discovered. It is claimed that dry boxes for at least one illicit laboratory were stolen from a nuclear facility, but in any case the equipment is sophisticated. Furthermore, the throughputs of tens to occasionally hundreds of kilograms per year for heroin laboratories are the same order of magnitude as would be required for preparing nuclear explosives. In these respects the illicit heroin industry is on the same scale as would be involved in converting plutonium nitrate to components of either plutonium oxide or plutonium metal.

20

**REAL PROBLEMS,
REAL SOLUTIONS**

Joerg H. Menzel

It has been implied that we are about to complete or have already completed some sort of transition from safeguards <u>techniques</u> to <u>implementing</u> nuclear safeguards. Indeed, we have made significant progress in many areas of safeguards techniques and in the practical application of prototype instrumentation. But certainly one must question whether we are really on the threshold of implementing nuclear safeguards on a nationwide basis when the nuclear fuel cycle contains tons of plutonium and highly enriched uranium scrap inventories based only on estimates, when a recent AEC Immediate Action Directive on the Scrap Management Program stresses the importance of "an <u>accurate estimate</u> of the quantity of special nuclear material" without a single mention of nondestructive assay technology, and when the nuclear industry—with few exceptions—places much unwarranted confidence in good analytical assays of often meaningless samples. Let me illustrate these points.

Several hundred cans containing low enriched uranium as incinerator oxide and ash were received by a recovery facility. Accompanying transfer documents listed the mass spectrometric isotopic analysis for each can to five significant figures. These enrichment values, which ranged from 1 to 5 percent, were of importance to the receiver not only for accountability but also for criticality

Work for this chapter was performed under the auspices of the U.S. Atomic Energy Commission.

FIGURE 24

Comparison of Shipper-Receiver Enrichment Values
on Cans of Uranium Scrap

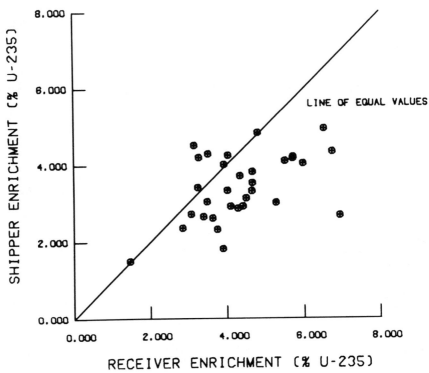

considerations of batch processing. Surprisingly, gamma ray measurements of these cans by Los Alamos Scientific Laboratory (LASL)
personnel revealed enrichment stratification and local enrichments
of up to 18 percent. The receiver consequently ground, blended, and
mass spectrometrically analyzed 36 cans of this shipment with the
results shown in Figure 34. The scatter of these data points illustrates
the sampling problem associated with this material. In addition to the
enrichment value, the shipper also had determined the respective
uranium content of each can by sampling/chemical analysis. The
shipper/receiver comparison of the uranium content is shown in
Figure 25. Clearly, the shipper had performed hundreds of costly
mass spectrometer and chemical analyses on meaningless samples.

Can blending solve this problem? Our experience has been that
blending simply does not guarantee that one will obtain a representative
sample. Table 15 shows significant discrepancies uncovered by nondestructive assay of a category of blended 93 percent enriched uranium
scrap. The discrepancy of item 2 was found to be due to mislabeling
of the can, but the cause of the other discrepancies must be attributed
to nonrepresentative sampling.

It should be noted that the first three cans listed in Table 15
contained more than one kilogram of ^{235}U each. We presently are
engaged in measuring an entire inventory of difficult-to-dissolve
scrap with an average ^{235}U content of three kilograms per can and
some cans exceeding six kilograms of ^{235}U; prior to these nondestructive measurements, the SS-value* of this inventory was based
only on estimates.

Another example of the sampling/chemical analysis problem is
shown in Table 16. The material is blended 97 percent enriched
uranium reject product and cleanout. After blending, four composite
samples (indicated by subtotals 1,2,3,4) from the eighteen bottles were
chemically analyzed. The blending for these samples was special; the
routine procedure is to take grab samples for analysis. The fact that
blending did not insure representative sampling is illustrated by the
additional 1,200 grams of ^{235}U found by nondestructive assay.

Space does not permit me to cite additional examples. But the
fact is that the quantitative uncertainty of scrap and "hold-up" inventories represents the largest loophole in nuclear materials

-----

*Source and special materials.

FIGURE 25

Comparison of Shipper-Receiver SS-Values
on Cans of Low-Enrichment Incinerator Ash

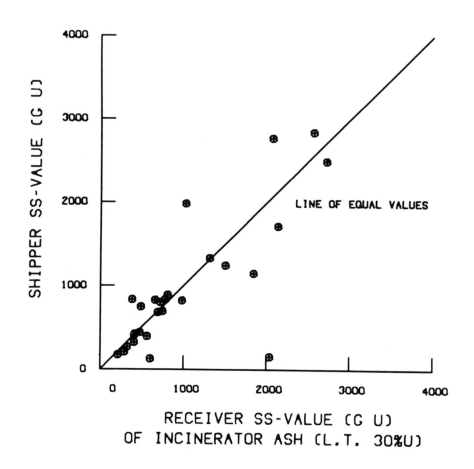

TABLE 15

Significant Discrepancies Among 146 Cans of Blended
93 Percent Enriched Uranium Scrap

Item Number	SS-Value (grams ^{235}U)	NDA-Active (grams ^{235}U)
1	32	1514
2	173	1428
3	706	1229
4	97	473
5	256	415
6	295	395
7	389	288
8	777	160

TABLE 16

^{235}U Assay Results on Blended
97 Percent Enriched Uranium Scrap

Item Number	Composite SS-Value (grams ^{235}U)	NDA Active/Passive (grams ^{235}U)
1		1874
2		1623
3		342
4		1371
5		1907
Subtotal 1	6377	7117
6		85
7		166
8		129
9		79
10		120
Subtotal 2	524	579
11		191
12		313
13		193
14		128
Subtotal 3	648	825
15		197
16		211
17		115
18		92
Subtotal 4	378	615
Total	7927	9136

accountability; the difference between the feed and product inventories at a particular plant may or may not lie in the "hold-up," recoverable scrap, or waste.

About a year ago, the Division of Nuclear Material Safeguards (DNMS) published the results of a study of random and systematic errors associated with sampling/chemical assay of inventory samples. Table 17 summarizes the data on 300 pairs of duplicate samples collected at many AEC licensed facilities. It is interesting to note that for four of the six material categories the systematic errors, or relative biases, exceed 2 percent. And since these systematic errors are between pairs of small samples there is no guarantee that the fissile content of the original material was in fact determined to this accuracy.

Nuclear safeguards can only be implemented on the solid foundation of direct measurement of all materials in the nuclear fuel cycle. Unless a safeguards system is based upon the proper tools and know-how to measure the kind and quantity of materials it is trying to safeguard, it will fail to provide even a minimum of assurance that a diversion could be detected. Specifically, the cornerstone of implementing nuclear safeguards must be nondestructive measurements since destructive chemical and isotopic analyses are not only more costly—by a factor of ten—but generally unsuitable for material in sealed or finished-product form and for the wide range of materials where representative sampling cannot be guaranteed.

Since 1966 the staff of the Los Alamos Nuclear Assay Research Group has been devoted to the development of nondestructive assay techniques and instrumentation for application to the broad spectrum of compositions and containers in which fissionable material is found throughout the nuclear fuel cycle. A mobile assay laboratory (MONAL) incorporating the major nondestructive assay capabilities is being deployed at key nuclear facilities to demonstrate, test, and apply these techniques to practical problems found in the nuclear industry. Vital liaison has been established with numerous nuclear facilities and government agencies to exchange technical information, to cooperate on particular assay problems, and to provide recommendations, engineering drawings, and even complete prototype assay systems. Here are just a few of the numerous examples of these strong ties to the real world of nuclear safeguards and material management, in other words, real solutions to real problems:

1. Measurement of the plutonium content of complete Southwest Experimental Fast Oxide Reactor (SEFOR) fuel elements to better than $\pm$ 3 percent

TABLE 17

Apparent Random and Systematic Errors Observed from AEC
Duplicate Samples Compared with Facility ^{235}U and
Plutonium Values

	Random (1σ)	Systematic (1σ)
1. Uranium compounds (UO$_2$ pellets, UNH crystals, UO$_2$ powder, UF$_4$, ADU, and U$_3$O$_8$ powder)	$\pm$ 0.5	+ 4.4
2. Uranium mixtures (UO$_2$-metal oxides, UPuC)	$\pm$ 0.3	+ 0.5
3. Plutonium mixtures (UO$_2$-PuO$_2$)	$\pm$ 2.0	+ 2.6
4. Uranium solutions	$\pm$ 0.1	- 8.5
5. Homogenous uranium scrap (U Al alloy, UO$_2$-metal oxides, UO$_2$ pellets)	$\pm$ 0.1	+ 0.1
6. Residues, calcined ash, press cake	$\pm$ 7.6	+ 30

Source: R. P. Wischow et al., "U.S. Safeguards Experience in Regulation and Inspection of the Private Nuclear Industry" in Safeguards Techniques, Vol. I (Vienna: IAEA, 1970), p. 442.

2. Measurement of the ^{235}U content of ninety cans of uranium aluminide doubly sealed in an argon atmosphere to an accuracy of $\pm$ 1 percent on an individual sample and $\pm$ 0.2 percent on the entire 300 kilogram inventory

3. Measurement of an entire 93 percent enriched uranium scrap inventory totaling over 500 kilograms of ^{235}U

4. On-site measurement of 314 bottles of uranium scrap varying in enrichment from 10-97 percent

5. Measurement of 144 DNMS inventory samples just prior to routine transmittal to the AEC New Brunswick Laboratory for chemical and mass spectrometer analysis

6. On-site measurement of over 200 cans of low enriched uranium oxide and ash

7. Nondestructive assay of hundreds of other items such as Fast Flux Test Facility (FFTF) fuel pellets, power reactor fuel rods and elements, ^{238}Pu scrap, process filter and duct "hold-up," UF$_6$ cylinders, uranium-thorium-fluoride scrap from Nuclear Materials Equipment Corporation (NUMEC), uranium-thorium-carbide High Temperature Gas-Cooled Reactor (HTGR) fuel and scrap from Gulf, high ^{241}Am containing molten salt plutonium residues from Rocky Flats, and so forth.

In short, literally thousands of items representative of all stages of the nuclear fuel cycle have been assayed nondestructively; many of these items previously had been considered unmeasurable or, even worse, poor measurements had become accepted as correct since they were allegedly the "best available." In the light of this background of broad practical accomplishment, we do not believe we are playing the role of "professional magicians who pile up only peer kudos."[1] The nuclear industry, as well as the AEC, is beginning to realize that these professionals have come up with real solutions to real problems and have developed practical assay systems that are ready to be produced by instrument manufacturers for in-plant use. However, there is no magic, no single nondestructive technique that suddenly provides a panacea for all measurement problems. Despite wishes to the contrary, a variety of nondestructive assay systems are required to accurately measure the wide range of material involved in fissile inventories. I shall now describe briefly four of the LASL-developed assay systems that are available for immediate application to more accurate fissile materials measurements.

Illustration 1 shows a neutron coincidence counter for assay of heterogeneous plutonium scrap in 30-gallon drums ready for installation at the Los Alamos plutonium facility. The sensitivity of this system is < 50 mg. ^{240}Pu (<0.5 g. plutonium containing 10 percent ^{240}Pu); the accuracy is $\pm$ 10 percent (1σ) for a single measurement; and the typical counting time is 200 seconds. The estimated cost of this system is $35,000 complete with direct automatic readout of the quantity of interest.

The second prototype system is shown in Illustration 2. This is an in-line fuel rod assay system for pressurized water reactor (PWR) fuel based on ^{252}Cf neutron interrogation. At the present time the system shown in Illustration 2 is being evaluated by Westinghouse personnel at their Columbia, South Carolina, fuel fabrication plant. A second version of this system, namely for boiling water reactor (BWR) fuel rods, has been acquired by the Division of Nuclear Material Safeguards and is in use at the General Electric Nuclear Fuels Division facility in Wilmington, North Carolina. The precision of both systems has been demonstrated to be $\pm$ 1.2 percent (1σ) for the measurement of the uranium content of an individual rod (dominated by statistics) and better than $\pm$ 0.25 percent (1σ) for 500 rods. The estimated cost is $35,000 per system. The demonstrated throughput is 240 to 320 rods per eight-hour shift including handling, coffee breaks, and so forth; to date about 10,000 rods have been assayed at General Electric.

Whereas the plutonium scrap assay system involves the counting of spontaneous fission neutrons from ^{240}Pu and the power reactor fuel rod assay system is based on the counting of prompt neutrons from the induced fission of ^{235}U, the following two systems rely on the detection of gamma ray signatures.

For quality control of "guaranteed" homogeneous finished products such as fuel plates and rods, gamma ray scanning is an established technique; however, for practical containers of scrap and waste, as well as feed material, gamma ray assay is complicated by sample attenuation and inhomogeneity. Nevertheless, quantitative assay of inhomogeneous samples can be accomplished with appropriate detection geometries and by applying attenuation corrections based on careful transmission measurements. If a package to be assayed can be divided by collimation into zones in which the transmission is reasonably constant, then the measured transmission of each zone can be used to derive an accurate attenuation correction to the observed fissile material response of that particular zone.

A versatile gamma scan system, suitable for this segmentation

ILLUSTRATION 1

4π Neutron Coincidence Counter for Assay
of Heterogeneous Plutonium Processing Scrap in 30-Gallon Barrels

294

ILLUSTRATION 2

Complete ^{252}Cf PWR Fuel Rod Assay System with 6-Channel Rod Handling Mechanism and Automated Data Acquisition, Reduction, and Printout

approach as well as more general rotation-collimation methods, has
been constructed for gamma ray assay of samples up to the five-gal-
lon size. This assay unit, as utilized for assay of ^{235}U in two-liter
bottles, is shown in Illustration 3. The sample rotates and is moved
in a vertical scan defined by a 0.5 inch slit in front of a Ge (Li)
detector. In this manner the sample is examined as a sequence of
independent thin segments, each of which is assumed to be homogeneous.
The fissionable material response and the gamma ray transmission
are recorded for each segment, and the attenuation-corrected vertical
distribution of material as well as the total mass is deduced automatically by the data acquisition system. The assay accuracy of this unit
is $\pm$ 5 percent (1σ) or better for a wide range of materials. Quantitative
results can be obtained for gamma ray transmissions through the
sample as low as 1 percent or uranium concentrations below 250 grams
per liter. The sensitivity of the system is better than 1 gram ^{235}U
or ^{239}Pu, and the time required for a complete assay is less than 10
minutes. Similar systems have been utilized for the assay of low
level uranium and plutonium waste in containers as large as a 55-gal-
lon drum.

    Several hundred containers of uranium and plutonium scrap have
been assayed with the segmented gamma ray scanning system. As an
example of the data produced by the system, the differential ^{235}U
activity and sample transmission of scrap in a two-liter bottle is
presented in Figure 26. The attenuation-corrected segmented scan
assay of this bottle was 137 grams ^{235}U; in contrast, 97 grams would
have been obtained using an uncollimated gamma count and the average
transmission from segments 2 through 16. A single transmission
measurement across the middle of the container would yield 168 grams
^{235}U, or 23 percent high.

    The severe attenuation of low energy gamma rays in highly
attenuating samples has been used to advantage in the development of
the so-called "enrichment meter." This "assay system" is unique
in the sense that it is a collection of techniques rather than instruments. The primary technique makes use of the fact that the 185-keV
gamma activity from a unit area of a dense, uniform object containing
primarily uranium is proportional to the enrichment of ^{235}U times a
factor F, a slowly varying function of density nearly equal to unity
for many practical cases. For pure metal, oxide (UO_2), and residue
containing only 50 percent uranium, F equals 1.00, 0.99, and 0.93,
respectively. Thus this principle can be used to measure fuel pins,
plates, or any reasonably homogeneous sample that is fairly rich in
uranium. The requirement that the sample be opaque to 185-keV
gamma rays is frequently not a limitation since 95 percent of the

ILLUSTRATION 3

Versatile Gamma Ray Scanning System

Used for Spatially-Segmented, Attenuation-Correction Gamma Ray Assay

FIGURE 26

Variation of Transmission and Uranium Activity
in a Two-Liter Bottle of Enriched Uranium Scrap

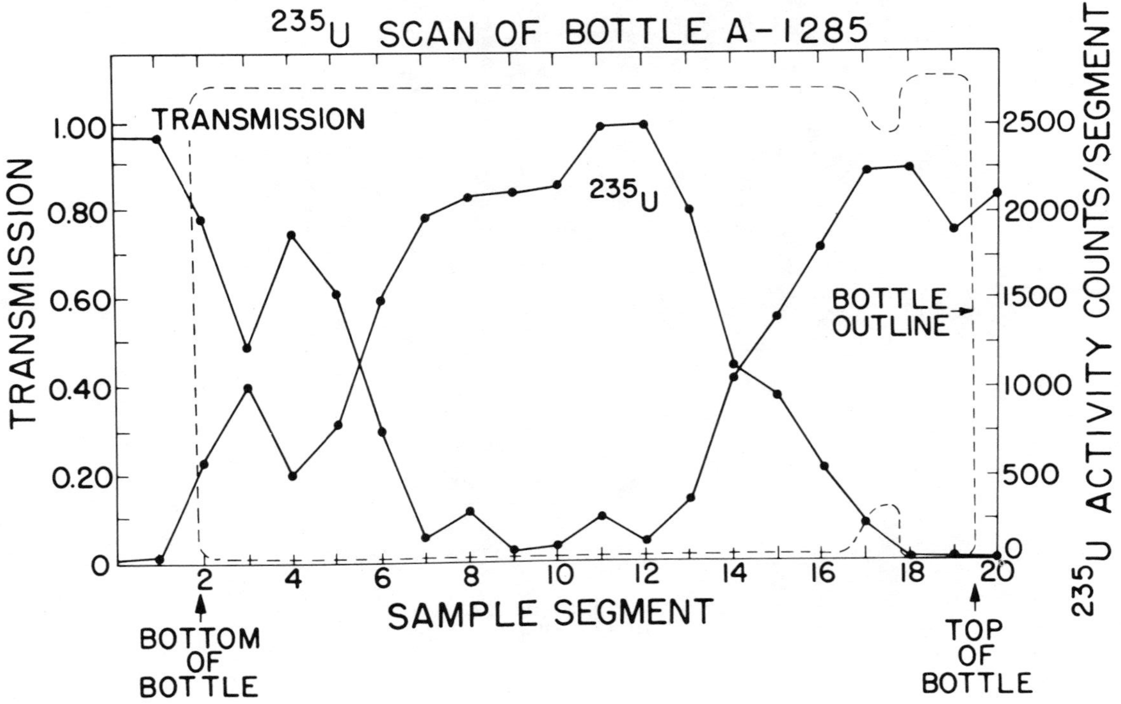

saturated count is achieved with one-millimeter-thick uranium metal
or 10 millimeters of a mixture of 50 percent by mass uranium with
a low-Z matrix.

Enrichment results obtained with equipment such as that associated with the segmented gamma scan assay system described earlier
indicate an achievable accuracy of about $\pm$ 1 percent (1σ). However,
of particular interest are the results of measurements made on an
assortment of fuel rods, cans of uranium compounds, incinerator ash,
and UF_6 cylinders with the handcarried unit shown in Illustration 4.
This system, costing about $1,300, consists of a shielded two by one-
half inch NaI detector connected to a battery-powered box of electronics
weighing about seven pounds. The system in Figure 26 contains
more sophisticated electronics but is not battery powered.

A wide variety of scrap fuel rods were assayed at National Lead
Company of Ohio (NLO). Some of the rods were actually uranium
metal slugs while others contained pelletized or vibra-packed UO_2
or UC. The comparison of the nondestructive assay (NDA) results
with mass spectrometric analyses is shown in Figure 27. Two rods
of known enrichments were used to calibrate the system; a single
enrichment measurement took five minutes. The results, which have
been corrected for gamma attenuation by the cladding, agree with
the mass spectrometric analyses to within $\pm$ 5 percent.

"Enrichment meter" results on blended uranium scrap again
measured at NLO are shown in Figure 28. It is interesting to note
that the range of applicability of this technique can be extended to
materials containing as little as 10 percent uranium if the uranium
concentration is at least approximately known.

Literally walking through the Portsmouth gaseous diffusion plant,
an experienced person carrying this portable unit can determine the
enrichment of UF_6 product in 5A and 48A cylinders with the results
shown in Figure 29. A 5A cylinder measures 5 inches in diameter by
30 inches long, has a one-quarter-inch Monel wall, and holds up to 55
pounds of UF_6 of greater than 12 percent enrichment; on the other
hand, a 48A cylinder measures 48 inches in diameter by 10 feet long,
has a five-eights-inch steel wall, and contains up to 21,000 pounds of
UF_6 of less than 3 percent enrichment. The calibrations for the
measurements at Portsmouth were made using two 4-inch diameter
cans of U_3O_8 (10 percent and 0.72 percent ^{235}U) and a one-quarter-
inch-thick plate of nickel to simulate the container wall. Corrections
for exact compositions and thickness of the walls of the actual containers were calculated during the course of the measurements. The

ILLUSTRATION 4

Commercially Available Portable Gamma Ray Assay Units

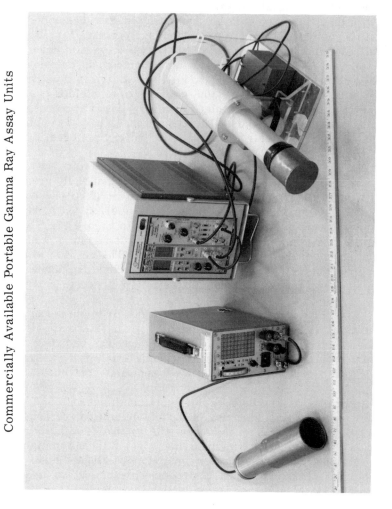

FIGURE 27

Results of "Enrichment-Meter" Measurements
on Scrap Fuel Rods

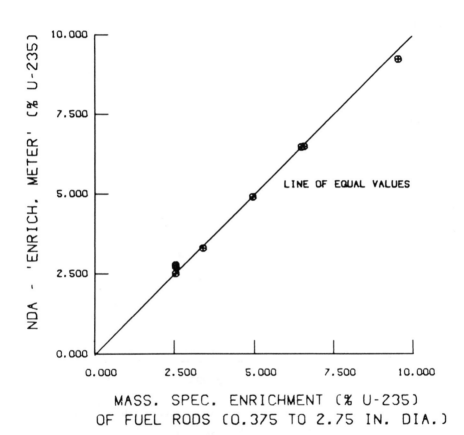

MASS. SPEC. ENRICHMENT (% U-235)
OF FUEL RODS (0.375 TO 2.75 IN. DIA.)

FIGURE 28

Results of "Enrichment-Meter" Measurements
on Cans of Blended Uranium Scrap

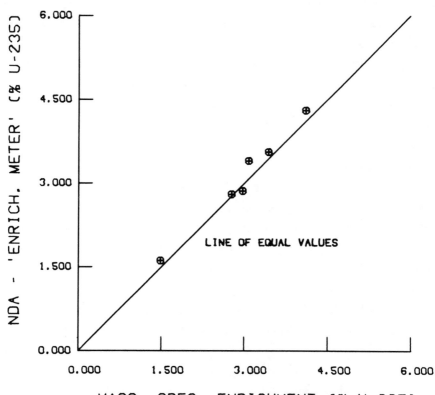

FIGURE 29

Results of "Enrichment-Meter" Measurements
on 5A and 48A UF$_6$ Cylinders

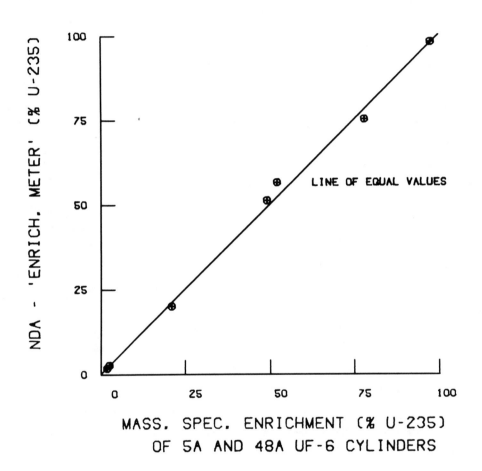

results of these measurements indicate that a simple portable NaI assay unit can be successfully used to spot-check enrichments of UF_6 in shipping containers. In regard to more precise measurements using a Ge(Li) detector, the accuracy seems to be dominated by the rather broad tolerance of the cylinder wall thickness.

During the recent deployment of our Mobile Nondestructive Assay Laboratory at Nuclear Material and Equipment Corporation (NUMEC), we demonstrated a rather imaginative method for verifying an 18.31 percent enriched uranium scrap inventory with simple, portable equipment. The material contained in 54 two-liter bottles was well-segregated, largely homogeneous, calcined scrap that had been evaluated by sampling/chemical assay methods. The uranium concentrations were high: approximately two-thirds of the bottles contained 75-88 percent uranium and the remainder contained 25-35 percent uranium. The SS-Value as well as the enrichment of each bottle was verified to within $\pm$ 5 percent by combining the "enrichment meter" with a 5 by 5 inch NaI plus ^{22}Na transmission source system to measure ^{238}U content. The results of these measurements are shown in Figure 30. The apparent bias of about 3-4 percent beyond 300 grams ^{235}U is within the uncertainty of these measurements and is due to increased gamma ray attenuation. However, six significant discrepancies were indeed found in this inventory: three bottles contained enrichments of 11, 27, and 51 percent instead of 18.31 percent and three bottles contained 1.1 kilogram more uranium at the 18 percent enrichment than was determined by sampling/chemical assay.

Another interesting extension of the enrichment meter concept is the fact that, knowing the isotopic constituents, it can be used to measure the blending ratio, that is, the relative concentration of plutonium and uranium in the reactor fuels of the future such as plutonium recycle and FFTF.

We have used the portable "enrichment meter" pictured in Illustration 4 at LASL and at numerous AEC contractors and licensees for the problems I have discussed as well as uranium "hold-up" in Raschig-ring-filled solution tanks, HEPA-filters, and just plain ducts. It is a simple but powerful tool in the hands of a knowledgeable person and as such should be—and I am sure will be—used more and more by the nuclear industry as well as by inspectors. However, it is not the answer to all problems and, because it can be fooled or misused, it requires a technical sophistication not to be taken for granted.

I have omitted discussion of the extensive development of NDA techniques and instruments which has been performed at LASL in

FIGURE 30

Verification of an 18. 31 Percent Enriched Uranium Scrap Inventory
with a Combination of a Portable "Enrichment-Meter"
and a 5-by-5-Inch NaI Detector for ^{238}U

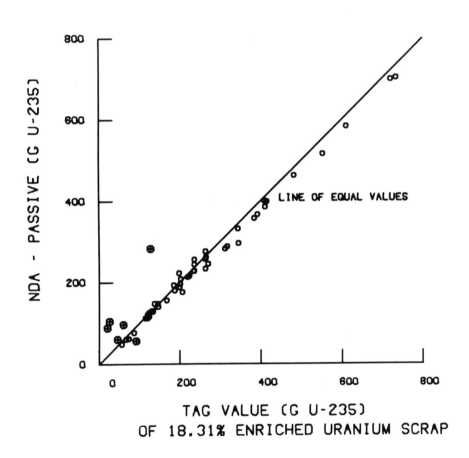

305

order to focus attention on some of the present problems and solutions of measuring the fissionable materials to be safeguarded. However, it is clear that the sheer quantity of nuclear material inventories and the associated safeguards problems will increase in the years ahead with new nuclear power plants and the scheduled introduction of plutonium recycle (BWR, PWR), highly enriched U-Th mixtures for the HTGR, and mixed Pu-U oxides for the FFTF. In addition, the expanding worldwide commerce in nuclear materials will present an increasing challenge to both national and international safeguards systems. Therefore, just as nuclear safeguards can only be implemented on the solid foundation of direct measurements of all materials in the nuclear fuel cycle, these direct measurements must be built on the solid foundation of a progressive program of technique and instrument development to be able to solve these new problems. In short, the inherently dynamic nature of fissionable material demands a correspondingly dynamic approach to safeguards and fissionable material measurements.

NOTE

1. C. D. W. Thornton, INMM Newsletter, 31 (September 1971), 7.

The need for a variety of instrumentation systems to handle the throughput of a modern nuclear fuel plant was emphasized by Joerg Menzel in response to an inquiry by Ralph Lumb (Nuclear Surveillance and Auditing Corporation). Examples cited by Menzel were gamma-ray scanning of individual pellets and interrogation of fissile content of a fuel rod by neutrons from ^{252}Cf. Gamma-ray scanning requires the longer time.

The distinction between the instrumentation needs for fuel assay and for detection against loss from a plant was made by Theodore Taylor (International Research and Technology). If safeguards of a plant are planned on a containment principle, then all the points of entrance and exit need to be monitored for passage of fissile materials. These points of penetration include passageways and also inlets and outlets for both air and water. Instrumentation required to assure that these are not channels for flow of unauthorized material needs to be continuous and capable of detecting to very low levels of activity, but it need not have great accuracy of measurement.

Work is under way on instrumentation of this sort. Menzel reported that the Los Alamos Scientific Laboratory is applying detectors for specific problems involving air and water effluence. Development of a passive-type doorway monitor sensitive to less than one gram of plutonium was mentioned by Richard Chanda (Dow Chemical Corporation). A prototype of this has been in operation and was sent for exhibit at the Fourth Geneva Conference. Rudolf Avenhaus (Kernforschungszentrum) confirmed that a similar system has been in operation at ALKEM in Karlsruhe, West Germany. To increase the sensitivity of such doorway monitors, Frank Morgan (United Kingdom Atomic Energy Authority) mentioned their practice of using these at places where people are held for some period of time, specifically at the location of hand and foot monitors of radioactivity.

CHAPTER 21

THE IAEA CATALOG
FOR PORTABLE SAFEGUARDS
ASSAY TECHNIQUES

L. A. Kull
G. M. Reynolds
J. R. Beyster

INTRODUCTION

During the last several years, safeguards programs in the United States and abroad have generated increasing amounts of information relating to nondestructive measurements and assay techniques for fissionable isotopes. This barrage of data, including ideas for new techniques, prototype design information, operating experience, and critical technical evaluations, has been stimulated by the concerned interest of a number of national and international agencies over the effectiveness of controls for the flow of nuclear materials in the fuel cycle. In anticipation of an international community that will depend increasingly on nuclear energy to satisfy its power requirements, responsible agencies have diverted resources, time, and talent into the development of more accurate measurements techniques since good measurements are one of the cornerstones of effective materials control.

This chapter concerns itself with a data management problem that is beginning to appear concomitant with the increase in the production rate of safeguards information.[1] The problem can be broken down into three parts:

Work for this chapter was supported by the International Atomic Energy Agency (IAEA). The authors would like to acknowledge the assistance of W. Higinbotham, M. Zucker, S. Suda, and W. Marcuse of the Brookhaven National Laboratory in collecting information for the data base and for valuable discussions of the problem.

1. The collection of all available data.

2. The condensation and arrangement of the data into a general format to form a data base.

3. The development of a retrieval system that provides convenient access to the data base for users with specific information requirements.

This additional effort is required in order that the information being generated can be readily put to use in the variety of tasks for which it was originally intended. Administrators of government research programs, plant operators and engineers, technical people working in the measurement field, and national and international inspectors charged with the enforcement of existing safeguards regulations and agreements all can easily be shown to benefit from a complete but condensed record of safeguards experience.

DESIGN OF THE IAEA HANDBOOK

As a start toward the resolution of this problem, the International Atomic Energy Agency has authorized a study to find how one might put together a safeguards information system. In the initial effort it was decided to limit the range of assay techniques for which data would be collected to those shown to be simple to use, capable of being easily transported, and relatively inexpensive. This was done so that a limited subset of the complete information system would in itself be useful to a selected set of the potential users—in this case, IAEA administrators and inspectors charged with the enforcement of regulatory functions. Table 18 gives a list of the techniques that were selected within these general guidelines. The list is not considered to be complete; however, it was felt that this mix does cover some of the more important techniques now receiving attention in the safeguards community and would be representative of the overall data management problem.

Considering the resources available, it was decided to initially collect about forty assay results, arrange the important facets from these results in an acceptable format, and use this as a data base from which to work. The format into which each of these individually reported results was fitted is shown in Figure 31. Each data sheet refers back specifically to a single reference in the published literature; however, more than one data sheet may be generated from a single reference if the variety of information presented would be confusing when reduced to a single data sheet.

TABLE 18

Techniques Selected for Inclusion in the
Safeguards Information System

1.   Gamma Spectroscopy

2.   Passive Neutron Yield

3.   Gamma Absorptiometry

4.   Active Neutron (Isotopic Sources)

5.   X-ray Fluorescence

As the data base grew in size, various indexing systems were
tried with the goal of providing convenient access to the system for
specific problems. It became apparent that a relatively simple index
would suffice for a system containing a small number of techniques
and limited data base. However, it was just as apparent that, as the
size and coverage of the system grew, more detail and flexibility in
the index would be useful for extracting certain information from the
data base.

The data base itself is ordered by technique (i.e., Section 1 contains all the gamma spectroscopy data sheets, Section 2 contains passive neutron, and so forth), so that questions related to the characteristics of a specific assay technique can be answered by scanning the
appropriate section. The present index, or variations of it, probably
are sufficient for a collection of data of catalog or handbook size. The
index is keyed to a description of the assay sample and first of all is
broken down by elements (uranium, plutonium, thorium) as well as
including a separate section for irradiated or spent fuels (see Figure
32). Each of these sections is further divided according to the physical
form of the material (bulk materials, fuel configurations, and scrap
and waste). The final breakdown under these classifications is shown
in Figure 33. Note that scrap and waste is broken down two different
ways: by the amount of material present per container and by the
container size irrespective of content.

As an example of how this index could be used, assume that a
particular query pertains to the assay of plutonium waste in one-gallon
containers with an expected material content of several grams per
container. With this information, the present limited data base would

FIGURE 31

Format for Each Individual Result in the Data Base

DATA SHEET 1-03

TECHNIQUE: Gamma-Spectroscopy

REFERENCE: J. Lovett, PIP Quarterly Progress Report, April-June 1970, BHO 69-1.

FISSILE MATERIAL: Plutonium   QUANTITIES PRESENT: 1-60 gms Pu per barrel.

PRECISION, ACCURACY, REPRODUCIBILITY, SENSITIVITY:

ACCURACY	SENSITIVITY	PRECISION
Measured Pu count rates can differ by up to 12% depending on the Pu location in the drum.	equivalent to approximately one 0.2 gm pellet of PuO_2	approximately 3.4% (2σ)

SNM CHEMICAL & PHYSICAL FORM: Plutonium oxides.

MATRIX MATERIALS: Solid glove box wastes (PVC bags, Nyo gloves, latex gloves, glass jars).

CONTAINER DESCRIPTION: 55 gallon drum. Each drum held 21 1.5 gallon cardboard scrap containers; the package arrangement was 3 layers of a ring of six with one in the middle.

HOMOGENEITY: Very poor.

SELF SHIELDING: A self shielding correction is applied to the results by comparing the response from a Pu source shining through the unknown drum, with that from a drum containing a know matrix. Relative self shielding factors ranged from .991 to 1.014 for a variety of sample matrices. This correction is considered relatively ineffective due to the fact that the source shines through gaps in the drum contents regardless of their specific composition. It indicates a strong need for a scrap segregation prior to drum loading.

BACKGROUNDS: The background correction subtracted from under the peaks of interest consisted of a flat Comption background plus a previously measured environmental background. The background under the Pu "384 KeV complex" was 1220 $\pm$ 44 counts/1000 seconds. (The signal was 1200 counts/sec. g Pu).

MEASURING PROCEDURES & THROUGHPUT:

> Detector - 55 cc Ge (Li)
> Detector to Barrel separation - 54 in.
> Barrel Rotation Rate - 4 RPM
> 1000 sec. count of unknown drum.
> 1000 sec. count of unknown drum with exterior Pu source in position for attenuation correction.

The amount of ^{239}Pu is determined from the measured intensity of the Pu "384 KeV complex".

STANDARDS & CALIBRATION: Four standard packages were made up containing known amounts of PuO_2 and were interspersed in the drum with dummy packages containing typical matrix materials. The calibration range was 0.2 to 19 grams PuO_2. The measured calibration coefficient for the system was 1.12 (g ^{239}Pu) (seconds)/(net count).

EQUIPMENT STABILITY:

SPECIAL CONSIDERATIONS:

1. Scrap should be segregated before being placed in drums.
2. More accurate results can be obtained by assaying individual packages before they are placed in the drum. See data sheet 1-02.
3. If packages can be screened for average attenuation prior to insertion in drums, assays of drums are considerably more accurate.

OTHER APPLICABLE REFERENCES: J. E. Lovett, D. B. James, PIP Second Quarterly Report, BHO-69-2 (1970).

FIGURE 32

Indexing System: Breakdown by Assay Sample Composition

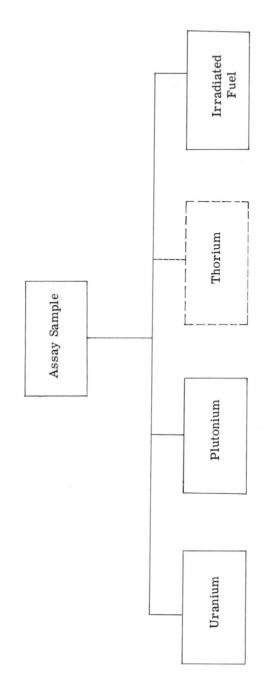

FIGURE 33

Indexing System: Further Breakdown by
Assay Sample Description

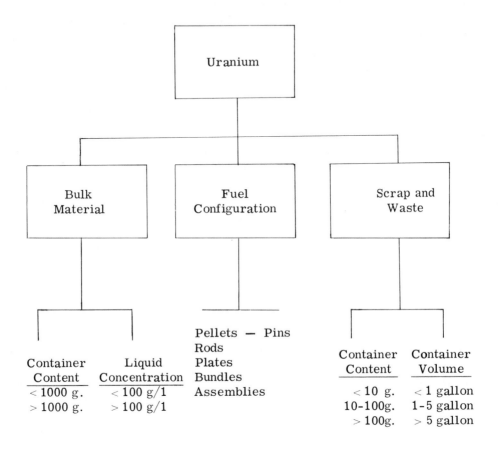

refer the user to one data sheet on gamma spectroscopy and three data sheets using the method of passive neutron yield. These data sheets in turn contain references to five papers available in the literature for elaboration of the information contained on the data sheets. It is apparent from the above description that the existing safeguards information system consists of a handbook or catalog containing a limited data base of essential details from published assay results. Convenient access to the information contained therein is attained by both the ordering of the data sheets and the use of an indexing system. The system is simple, but it illustrates the usefulness of the concept.

FUTURE NEEDS

It is now appropriate to consider what lies ahead. The first and most immediate need is to expand the data base under the present limited set of techniques and to get this handbook into the field. There it can be improved upon and refined, based on suggestions and complaints from the users. Second, the system should broaden out in scope so as to include all important assay techniques now in use or under serious development. Finally, once the coverage of the system has been expanded, a responsibility needs to be established to update the information system on a periodic basis. Once the systems comes "up to speed," i.e., all the relevant existing data has been fed into the system, the reviewers also can spend some time insuring that all the possible pertinent data from newly reported measurements or operating experiences is recorded. There are important omissions in many earlier reports that possibly might have been avoided if the authors had been contacted soon after publishing their data.

As the data base expands and the number of techniques grows, it may be more effective to move from the "handbook" stage and program the information system on a computer. This is especially true if it becomes desirable to query the system in considerably more detail than was presented here. For example, if the same problem mentioned earlier were put to the system and thirty data sheets for a variety of techniques were referenced, it might be more effective to refine the problem further by defining the range of accuracy desired, isotopic content, enrichment, and so forth. As the data base develops, it also may be desirable to subdivide the data under such additional major headings as mixed oxides and burnup determination.

The effort described here is a small but significant step toward more effective management of the flow of safeguards measurement data. The problem of collection, evaluation, display, and dissemination of this information concerns us all even though we work on different facets of the safeguards problem. Stated very simply, accurate and up-to-date knowledge of our ability to measure forms a vital background for any decisions that are made with the object of bringing about more effective control of nuclear materials.

NOTE

1. L. Kull, S. Suda, and W. Marcuse, "Generation of a Measurement Catalog for Safeguards," paper presented at the Twelfth Annual Meeting of the Institute for Nuclear Materials Management (INMM), June 1970, (proceedings to be published).

■ **DISCUSSION**

In answer to an inquiry by Ralph Lumb (Nuclear Surveillance and Auditing Corporation) about the expected availability of the catalog, Lorenz Kull replied that it will be delivered to the International Atomic Energy Agency by the end of 1971. Copies published by the IAEA should be ready sometime in 1972.

22

**APPLICATION
OF THE THEORY
OF GAMES
TO SAFEGUARDS
PROBLEMS**

Rudolf Avenhaus

INTRODUCTION

It is an important assumption within the application of safeguards of nuclear material that the chance of a diversion from the facilities to be safeguarded is finite. This means that human beings are involved in the basic considerations of safeguards. The safeguards situation may be considered to be a conflict situation in which a group of persons is assumed to be in a position to divert nuclear material and another is chosen to detect or deter such a diversion. In such a situation the second group has to take into consideration the possible strategies of the first group if it wants to determine the optimal strategy, and vice versa. This has been pointed out by, for example, Häfele.[1] These types of situations normally cannot be handled by classical statistical methods as they are meant to deal with problems created by objective inanimate nature and not those created by scheming human beings. However, they can be tackled at least in part by the methods of game theory and decision theory.

The Karlsruhe group has been studying the possiblity of applying game theory to safeguards problems for three years. In this chapter a survey will be given on the basic considerations as well as the different models that were developed for the various problems occurring

---

The author would like to thank W. Häfele, D. Gupts, R. Reinhauer, and especially E. Höpfinger for valuable discussions and suggestions.

in the field of systems analysis of safeguards. In the first part, the
question of application of non-zero-sum games and zero-sum games
is discussed and, furthermore, what can be reached in view of the difficult problem of giving realistic figures for the payoff parameters.
Thereafter, the ideas developed will be illustrated with the help of a
characteristic example, namely, the problem of the relative importance
of different strategic points in a nuclear plant. In the second part, the
models and the solutions developed by the Karlsruhe group thus far
are reviewed.

BASIC CONSIDERATIONS

Two-Person Non-Zero-Sum Games

One possibility of applying game theory to the problem of safeguarding nuclear material may be the analysis and description of the
conflict situation by a systems analyst who is completely uninvolved
in the gains and losses of the involved parties. In this case one starts
with the consideration of the sets of possible strategies of the two
parties and the estimation of the values of the possible outcomes for
each party. This does not lead necessarily to a zero-sum game, i.e.,
a game where the gain of one party is the loss of the other and vice
versa. One can imagine, for example, that the gain of the operator in
the case of an undetected diversion is not the same as the loss of the
inspector in the same case. In such a case the intentions of the parties
must be taken into consideration (e.g., whether the inspector intends
to maximize his profit or minimize the profit of the operator). This
difficulty is expressed in the problem of establishing the appropriate
utility functions. A further difficulty in a general noncooperative two-
person game is that, even if the utility functions are given, it is not
yet predetermined what pairs of strategies are to be considered by
the two parties as pairs of optimal strategies.

A further complication is that perhaps each of the two parties
does not have full information about the intentions of the other party;
this must be considered as well. As an example, a sequence of inventory periods in a nuclear plant is considered, where each inventory
period represents one stage of the game. The situation after the first
and before the second inventory period may depend on the result of
the first inventory period. Each party might have obtained some
knowledge on the utility function of the other party through the actions
already performed. Therefore, one must take into consideration the
possibility of dynamic behavior by both parties in the course of the
sequence of inventory periods.

Two-Person Zero-Sum Games

The "impartial analysis" of the problem of safeguarding nuclear material is one field for applying game theory. Another field that is more interesting from the practical point of view is the solution of the "inspection problem" which means the solution to the problem of finding the optimal inspection strategy for a fixed safeguards budget and, furthermore, finding the safeguards budget necessary for effective safeguards. For the solution of this problem it is necessary to define the motivation of the inspection authority. It is assumed here that the inspection authority considers the gain of the operator in the case of an undetected diversion of nuclear material as its own loss and, inversely, the loss of the operator as its own gain. Furthermore, it is assumed that the inspection authority considers the "minimax-solution" in the sense of game theory, i.e., the maximum payoff for one partner among all minimum payoffs with respect to the different possible strategies of the opponent as the solution of the inspection problem; in this case the optimal inspection strategy is given by the minimax-strategy.

Thus one is led to a two-person zero-sum game with the following payoff function which defines, in the sense as described above, the payoff of the operator as player 2 to the inspection authority as player 1:

O in case of no diversion
c in case of detected diversion
-d in case of undetected diversion.*

In the case that there exists the possibility of a false alarm (error first kind α), i.e., in all cases where normal distributed measurement errors are involved, one has furthermore to define the payoff:

---

*One can discuss whether these payoffs should not be proportional to the amounts of material to be diverted. In the case of detected diversion this does not seem to be very meaningful since in this case the loss to the operator (withdrawn license, etc.) is probably very highly independent of the amount of diverted material. In the case of undetected diversion it depends on the purposes for which the diverted material will be used. In the case of a "mafia-type" diversion, a gain proportional to the diverted amount might be reasonable; in the case of safeguards in the framework of NPT, a gain independent of the diverted amount seems to be more reasonable. This question is important in connection with the determination of the safeguards budget but not for the determination of the optimal inspection strategy.

e in case of false alarm.

It is assumed that e is different from c since it is assumed that in the case of an alarm the inspection authority will find out in a second action level if the alarm was correct or false.

At first sight the fact that the gain or the loss of the operator is not given in the same units from the beginning represents a serious problem. The gain, for example, in the case of successful diversion is given in kilograms of nuclear material, the value of which is difficult to estimate and depends on the intention of the operator, whereas the loss in the case of unsuccessful diversion means a withdrawn license, jail, or political disadvantages. As has been used in many other spheres of human activities, it is assumed here that the gain and the losses can be expressed in the same utility units.

Finally, one must fix the overall objectives of the inspection authority, i.e., establish the necessary and sufficient safeguards effort, whereas the game theory treatment gives the solution of the inspection problem in the form of minimax-solutions and minimax-strategies for a fixed effort, i.e., budget for analyses or number of inspectors. One furthermore must develop a criterion in order to be able to determine what budget and what number of inspectors is necessary for a given safeguards task.

Among other considerations, two main criteria have been developed:

1. The first criterion states that the effort must be sufficient to induce the operator to behave legally. This will be the case if the expected gain to the operator in case of attempted diversion is smaller than his expected gain in case of no diversion.

2. The second criterion—which is taken from quality control statistics—states that a diversion of at least 5 percent of the nuclear material available must be detected with a probability of at least 95 percent.

In order to formulate these criteria quantitatively, it is assumed that for a given safeguards budget K the minimax-strategy of the inspector leads in case of a diversion to the probability of detection $p(K)$. In this case the expectation value of the gain of the operator is given by

$$-cp(K) + d(1-p(K)), \tag{1}$$

whereas the gain of the operator in the case of no diversion is zero (if one assumes that there is no error first kind α). Therefore, the operator will be induced to behave legally if

$$O \geq -cp(K) + d(1-p(K))$$

or

$$p(K) \geq \frac{1}{1+c/d} \ . \tag{2}$$

This relation represents a necessary and sufficient condition for the safeguards effort K according to the first criterion. Since $p(K)$ is a monotonically increasing function of K and since $O \leq p(K) \leq 1$, there always exists a value of K that fulfills the condition (2). As one sees, this condition is only dependent on the ratio of c and d. This is the first important remark.

Furthermore, one can compare the first criterion with the second. One sees that a choice of $p(K) = 0.95$ corresponds in the limiting case to a value of $c/d = 0.05$. Thus one sees that any choice of a detection probability may be expressed as an estimate of the ratio of the payoff parameters.

The second important remark results from the fact that in the case of a two-person zero-sum game the minimax-strategies do not change if one performs a linear transformation of the payoff function (1) of the following form:

$$-cp(K) + d(1-p(K)) \rightarrow -p(K).$$

Since in most cases the total budget—for example, for one plant or one country—is given, the only problem is to determine the optimal distribution of the safeguards efforts. However, this optimal distribution does not depend on the payoff parameters. This will become clearer in the example given in the following section.

The important results of this section are now summarized: For a given effort only the structure of the payoff function, not the values of the payoff parameters, must be given for the determination of the optimal distribution of safeguards efforts. If one wants to determine the necessary safeguards effort, the payoff parameters must be estimated; however, only the ratio of the gain in the case of successful diversion and the loss in the case of detected diversion must be estimated. As already stated, this problem of comparing different parameters represents a problem of daily life. An airline company, for example, in the case of bad weather must compare the economic loss in case the airplane does not fly with the risk of human life.

Example: The Relative Importance of Strategic Points

In the following discussion, the input of a reprocessing plant is considered. The spent fuel elements are dissolved and measured in the accountability tank. The content of plutonium, which is the more interesting material from the safeguards standpoint, varies for technical reasons from batch to batch; a realistic example is given in Table 19. The inspector who has the task of verifying the data of the input measurements reported to him by the operator has at his disposal a budget K that allows him to analyze k batches of a campaign consisting of m batches in total. In order to be able to determine the most effective use of the inspector's budget, it must be assumed that the operator has the intention of diverting nuclear material. One strategy considered here is that the operator reports for some batches a smaller amount than corresponds to reality and hopes that the falsified batches will not be analyzed by the inspector. The amount of material corresponding to the difference between reported and real values then can be diverted by the operator. However, one single batch cannot be falsified in an arbitrary way; if the reported amount is outside the batch-to-batch variation ρ, which is assumed as known to the inspector, the inspector will not believe that reported value.* On the other hand, the operator will falsify as few batches as possible in order to keep the probability of detection low. Therefore, if the operator wants to divert in a certain time period the amount M of nuclear material, he will falsify r batches where r is given by

---

*It is assumed here that the measurement errors are small compared to the batch-to-batch variation. In case considerable measurement errors exist, the operator must estimate whether it is better for him to divert in the framework of measurement errors, i.e., to falsify many batches within the range of the measurement standard deviation, or to divert in the framework of the batch-to-batch variation. Furthermore, as stated above, only one diversion strategy is considered here (falsification of information). One can extend these considerations by taking into account the diversion strategy that consists in diverting material without any falsification of information; such a diversion could be detected, for example, with the help of the material balance.

TABLE 19

Realistic Example for the Batch-to-Batch Variation at the Input of a Reprocessing Plant for One Campaign

Batch	Concentration of Pu (milligrams per liter)	Standard Volume (liters)	Pu($=a_i$) (grams)
1	1,956.0	2,462.3	4,820
2	1,794.0	2,490.2	4,470
3	1,782.0	2,631.9	4,690
4	1,848.7	2,394.9	4,420
5	1,832.0	2,535.6	4,650
6	2,045.0	2,565.5	5,250
7	1,877.0	2,361.5	4,430
8	2,007.0	2,119.01	4,250
9	1,639.0	2,726.4	4,290
10	1,788.0	2,508.1	4,480
11	1,825.0	2,431.2	4,440
12	2,168.0	2,687.0	5,830
13	2,206.0	2,695.0	5,950
14	1,462.0	2,773.1	4,050

Note: The average $\bar{a}$ plutonium content of a batch is given by $\bar{a} = \frac{1}{14} \sum\limits_{i=1}^{14} a_i = 4760$ g Pu

and the standard deviation ρ is given by $\rho = \left[\frac{1}{13} \sum\limits_{i=1}^{14} (a_i - \bar{a})^2 \right]^{\frac{1}{2}} = 351$g Pu $\hat{=} 7.5\%$.

$$M = \rho\, r. \tag{3}$$

The game theory treatment shows that the minimax-strategies are given by equal distributions, which means that both the inspector and the operator must select randomly k and r batches out of the total of m batches.[2] This is not a surprising result if one considers the symmetry of the problem. The probability of detection, i.e., the probability of detecting at least one falsified batch is then given by

$$p(r,k;m) = 1 - \prod_{v=0}^{r-1} (1 - \frac{k}{m-v}). \tag{4}$$

If r is small compared to m, one has

$$p(r,k;m) = 1 - (1 - \frac{k}{m})^r. \tag{5}$$

From relation (2) one obtains the number k of inspector's analyses that are necessary to induce the operator to act legally:

$$\frac{k}{m} \geq 1 - \frac{1}{r\sqrt{1 + \frac{d}{c}}}. \tag{6}$$

The smallest integer greater or equal to k_o therefore is the necessary and sufficient number of inspector's analyses. This is given by

$$\frac{k_o}{m} = 1 - \frac{1}{r\sqrt{1 + \frac{d}{c}}}. \tag{7}$$

If one assumes, for example, that the gain d of the operator in case of undetected diversion is smaller than his loss c in case of detected diversion, one obtains from (7)

$$\frac{k_o}{m} < 1 - \frac{1}{r\sqrt{2}}. \tag{8}$$

As mentioned before, in this simple case the optimal strategies could have been guessed without sophisticated application of game theory. However, let us consider the following generalized problem. The operator tries to divert nuclear material either from the input stream of the plant or from the output stream. The situation at the output is somewhat different from the situation at the input. At the output the operator wants to report a value greater than the true value because he wants to hold back material. Therefore, in principle he can hold back the total amount which means that he ships an empty birdcage (this is only possible if the receiver collaborates with the shipper). Thus, at the output the batch-to-batch variation in the framework of which the operator can divert is given by the average amount of material in the birdcages. Furthermore, one must take into account the possibility that the costs for input analyses and output analyses are different.

In this case, the solution of the inspection problem means the optimal distribution of the safeguards budget K between input and output. As a byproduct, the optimal distribution of the amount of material to be diverted will be obtained. The relevant parameters for this problem are summarized once more in Table 20.

This problem can be solved exactly under the condition that both the operator and the inspector decide (with a result not known to the opponent) to divert and to safeguard either at the input or at the output.[3] This means in mathematical terms that the pure strategies of

TABLE 20

Relevant Parameters in the Problem of
the Relative Importance of Strategic Points

Parameter	Input	Output
Number of batches per year	m_1	m_2
Number of inspector's analyses	k_1	k_2
Number of batches to be falsified by the operator	r_1	r_2
Costs per analysis	ε_1	ε_2
Amount assumed to be diverted per batch	ρ_1	ρ_2

the inspector consist in the choice of either k_1 input batches or k_2 output batches where

$$K = \epsilon_1 k_1 = \epsilon_2 k_2,$$
(9)

whereas the pure strategies of the operator consist in the choice of r_1 input batches or r_2 output batches where

$$M = \rho_1 r_1 = \rho_2 r_2.$$
(10)

The optimal inspection strategy, i.e., the minimax-strategy, is a mixed strategy: the inspector controls with probability p^+,

$$p^+ = \frac{p_1}{p_1 + p_2},$$
(11)

the input stream, where

$$p_v = 1 - \prod_{\mu=0}^{r_v - 1} \left(1 - \frac{k_v}{m_v - \mu}\right); \ v = 1, 2$$
(12)

are the probabilities of detection corresponding to (4) and with probability $1 - p^+$ the output stream. The operator diverts with probability $q^+ = p^+$ from the input stream and with probability $1 - q^+$ from the output stream.

It is interesting to determine the ratio of the expectation values of the numbers of the inspector's analyses of input and output and the ratio of the expectation values of the numbers of the falsified batches of input and output. One obtains

$$\frac{\bar{k}_1}{\bar{k}_2} = \frac{k_1 p^+}{k_2 (1 - p^+)} = \frac{k_1 p_2}{k_2 p_1},$$
(13)

$$\frac{\bar{r}_1}{\bar{r}_2} = \frac{r_1 q^+}{r_2 (1 - q^+)} = \frac{r_1 p_2}{r_2 p_1}.$$
(14)

If one assumes that

$$r_v, k_v << m_v, \quad v = 1, 2, \tag{15}$$

one obtains

$$\frac{k_1}{k_2} = \frac{\rho_1 m_1}{\rho_2 m_2}, \quad \frac{r_1}{r_2} = \frac{\varepsilon_1 m_1}{\varepsilon_2 m_2}. \tag{16}$$

This can be formulated in the following way: The ratio of the optimal average number of inspector's analyses is proportional to the maximum amounts of material that can be diverted from the different streams. The ratio of the optimal average numbers of falsified batches is proportional to the costs necessary to control the complete stream.

A numerical example is given in Table 21. The different probabilities occuring in this problem are given in Table 22 for different values of the inspector's budget K. According to equation (16) one obtains $k_1/k_2 = 0.103$, $r_1/r_2 = 0.35$.

One can immediately conclude from these considerations that the waste stream in a reprocessing plant must not be controlled virtually at all, which is a reasonable result if one considers the quantities of nuclear material occurring there in comparison with the other streams.

So far an exact solution of the approximatively formulated problem of the relative importance of strategic points was given; the approximation consisted in the assumption that the inspector and the operator decided to control and to divert either at the input or at the output stream. One can assume from the beginning that both the inspector and the operator choose a combination of input batches and output batches, which means that a pure strategy for the inspector consists in choosing k_1 input batches and k_2 output batches such that the condition

$$K = \varepsilon_1 k_1 + \varepsilon_2 k_2 \tag{17}$$

is fulfilled, while a pure strategy for the operator consists in choosing r_1 input batches and r_2 output batches such that the condition

$$M = \rho_1 r_1 + \rho_2 r_2 \tag{18}$$

TABLE 21

Numerical Example for the Problem of the
Relative Importance of Strategic Points

Parameter	Input	Output
Number of batches per year	168	1,200
Number of batches to be falsified by the operator	9	7
Cost per analysis (German marks)	1,000[a]	400[b]
Amount assumed to be diverted per batch (kilograms Pu)	1.1	1.5

[a]Isotopic dilution analysis.

[b]Mass spectrometrical and chemical analysis.

Note: 1800 kilograms Pu input per year; 10 kilograms Pu assumed to be diverted per year.

TABLE 22

Probabilities of Detection for Different
Budget Values K for the Numerical
Example Given in Table 21

K (German marks)	k_1	k_2	p_1	p_2	p^+
10^4	10	25	0.43	0.14	0.246
5.10^4	50	125	0.94	0.53	0.361
10.10^4	100	250	0.9995	0.80	0.444

is fulfilled. Up to now no exact solution of this problem has been
found. However, if one treats all the integers occurring in this problem
as continuous variables, then one can again determine the optimal
strategies. With the same approximation that was necessary to come
to the result (16), one obtains as minimax-strategies pure strategies
that fulfill the relations (16). In other words, whereas in the first
case the relations (16) were obtained for average numbers, in the
second case the relations (16) were obtained for the actual numbers for
one year. Thus, one obtains the same result in the case of the exact
solution of the approximate problem and in the case of the approximate
solution of the exact problem.

REVIEW OF MODELS DEVELOPED THUS FAR
BY THE KARLSRUHE GROUP

Introductory Remarks

The last phrase of the preceding paragraph characterizes the
intention of the Karlsruhe group in the course of the work in this field
over the last three years. On the one hand, effort were made to develop simple models that could be treated exactly in order to get a
feeling for the mathematics involved in this field. On the other hand,
efforts were made to treat realistic problems occurring in the field of
safeguarding nuclear material; this naturally led in most cases to
models that could not be treated exactly in the mathematical sense.
The aim was, first, to combine these two different approaches and,
second, to develop a kind of simplified but applicable formalism. It
is well known that one of the objections to game theory is that it is
too complicated for practical people.

Since the Karlsruhe group was interested mainly in the study of
the decision theoretical problem of safeguarding nuclear material,
i.e., in the problem of determining the optimal inspection strategies
and the necessary safeguards effort. For the reasons discussed above,
thus far only two-person zero-sum games have been considered.

Models for Surveillance and Random Sampling Problems

These models were the first to be developed, but some slightly
differing variants were considered. In the simplest variant, at m
different places of a plant there exists the possibility of a diversion
of nuclear material; k inspectors, each of whom can control at a certain

time point one of the m places, are available for safeguarding the plant.
The set of possible strategies for the operator is given by the set of
possibilities of choosing the places where he intends to divert nuclear
material in a given interval of time; the set of possible strategies for
the inspection authority is given by the set of possibilities of choosing
for every point of time the places where the k inspectors should control.
Solutions are given that determine the minimax-strategies of the inspection authority and the operator and that furthermore determine
that number k_0 of inspectors necessary to induce the operator to behave legally.

These models can be applied to random sampling problems of
the kind described above. The results obtained were used in determining
the effort necessary to safeguard a complete fuel cycle.[4]

Models for Safeguards
by Means of Inventory Taking

Common to all models developed for the problem of safeguards
by means of inventory taking is the following: One considers a sequence of inventory periods of varying lengths of time. A material
balance can be closed by an inventory carried through by the inspection
authority at a time point that is not known in advance to the operator.
It is assumed that the inventory will detect any illegal action. An
illegal action of the operator lasts τ units of time; τ is called the critical time. If the inventory takes place before the end of the critical
time, the operator has lost the play; he has won it if the inventory
takes place after the end of the critical time. The set of possible
strategies for the operator is given by the set of possibilities of choosing the starting time point of the illegal action; the set of possible
strategies for the inspection authority is given by the set of possibilities
of choosing the starting points of the inventory takings. (In the first
two variants described below it is assumed that the time necessary for
one inventory taking can be neglected in the last variant if it is assumed
that one inventory taking lasts $o > 0$ time units.)

One sees immediately that these models also can be applied to
questions in connection with the safeguarding of sealed stores of nuclear
material.

The following different variants have been worked out thus far:

Variant 1: Infinite interval of time; time is taken continuous.[5]
In this variant no limitation of the time interval in which a plant is

safeguarded is given. The budget of the inspection authority permits
an inventory taking all L days in the mean. An inspection strategy is
given against which the legal strategy of the operator is his only optimal strategy for the case $L<\tau(1+\frac{c}{d})$.

Variant 2: Finite interval of time; time is taken discrete.[6] Here,
a time interval of finite length T is considered; the budget of the inspection authority permits at most J inventories in this interval of
time. The inventories as well as the starting points of the illegal
actions can only take place at discrete time points. An inventory leads
only with probability $\Pi<1$ to the detection of an illegal action in case
the inventory takes place during the time of the illegal action. The
minimax-strategies for the inspection authority and for the operator
are determined as well as the probability of detection as a function of
J and Π. In this variant the operator fixes the starting point of the
illegal action before the beginning of the "play" and does not take any
notice of the inventories performed up to the starting point of the illegal action. This can be interpreted as though the operator were not
informed on the inventories, i.e., this variant can be interpreted as a
game with incomplete information for the operator.

This variant has been generalized by the assumption that a plant
consists of m places at each of which an inventory can be taken independently.[7] The probabilities of detection for those cases where it
was possible up to now to determine minimax-strategies are given
in Table 23.

Variant 3: Finite interval of time, time is taken discrete, sequential behavior of inspection authority and operator.[8] Again a time
interval of finite length T is considered, and again the budget of the
inspection authority permits at most J inventories in this interval of
time. However, in this case both the inspector and the operator behave strictly sequentially: In every time point both players decide
whether they will start an action or not by considering the number of
inspectors and the starting points of those inspections already performed.

In closing the discussion of this type of model, the value of these
considerations should be pointed out once more. Consider the simple
case of variant 2 (m=1). For a given number of inventories and a
given conditioned probability of detection Π, the minimax-strategies
lead to an overall (unconditioned) probability of detection (see Table
23) of

$$p(J, \Pi) = 1 - (1-\Pi)^{\zeta}(1-\frac{\eta\Pi}{g}), \qquad (19)$$

TABLE 23

Probabilities of Detection in the Generalized
Model for Safeguards by Means of Inventory Taking

Case		Probability of Detection
$0 < J \le g$ (i.e., $\zeta=0, n=J$)	$k < m$	$\dfrac{Jk\Pi}{gm}$
	$\zeta k \bmod m$	$1 - h_\zeta \dfrac{m - \gamma \zeta \Pi}{m\Pi}$
$J = \zeta g$ (i.e. $\zeta \le 1, n=0$)	ζk arbitrary $\Pi_1 = \ldots = \Pi_m =: \Pi$	$1 - (1-\Pi)^{\alpha\zeta}(1 - \dfrac{\gamma\zeta\Pi}{m})$
	$m = 1$	$1 - (1-\Pi)^\zeta (1 - \dfrac{n\Pi}{g}$
$J = \zeta g + n$	$(\zeta+1)k < m$	$\dfrac{Jk\Pi}{gm}$
	$(\zeta+1)k \le m$ $\Pi_1 = \ldots = \Pi_m =: \Pi$	$\dfrac{Jk\Pi}{gm}$

Notes: T=interval of time considered.
τ =critical time.
$g = \dfrac{T-1}{\tau}$ (positive integer).
J=number of inventories in T.
$\zeta, n = J = \zeta g + n$ (ζ, n positive integers, $n < g$).
k=number of inspectors.
m=number of areas in the plant
$\alpha\zeta, \gamma\zeta = \zeta k = \alpha\zeta m + \gamma\zeta$ ($\alpha\zeta, \gamma\zeta$ positive integers, $\gamma\zeta < m$).
$\Pi\mu$=probability of detection for area $\mu (\mu = 1, \ldots, m)$.
$$\Pi = (\frac{1}{m} \sum_{\mu=1}^{m} \frac{1}{\Pi\mu})^{-1}$$
$$h\zeta = (\frac{1}{m} \sum_{\mu=1}^{m} \frac{1}{\Pi\mu(1-\Pi\mu)^{\alpha\zeta}})^{-1}$$

where

$$J = \zeta g+n, \quad g = \frac{T-1}{T}, \quad 0 \le n < g. \tag{20}$$

The parameters J and Π determine the safeguards budget $K = K(J, \Pi)$. Thus, a safeguards authority that has a fixed budget K at its disposal must choose the values of the parameters J and Π in such a way that the budget boundary condition is fulfilled and the probability of detection (18) becomes a maximum.

A safeguards authority that wants to determine the necessary budget K must first define what "necessary budget" means. If it means that the operator shall be induced to act legally, then the necessary budget is determined by the relation

$$P_o(K) \ge \frac{1}{1+\dfrac{c}{d}} \tag{21}$$

where $p_o(K)$ is the probability of detection (19) optimized in the sense described above and c and d are the payoff parameters defined above.

Model for the Determination of Significance Thresholds in Case of a Sequence of Inventory Periods[9]

Here, a sequence of inventory periods is considered where measurement errors of the flow measurements as well as measurement errors of the physical inventory determination are taken into consideration. For a fixed error of the first kind for the total sequence of inventory periods considered, the set of possible strategies for the inspection authority is given by the set of possibilities of choosing the starting inventory and the significance thresholds for the difference between book and physical inventory material unaccounted for at the end of an inventory period. The set of possible strategies for the operator is given by the set of possibilities for distributing the total amount M of nuclear material to be diverted on the different inventory periods. The treatment of this model runs into very difficult analytical problems; an example is given in Table 24 for the case of only two inventory periods and zero error of the first kind (which is possible if one deals with rectangular error distributions).

TABLE 24

Optimal Strategies and Probability of Detection
for a Sequence of Two Inventory Periods

Case	Optimal Inspector Strategy	Optimal Operator Strategy	Probability of Detection
$4v+2u \leq M$	$a=0$ $B_1 = u+v$ $B_2 = u+2v$	arbitrary	1
$M \leq 4v$ $u=0$	$a=1$ $B_1 = B_2 = v$	$(\frac{M}{2}, \frac{M}{2})$	$1-(1-\frac{M}{4v})^2$
$M \leq 2v$ $u \leq v$	$a=0$ $B_1 = u+v$ $B_2 = u+2v$	(O,M)	$\dfrac{M^3}{48uv^2}$
$7u \leq M \leq 2v$ $u \leq v$	$a=1$ $B_1 = u+v$ $B_2 = v+2u$	$(\frac{M-u}{2}, \frac{M+u}{2})$	$1-(1-\frac{M-u}{4v})(1-\frac{M-5u}{4v})+\frac{1}{6}(\frac{u}{v})^2$

Notes: Measurement errors equally distributed, error first kind $\alpha=0$.

M=total amount assumed to be diverted.

$B_{1,2}$=significance thresholds after the first and second inventory period.

a characterizes the starting inventory after the first inventory period: a=0(1) means book (physical) inventory as starting inventory.

$u=\sqrt{3}$. standard deviation of the physical inventory,

$v=\sqrt{3}$. standard deviation of the book inventory.

Model for Action Levels[10]

Only one inventory period is considered here. After the physical inventory, the inspector checks whether the book-physical-inventory difference is greater than a fixed significance threshold or not. If it is greater, a second and more accurate inventory is taken. The set of possible strategies for the inspector consists of the set of possible significance thresholds. The set of possible strategies for the operator consists of the set of possible amounts of nuclear material to be diverted. Minimax-solutions are given for special error distributions.

CONCLUSION

A survey of the last three years' work of the Karlsruhe group in the field of applying game theory to safeguards problems has been given. In conclusion, something should be said on what is planned for the future.

First, all the models presented can and shall be further developed; however, this is connected with increasing mathematical difficulties. This is especially true for the problem of the sequence of inventory periods. Because of its importance for the most important safeguards measure of material accountancy, a high priority is given to a further analysis of this problem. Furthermore, the consideration of random sampling problems in connection with measurement errors seems to be important at some strategic points in the fuel cycle. This problem has been attacked already, but again the analysis runs into serious mathematical difficulties.

A second category of problems that are important and interesting is given by problems concerning the fuel cycle as a whole. Here, correlations of various types (e.g., shipper-receiver correlations) come into play and coalitions between operators of different plants must be considered.

It is clear that the ultimate goal of safeguards systems analysis is to determine for a given budget the optimal inspection strategy for a complete fuel cycle, taking into consideration all existing boundary conditions. But it also is clear that this problem is too complicated for a rigorous mathematical treatment; experience and judgment must also be taken into consideration. However, we think that, for the treatment of isolated and detailed problems in connection with optimization of safeguards efforts, game theory may be a very helpful tool.

NOTES

1. W. Häfele, "Systems Analysis in Safeguards of Nuclear Material," paper presented at the Fourth United Nations International Conference on the Peaceful Uses of Nuclear Energy, Geneva, 1971.

2. D. Bierlein, "Direkte Überwachungssysteme," Operations Research Verfahren, Vol. VI (1968), 57-68.

3. R. Avenhaus and E. Höpfinger, "Optimale Stichprobenpläne," Internal Notice, No. 52 (1971).

4. R. Avenhaus and D. Gupta, "Effective Application of Safeguards Manpower and Other Techniques in Nuclear Fuel Cycles," in Safeguards Techniques, Vol. I (Vienna: IAEA, 1970), pp. 345-73.

5. D. Bierlein, "Auf Bilanzen und Inventuren basierende Überwachungssysteme," Operations Research Verfahren Vol. VIII (1969), 36-43; R. Beinhauer and D. Bierlein, "Games Theoretical Models for Inspection Procedures," in Safeguards Techniques, Vol. II (Vienna: IAEA, 1970), pp. 425-46.

6. Beinhauer and Bierlein, "Games Theoretical Models."

7. R. Beinhauer, "A Game Theoretical Model for Safeguarding a Facility with m Different Areas," Internal Notice No. 51 (1971).

8. E. Höpfinger, "A Game Theoretical Analysis of an Inspection Problem," Internal Notice No. 53 (1971).

9. R. Avenhaus and E. Höpfinger, "Optimal Inspection Procedures in a Nuclear Facility for a Sequence of Inventory Periods," in Safeguards Techniques, Vol. II, pp. 411-24.

10. E. Höpfinger, "Criteria for Action Levels for Inspection Based on a Game Theoretical Model," Kernforschungszentrun Karlsruhe unpublished report KFK 909 (1969).

In the discussion <u>Frank Morgan</u> (United Kingdom Atomic Energy Authority) endorsed the concluding remarks of Rudolf Avenhaus concerning the limitations of game theory.

Leaving game theory, <u>Carl Bennett</u> (Battelle Seattle) brought up the problem of false positives that can arise in any decision process based on a series of measurements. False positives are those cases where the decision process, due to errors of measurement, concludes that diversion has occurred when in fact it has not. For safeguards, Bennett essentially asked what quota of false positives an operating safeguards system should expect even when no diversion has occurred. Also unanswered was the question of whether the quota should be some number of false positives per day or per batch.

The importance of false positives, as stressed by Bennett, lies in the opportunities that their existence provides to possible diverters. Logically, the more complicated the decision process, either due to the number or complexity of the measurements involved, the more difficult it becomes to distinguish between a false positive and a true diversion. This increases the "gray zone" within which a potential diverter can operate.

The political limitations in the application of game theory were noted by <u>Charles Van Doren</u> (Arms Control and Disarmament Agency). Practical limitations of international safeguards would not allow a concentration of effort on one country even if the need for a concentration of effort were to result from such analyses as game theory. Avenhaus responded by stating that his group's undertaking was for a limited and well-defined problem and that such political limitations were beyond the scope of the group's effort.

23

STUDIES
OF SAFEGUARDS
AS A
SYSTEMS PROBLEM

F. A. Costanzi
F. A. Tillman
S. Chatterjee

INTRODUCTION

This chapter discusses the studies of cost optimization applied to safeguards in the nuclear fuel cycle. The fuel cycle employed as a basis for our studies is that chosen by Avenhaus and Gupta in their 1970 Karlsruhe paper.[1] In our work, we regard safeguards as a systems problem and translate safeguards effectiveness over the entire fuel cycle into system reliability. Cost optimization via nonlinear programming techniques is then applied to the systems problem as a means of obtaining maximal system reliability at any given cost.

The program is next expanded in consideration of the fact that attempts to divert fissile material may not be equally likely for all forms of fissile material. We do this by introducing the concepts of diverter preference and vulnerability index.

Research for this chapter was supported under the Research Applied to National Needs (RANN) Program of the National Science Foundation.

The authors wish to thank C. L. Hwang, Associate Professor in Industrial Engineering, for assistance with the use of SUMT, and C. R. Rudy, Research Associate in Physics, for assistance with the appendix, and both for reading the manuscript. They also wish to thank Robert Leachman, Director of the Diversion Safeguards Program for many useful and informative discussions.

In the following section we discuss the Avenhaus and Gupta fuel
cycle and detail our program for optimization of safeguards in the fuel
cycle. The nonlinear programming employed in this study is treated
in the third section. The results of our studies under strict cost optimization are presented in the fourth section. The fifth section introduces diverter preference and vulnerability index into the study, and
these notions are incorporated into the program in the sixth section.
In the final section we display the results of cost optimization employing
diverter preference and vulnerability index and compare these results
with those presented in the fourth section.

THE MODEL

In our optimization studies we have used the nuclear fuel industry
of Avenhaus and Gupta which serves twelve reactors, each of 500-MWe
capacity. (See Figure 34.) The six components of the system—reactors,
reprocessing, two conversion, isotope separation, and fabrication—are
taken to be self-contained. Thus, nuclear material does not enter nor
leave this cycle except for the 103t ADU monthly input at Conversion
II. Furthermore, the accessible points for diversion in these six components are limited to fifteen.

To allow comparison with the Avenhaus and Gupta analysis,
which is of a somewhat different nature, all the quantitative parameters
were taken to be the same and are displayed in Table 25. For the one-
year time considered, these include: the number (n_i) of measurements
made at each facility; the cost of checking each measurement (c_i); and
the amount of material considered to be a hazard if diverted (10-kilo-
gram effective).

As in Avenhaus and Gupta, the cumulative systematic and random
measurement errors for all the facilities are assumed to be insignificant compared to the hazard value of 10-kilogram effective, such that
the plant operator can only divert by falsification of gross measurements and would not attempt to divert by taking advantage of measurement errors. We also assume, as do Avenhaus and Gupta, that the
inspectorate can verify with certainty the legitimacy of a measurement
performed by the operator. Thus the probability of detecting a diversion at point i is the probability that a falsified measurement will be
checked by the inspector. Avenhaus and Gupta give the specific values
of measurement errors.[2]

Our model portrays safeguards as a reliability problem with
system reliability defined as the overall, or system, probability of

FIGURE 34

System I Fuel Cycle: Safeguards and Throughputs Per Month

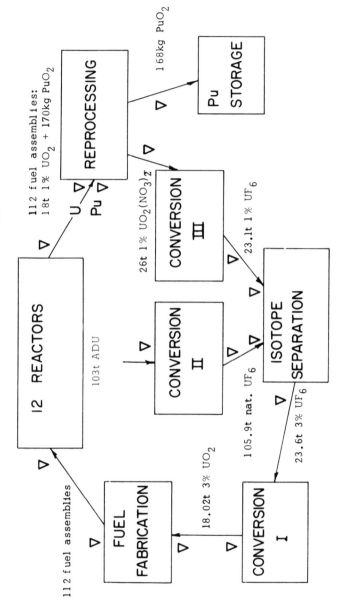

∇ — POINTS FOR SAFEGUARDS (STAGES)

343

TABLE 25

Time and Cost of Safeguard Measures

Facility	Effective Kilograms Unit Measure	r	n	Unit Costs and Times — ID&S[a] Cost (dollars)	ID&S[a] Time (hours)	M&A[b] Cost (dollars)	M&A[b] Time (hours)	Fixed Costs — Inventory (dollars)	Fixed Costs — Data Computer./Reports etc. (dollars)
Reactors									
Input	0.64	15	1344	5.00	0.25 }	none made			5,390
Output	1.41	15	1344	10.00	0.50				
Reprocessor									
U stream input	0.58	168	168 }	included in reactor	0.50	252.50	4.00	17,686	624
Pu stream input	11.00	9	168						
U stream output	0.34	27	252 }	0.50	0.25	101.25	4.00		
Pu stream output	1.50	7	1200						
Conversion I									
Input	4.47	3	192	in isotope separation	0.17 }	none made		8,937	624
Output	0.23	44	3840	0.50	0.25				
Conversion II									
Input	1.50	60	60	none made	0.25	13.75	4.00	1,890	312
Output	0.10	100	840	0.50		none made			
Conversion III									
Input	0.34	27	252	in Reprocessing	0.17 }	none made		3,062	312
Output	0.52	20	180	0.50	0.25				
Isotope separation									
Natural input	0.10	100	840	Conversion II }	0.17	38.75	3.00	11,405	624
Enriched input	0.52	20	180	Conversion III					
Output	4.47	3	192	0.50	0.25	101.25	3.00		
Fabrication									
Input	0.23	42	3840	1.00	0.17	38.75	1.50	24,082	624
Output	.64	15	1344	in measurement cost	0.50	.25	.17		

[a] ID&S = identification and sealing.
[b] M&A = measurement and analysis.

Source: Data from R. Avenhaus and D. Gupta, "Effective Application of Safeguards Manpower and Other Techniques in Nuclear Fuel Cycles," in Safeguards Techniques, Vol. I (Vienna: IAEA, 1970), pp. 345–73.

detecting diversion of nuclear materials. Proper consideration was taken of both the number (r_i) of measurements that need to be falsified at each of the accessible points, i, to accumulate the hazardous quantity and the probability (P_i) of detecting the successive falsifications through the number (k_i) of inspector measurements made at random at each point i within the cost budget (C) of the inspectors. The problem is then to maximize the system probability of detection, $P_S = \prod_i P_i$, subject to the inspection cost constraint,

$$\sum_i c_i k_i \le C. \tag{1}$$

Under the assumption of random inspections, the probability of detection at point (see appendix) i is given by the following:

$$P_i = 1 - \left(1 - \frac{k_i}{n_i}\right)^{r_i}. \tag{2}$$

SUMT

To execute our program we employed the Sequential Unconstrained Minimization Technique (SUMT), which is a simple and efficient method for solving constrained nonlinear programming problems.[3] The transformation of a constrained minimization problem into a sequence of unconstrained minimization problems is the principle behind SUMT. The method was first proposed by Carroll in 1959 and further developed by Fiacco and McCormick.[4]

In large size or complex nonlinear programming problems, difficulties arise when one has to find first order and second order derivatives when using the second order gradient method for the unconstrained minimization technique. Since most practical problems fall into this category, Lai developed a modified version of SUMT that avoids this difficulty.[5] Basically, it incorporates the Hooke and Jeeves pattern-search method which does not require taking derivatives.[6] The direction of search in the gradient method is the steepest descent direction, whereas in the Hooke and Jeeves pattern-search technique it is determined by a direct comparison of two values of the objective function (in our case, $1-P_S$) at two points separated from each other by a finite step. However, when the pattern-search is close to the boundary of some inequality constraint, the search may fall into the infeasible region—that is, the constraint is violated. When this happens a technique developed by Paviani and Himmelblau can be employed to direct the search back into the feasible region.[7]

The general nonlinear programming problem with nonlinear inequality and equality constraints is formulated as the problem of finding the n dimensional vector, $x = (x_1, x_2, \ldots, x_n)$ that minimizes the objective function $f(x) = 1-P_s$, subject to the inequality constraints

$$g_j(x) \geq 0, \qquad j = 1, \ldots, m \qquad\qquad (3)$$

and the equality constraints

$$v_j(x) = 0, \qquad j = 1, \ldots, p. \qquad\qquad (4)$$

The SUMT formulation is based on the minimization of a penalty function, $Q(x, t_h)$,

$$Q(x, t_h) = f(x) + t_h \sum_{j=1}^{m} \frac{1}{g_j(x)} + t_h^{-1/2} \sum_{j=1}^{p} v_j^2(x), \qquad (5)$$

over a strictly monotonic decreasing sequence of the penalty coefficient $\{t_h\}$. The sequence of values of the Q function are respectively minimized by a sequence of $\{x(t_h)\}$ over a strictly monotonic decreasing sequence $\{t_h\}$ and converges to the constrained optimum values of the original objective function $f(x)$.

The second term of the Q function, $t_h \sum_{j=1}^{m} \frac{1}{g_j(x)}$, will approach infinity as the value of x approaches any one of the boundaries given by $g_j(x) = 0$ and hence the values of x will tend to remain within the inequality constrained feasible space.

Since the sequence $\{t_h\}$ is strictly monotonic decreasing, as $t_h \to 0$ the third term of the Q function in equation (5), $t_h^{-1/2} \sum_{j=1}^{p} v_j^2(x)$, will approach infinity unless $v_j(x) = 0$ for $j = 1, 2, \ldots, p$. By the process of minimizing the Q function, equation (5), this formulation will force all equality constraints to zero.

The solution process for the nonlinear programming problem as defined by the Q function in equation (5) is started by selecting an arbitrary point inside the feasible region and selecting a value of t_h. A search is made for the minimum value of the Q function. After a minimum value is obtained, the value of t_h is reduced and the search is repeated starting from the previous minimum point of the Q function. By employing a strictly monotonic decreasing sequence $\{t_h\}$, a monotonically decreasing sequence $\{Q_{min}(x,t_h)\}$ inside the feasible region is obtained. As t_h tends to zero the equality constraints are satisfied and the second term of equation (4), $t_h \sum_{j=1}^{m} \frac{1}{g_j(x)}$, also approaches zero. Thus, t_h approaches zero and $Q(x,t_h)$ approaches $f(x)$ such that x is the optimum point that yields the minimum $Q(x,t_h)$ and thus the optimum point of the original problem.[8]

As mentioned, the objective function in our application of the SUMT procedure is $1 - P_s$. The vector x is $x(k_i, r_i, n_i)$ and thus

$$f(x) = f(k_i, n_i, r_i) = 1 - \prod_{i=1}^{m} P_i(k_i, n_i, r_i), \qquad (6)$$

with $P_i(k_i, n_i, r_i)$ given by equation (2), and m is the number of safeguards points i. We employ $2m+1$ inequality constraints and no equality constraint. The cost constraint is constructed as follows:

$$g_{2m+1} = C^* - C, \qquad (7)$$

with C given by equation (1) and C^* an arbitrary cost upper bound. The value of C^* is varied with each run of the program to obtain a different P_s at differing costs. The remaining 2m inequality constraints place the limits on the k_i:

$$g_i(x) = k_i, \qquad i = 1, 2, \ldots, m \qquad (8a)$$

$$g_j(x) = n_i - k_i, \qquad j = m + 1, \ldots, 2m, \qquad j = i + 8. \qquad (8b)$$

As examples of inequality constraints we list in Table 26 the g_j of a safeguards model we will discuss elsewhere in the chapter.

RESULTS OF STRICT COST OPTIMIZATION

Table 27 displays the results of our optimization studies of the Avenhaus and Gupta System (hereafter termed System I) for an overall safeguards cost of $260,000. In this system the material costs (as opposed to inspector hour costs) for identification and tagging in the

TABLE 26

P_i and Inequality Constraints for System II

i	$G_i(k_i, n_i, r_i)$	$P_i(k_i, n_i, r_i)$
1	k_1	$1 - (1 - k_1/168)^9$
2	k_2	$1 - (1 - k_2/252)^{27}$
3	k_3	$1 - (1 - k_3/1200)^7$
4	k_4	$1 - (1 - k_4/180)^{20}$
5	k_5	$1 - (1 - k_5/840)^{100}$
6	k_6	$1 - (1 - k_6/192)^3$
7	k_7	$1 - (1 - k_7/3840)^{44}$
8	k_8	$1 - (1 - k_8/1344)^{15}$
9	$168 - k_1$	
10	$252 - k_2$	
11	$1,200 - k_3$	
12	$180 - k_4$	
13	$840 - k_5$	
14	$192 - k_6$	
15	$3,840 - k_7$	
16	$1,344 - k_8$	
17	$C^* - C(k_i, n_i, r_i)$	

Note: For System II, m (the number of safeguard points) = 8

$^*C = 283.75(k_1) + 132.50(k_2 + k_3) + 62.19(k_4 + k_5) + 124.69(k_6) +$
$50.47(k_7) + 1.55(k_8)$

reactors, reprocessing, and fuel fabrication facilities are assumed fixed, as are bookkeeping and inventory costs, and therefore independent of the number of articles tagged and identified by the inspector.[9] These fixed costs are added to the cost computed by the SUMT program to give overall cost. This is not assumed for the remainder of the fuel cycle, i.e., in the three conversion plants and the isotope separation

TABLE 27

Safeguards Costs and System Reliabilities

	Avenhaus and Gupta	Optimization	
Safeguards costs	$260,000	$260,000	$300,000
System reliability (percentage)	46	94	99

plant. We compare our results with the results of Avenhaus and Gupta for the same overall $260,000 cost and with their uniform 95 percent probability of detection at each safeguards stage (P_i = 95% for all i). We note that the system reliabilities, P_s, are 94 percent for our method and 46 percent for the method of Avenhaus and Gupta.[10]

The advantage of our procedure is that true cost optimization is employed, i.e., the safeguards effort is varied at each stage to produce the highest overall system reliability subject to a cost constraint. This is obviously more flexible than the Avenhaus and Gupta prescription of setting a definite probability of detection at all stages and summing the costs. Further, we see that system reliability varies with cost such that modest increases in cost produce reasonable increases in reliability even at high levels of overall reliability. This is illustrated in the third column of Table 27. Here an increase of $40,000, about 15 percent, to a total cost of $300,000 increases reliability to the 99 percent level.

We now turn our attention to a system we feel is a bit more realistic, which what we term System II (see Figure 35). System II is the identical fuel cycle as System I, and the measurement costs are also the same; however, under System II all articles are identified and counted by inspectors at all stages in the fuel cycle. System II obtains a fixed cost of $107,000 (including inspector hour costs), a bit higher than the $71,000 fixed costs of System I. However, we note that the system reliability has also increased from 94 percent (System I) to 97 percent (System II) at the same overall cost of $260,000, and further, under the assumptions of Avenhaus and Gupta, the possible points of diversion are effectively limited to eight.[11] This increase in protection can be seen in Table 28 and corresponding Figure 36, which lists system reliabilities as a function of safeguards costs for

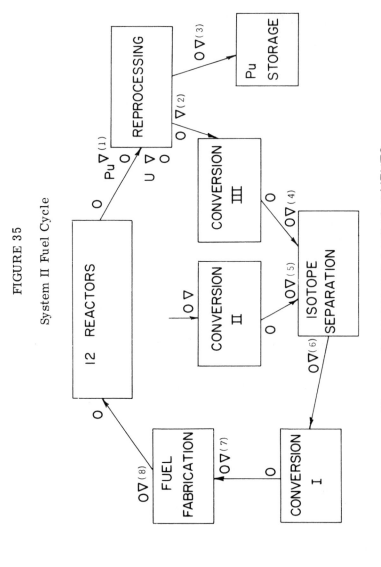

FIGURE 35

System II Fuel Cycle

∇( ) — SAFEGUARDS : MEASURMENTS

O — SAFEGUARDS : COUNTING AND TAGGING

TABLE 28

System Reliability as a Function of Safeguards Cost

System Costs (thousands of dollars)	System Reliability (percentage)
193	67.6
203	75.6
218	85.5
240	93.1
249	95.4
262	97.4
282	99.1
293	99.5
315	99.9
631(full coverage)	100.0

System II. In Table 29 we list the probabilities of detection at the various points of the System II fuel cycle as a function of cost. These probabilities are displayed graphically in Figure 37. We note from Figure 37 that a probability of detection at the 99 percent + level for all stages requires an expenditure of $300,000 per year and gives a system reliability at the 99 percent level. In Figure 38, we show how increases in cost vary with increases in overall protection. We note that the ratio of percent increase in cost to percent increase in reliability varies slowly with reliability until the system reliability reaches about 90 percent. Above $P_S = 97\%$ the ratio increases asymptotically with P_S. We also note that between $P_S = 65\%$ and $P_S = 90\%$ the average ratio is unity, i.e., the percent increase in safeguards cost is roughly proportional to the percent increase in system reliability.

VULNERABILITY INDEX AND DIVERTER PREVERENCES

In applying strict cost optimization to safeguards, the assumption of equality of all forms of nuclear materials (except wastes) was made, i.e., all forms of fissile material were safeguarded with equal intensity. Although this assumption greatly simplifies the cost optimization problem, it oversimplifies reality. To remove this assumption, one must

FIGURE 36

Costs Versus System Reliability in Safeguards System II

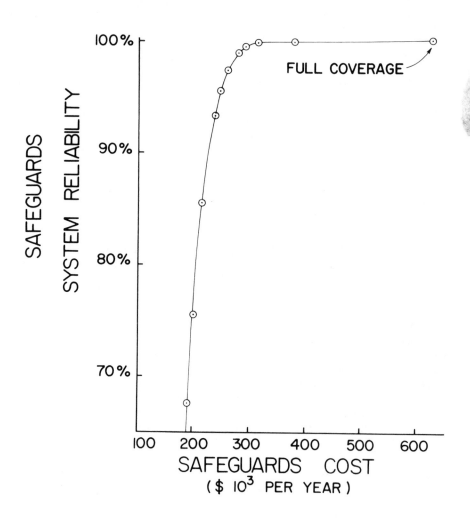

TABLE 29

Cost and Probability of Detection at Safeguard Points in the System II Fuel Cycle

System Reliability	Reprocessor Input		Reprocessor Output U Stream		Reprocessor Output Pu Stream		Isotope Separation Input Natural		Isotope Separation Input 1% Enriched		Isotope Separation Output		Fabrication Input		Fabrication Output	
	P_i[a]	C_i[b]	P_i	C_i	P_i	C_i	P_i	C_i	P_i	C_i	P_i	C_i	P_i	C_i	P_i	C_i
0.6762	0.9533	13.62	0.9816	4.64	0.8146	34.05	0.9921	2.30	0.9917	2.43	0.9607	15.83	0.9405	12.01	0.9981	0.71
0.7563	0.9625	14.47	0.9888	5.17	0.8531	38.16	0.9954	2.61	0.9946	2.67	0.9791	17.32	0.9620	13.88	0.9991	0.77
0.8548	0.9788	16.74	0.9936	5.67	0.9167	47.57	0.9974	2.86	0.9969	2.92	0.9890	18.57	0.9755	15.65	0.9995	0.82
0.9312	0.9955	21.51	0.9976	6.63	0.9622	59.49	0.9980	2.99	0.9978	3.11	0.9887	18.42	0.9902	19.33	0.9997	0.87
0.9539	0.9967	22.42	0.9978	6.76	0.9742	64.79	0.9987	3.17	0.9986	3.36	0.9936	19.44	0.9937	21.10	0.9998	0.89
0.9735	0.9987	24.40	0.9982	7.02	0.9872	73.67	0.9993	3.42	0.9991	3.55	0.9960	20.06	0.9950	22.01	0.9999	0.93
0.9905	0.9989	24.97	0.9996	8.22	0.9960	84.80	0.9998	3.98	0.9998	4.23	0.9997	22.55	0.9981	26.09	1.0000	1.03
0.9945	0.9993	26.39	0.9998	9.01	0.9972	90.37	1.0000	4.35	0.9999	4.79	0.9996	22.18	0.9986	26.95	1.0000	1.09
0.9985	0.9998	29.51	0.9999	9.94	0.9993	102.29	1.0000	4.54	1.0000	5.04	0.9999	23.05	0.9997	32.20	1.0000	1.15

[a] P_i = probability of detection at point i.
[b] C_i = costs of checking measurements at point i, including inspector hour costs(in thousands of dollars).

FIGURE 37

Stage Probability of Detection Versus System Cost

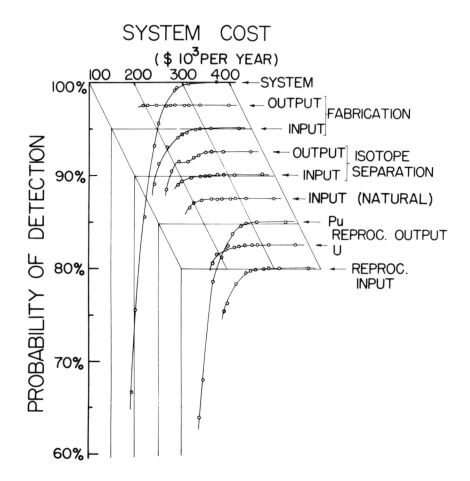

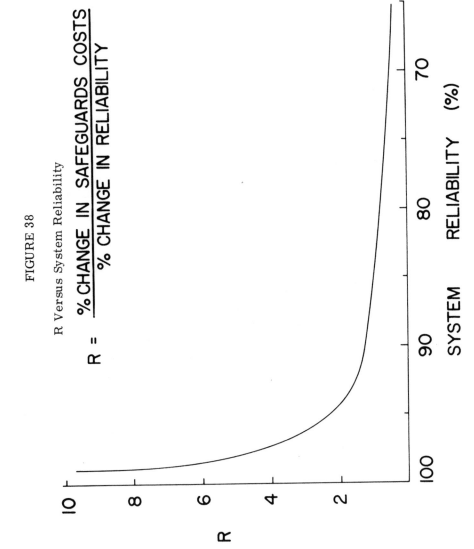

FIGURE 38

R Versus System Reliability

$$R = \frac{\% \text{ CHANGE IN SAFEGUARDS COSTS}}{\% \text{ CHANGE IN RELIABILITY}}$$

SYSTEM   RELIABILITY   (%)

R

know the relative weights of the various forms of fissile material,
i.e., the relative likeliness of attempted diversions of the various
forms of material. One also must know how to incorporate these
weights into the optimization model of the system to obtain safeguard
measures that correspond to the likelihood of attempted diversions.

We do not believe that anyone would dispute the assessment that
plutonium is of greater interest to the potential diverter than is depleted
uranium. However, the conclusion that one therefore must safeguard
plutonium with greater intensity than one safeguards depleted uranium
is meaningless for any analytical treatment of safeguards unless one
can quantify the difference in diverter preference between plutonium
and depleted uranium. Such quantification can then be translated into
the statement: The intensity of safeguards of plutonium should exceed
that of depleted uranium by a stated amount X. On the other hand, if
we make the protection of the two forms equal, then we might say that
plutonium is X amount more vulnerable to diversion as is depleted
uranium.

Since no history of attempted diversions exists that would lend
statistics of likeliness of attempts to divert the various forms of fissile
material, we cannot directly obtain quantified diverter preferences.
However, we have at our disposal the results of a survey conducted
by L. H. Rappoport and J. D. Pettinelli in which the respondents graded
on a scale of 1 to 5 their concern with regard to diversion of various
forms of fissile material[12](see Chapter 13). Normalizing the scale to
unity, we obtain the entries of Table 30. We define the respondents'
normalized level of concern for a particular material as the diverter
preference and translate this to the probability that a potential diverter
will attempt to divert that type of material. For example, we take the
probability that an attempted diversion of low enriched UF_6 will be
0.17. Thus having quantified to some degree the diverter preferences,
we proceed to the second requirement, that is, incorporating this
preference into the cost optimization model.

COST OPTIMIZED VULNERABILITY
INDEX PROCEDURE

We begin by defining the function we termed the vulnerability
index. This function is akin to the expectation of success of a diverter
if he distributes his efforts over the various forms of material according to the diverter preferences assumed above. The vulnerability
index is defined as:

TABLE 30

Concern for Various Forms of Fissile Material

	Material			
	UF_6	UO_2	$P_u(NO_3)_4$	P_uO_2
Normalized Mean	0.17	0.19	0.31	0.33

Source: Computed from data supplied by L. H. Rappoport and J. D. Pettinelli. Statistical tests, both parametric and nonparametric, indicate that the unnormalized means for the above forms of fissile material are statistically independent at better than the 90 percent confidence level.

$$VI = \sum_i \pi_i y_i, \tag{9}$$

where VI is the index, π_i is the diverter preference of the type of material at the safeguards point i, and y_i is the probability that a diversion at point i would not be detected. We observe that the vulnerability index is not strictly an expectation of success since the same form of material might be at more than one safeguards point; furthermore, an actual diversion is assumed to be attempted at one safeguards point only, and hence the diverter's efforts are not actually distributed in the statistical sense.

As before, safeguards in this fuel cycle is effected by item count, identification and sealing, and inspector verification of measurements made at each of the six facilities comprising the fuel cycle. Diversion is assumed successful if undetected and of an amount of material equal to the hazard amount, 10-kilogram effective. We deal with the fuel cycle of System II, and we make no distinction with regard to diverter preference between the various enrichments of UF_6 and similarly between the two forms of UO_2 occurring in the fuel cycle since the enrichments are all low, i.e., 3 percent or less. This allows us to write the vulnerability index (VI), equation (9), as a function of four π_i and eight y_i values:

$$VI = 0.17\,(y_4 + y_5 + y_6) + 0.19\,(y_2 + y_7 + y_8) + 0.30\,y_1 + 0.33y_3. \tag{10}$$

The vulnerability index optimization model is constructed to minimize the overall cost at a given system reliability subject to a vulnerability index constraint

$$VI \leq VI^*, \tag{11}$$

with the overall cost defined as:

$$C = C_0 + \sum_i c_i k_i, \tag{12}$$

where C_0 is the same fixed cost of \$107,000 mentioned earlier and c_i is the same cost of checking each of the k_i measurements checked at point i.

The optimization of the model is accomplished again using the SUMT procedure. However, in this application we have one equality constraint,

$$v(x) = (P_s - P_s^*) \times 10^2 \tag{13}$$

and 17 inequality constraints,

$$g_i(x) = k_i, \qquad i = 1, \ldots, 8, \tag{14a}$$

$$g_j(x) = n_i - k_i, \qquad j = 9, \ldots, 16, \quad j = i + 8, \tag{14b}$$

$$g_{17}(x) = VI^* - VI. \tag{14c}$$

In equation (13), P_s^* is an arbitrary value of system reliability inserted into the program and the factor of 10^2 insures that the final P_s calculated by the program differs from the chosen value P_s^* by less than 1 percent.[13] In equation (14c), VI^*, is an arbitrary value that provides an upper bond on the vulnerability index.

RESULTS OF VULNERABILITY INDEX COST OPTIMIZATION

The optimization was carried out by selecting a value of P_s^* and several values of VI^* and running the program for each VI^*. A new value of P_s^* was taken and the above procedure repeated for each of the VI^*. Table 31 displays some combinations of P_s^* and VI^* chosen and the corresponding values of P_s, VI, and C computed by the

TABLE 31

P$_s$, C, VI as a Function of P$_s$* and VI*

P$_s$*		VI*							
		0.0200	0.0175	0.0150	0.0125	0.0100	0.0075	0.0050	0.0025
0.9300	P$_s$	0.9298	0.9357						
	C	132.29	133.95						
	VI	0.0184	0.0171						
0.9500		0.9488	0.9494	0.9498	0.9505				
		138.70	138.42	138.92	143.21				
		0.0141	0.0144	0.0140	0.0125				
0.9700				0.9676	0.9689	0.7692	0.7712		
				148.85	149.75	150.01	155.33		
				0.0092	0.0088	0.0087	0.0070		
0.9900						0.9831	0.9848	0.9903	0.9903
						162.88	165.18	174.924	176.04
						0.0048	0.0043	0.0025	0.0024

program. The missing entries in Table 31 indicate incompatible values of P_S^* and VI^*. We observe that several values of VI and C are possible for a given P_S^*. This is not surprising since the P_i at the individual points i can be varied in several ways to obtain approximately the same overall P_S. As an example, Table 32 lists the individual P_i values for $P_S^* = 0.9500$ and varying VI^* values, along with the corresponding cost of safeguards at each point i. We observe the fluctuation in the individual costs as VI^* is varied over the selected range.

At this point, it is useful to compare the results here with the results of the optimization based on system reliability given above. We do this by listing in Table 33 the P_i values, costs, and k_i values for both the procedure with the vulnerability index and the previous procedure at values of P_S equal to 67, 86, and 93 percent, respectively. We note from these tables that the overall costs are similar but that the distribution of costs is very different. We emphasize that the use of diverter preference places more safeguards effort at the points where diversion is more likely to be attempted. Hence, the Pu stream inputs and outputs are more heavily safeguarded under this procedure than under strict reliability optimization while the UF_6 stream receives a bit less safeguarding. The UO_2 and $UO_2(NO_3)_2$ streams receive about the same level of safeguards under both procedures. This correlation of safeguards effort to the likeliness of attempted diversion of the various forms of fissile material is the obvious advantage of the vulnerability index procedure over strict reliability optimization. Although the latter is an effective means of obtaining the greatest overall protection per safeguards dollar, by its structure proportionately less effort is expended on points that are more expensive to safeguard. Furthermore, if a diversion is attempted at any given point, the probability of the diversion being detected is only the probability of detection at that point, regardless of the system reliability. We see from Table 29 above that this property of strict reliability optimization becomes a critical factor for relatively low values of P_S. However, with the vulnerability index procedure, the points where attempted diversions are most likely to occur are given relatively high values of P_i, even though the cost of checking measurements at those points may be high, e.g., the Pu stream output of the reprocessor.

A criticism might be raised that the diverter preferences are really quite arbitrary and have no basis in fact in that no history of thefts of fissile material exists. In response, we remark that our diverter preferences are based upon the subjective concerns of industry and government officials and their estimates of the need for safeguards of the various forms of material. We cannot argue that this affords an accurate diverter preference; however, we can state that

TABLE 32

VI*, VI, P_i, k_i, and Cost, $C = c_i k_i$ for $P_s^* - 0.9500$

Safeguard Point	Location	Material	VI* = 0.0200, VI = 0.0141, P_s = 0.9488			VI* = 0.0175, VI = 0.0144, P_s = 0.9494			VI* = 0.0150, VI = 0.0140, P_s = 0.9498			VI* = 0.0125, VI = 0.0125, P_s = 0.9505		
			P_i	k_i	c_i	P_i	k_i	c_i	P_i	k_i	c_i	P_i	k_i	c_i
	Reprocessor													
1	Input	Pu	0.9923	71	20.15	0.9923	71	20.15	0.9923	71	20.15	0.9967	79	22.42
2	Output	U	0.9974	49	6.49	0.9977	51	6.76	0.9975	50	6.63	0.9980	52	6.89
3	Output	Pu	0.9762	497	65.85	0.9729	483	64.00	0.9758	500	66.25	0.9799	513	67.97
	Isotope Separation													
4	Input	Nat	0.9990	52	3.23	0.9991	53	3.30	0.9990	52	3.23	0.9945	41	2.55
5	Input	1%	0.9986	53	3.30	0.9988	55	3.42	0.9988	54	3.36	0.9969	47	2.92
6	Output		0.9967	163	20.32	0.9969	164	20.45	0.9969	161	20.08	0.9910	152	18.95
	Fabrication													
7	Input		0.9877	365	18.42	0.9902	383	19.33	0.9889	368	18.57	0.9928	407	20.54
8	Output		0.9998	579	0.90	0.9998	584	0.91	0.9998	581	0.90	0.9999	602	0.93

<u>Note</u>: C=cost in thousands of dollars.

361

TABLE 33

Comparison of VI Procedure with Straight Optimization

| | | | System Reliability (P_s) = 0.6762 | | | | System Reliability (P_s) = 0.7563 | | | | System Reliability (P_s) = 0.8548 | | | |
| | | | VI = (0.1009) Cost = 193 | | 0.0786 208 | | VI = (0.0755) Cost = 203 | | 0.0564 217 | | VI = (0.0432) Cost = 218 | | 0.0331 230 | |
Safeguard Point	Location	Material	P_i	c_i	P_i	c_i	P_i	c_i	P_i	c_i	P_i	c_i	P_i	c_i
Reprocessor														
1	Input	Pu	0.9533	13.62	0.9722	15.61	0.9625	14.47	0.9934	20.43	0.9788	16.74	0.9888	18.73
2	Output	U	0.9816	4.64	0.9744	4.24	0.9888	5.17	0.9888	5.17	0.9936	5.67	0.9879	5.04
3	Output	Pu	0.8146	34.05	0.9464	54.33	0.8531	38.16	0.9483	54.86	0.9167	47.57	0.9704	62.81
Isotope Separation														
4	Input	Nat	0.9921	2.30	0.9660	1.74	0.9954	2.61	0.9811	1.99	0.9974	2.86	0.9801	1.99
5	Input	1%	0.9917	2.43	0.9903	2.36	0.9946	2.67	0.9968	2.92	0.9969	2.92	0.9914	2.43
6	Output		0.9607	15.83	0.8900	12.47	0.9791	17.32	0.8900	12.44	0.9890	18.57	0.9473	14.96
Fabrication														
7	Input		0.9405	12.01	0.8928	9.57	0.9620	13.88	0.9562	13.32	0.9755	15.65	0.9808	16.66
8	Output		0.9981	0.71	0.9923	0.58	0.9991	0.77	0.9757	0.46	0.9995	0.82	0.9990	0.77

<u>Note</u>: P_s = system reliability obtained by writing the equality constraint $H(1) = (P_s^* - P_s) \times 10^4$.

VI = for straight optimization obtained for equation (10). VI for straight optimization marked ( ).

Cost = overall cost in thousands of dollars.

it is reasonable to suppose that the judgments of these individuals are representative of actual diverter preferences. Furthermore, we are exhibiting a methodology and the use of a new measure of safeguards integrity: vulnerability index. Therefore, we argue that the validity of the method is independent of the above criticism. Finally, estimates of diverter preference possibly can be made in other ways, such as using the relative ease of fabricating a bomb based upon the estimates of such factors as the time required and equipment needed, which would be more analytical than the survey results used here.

SUMMARY

In this chapter we have demonstrated the use of cost optimization applied to nuclear safeguards. We have shown that by this method safeguards can be efficiently increased to very high levels of overall protection (above 90 percent) with only proportionate increases in costs. Still further increases in protection require cost increases in greater proportion; however, levels as high as 99 percent overall can still be achieved within reasonable costs limits.

We also have demonstrated that the use of cost optimization in safeguards can incorporate a measure of safeguards integrity by the use of the vulnerability index. By this procedure, the forms of fissile material as well as costs of inspection are inputs to the program. Consideration of both the likeliness of an attempted diversion and the costs of inspection at any given safeguards point provides for cost effectiveness at each safeguards point as well as for the overall system, resulting in a safeguards system in which safeguards efforts are commensurate with the likelihoods of attempted diversion.

An obvious extension of the vulnerability index procedure would be to utilize the notion of "critical time" based upon the supposition that time from diversion to weapon manufacture would vary with the form of fissile material.[14] Use of this notion would require restructuring of safeguards procedure to take into account the frequency of inspections as well as the number of inspections.

NOTES

1. R. Avenhaus and D. Gupta, "Effective Application of Safeguards Manpower and Other Techniques in Nuclear Fuel Cycles," in Safeguards Techniques, Vol. I (Vienna: IAEA, 1970), p. 345.

2. Ibid., Table V, p. 358-59.

3. F. A. Tillman, C. L. Hwang, L. T. Fan, and K. C. Lai, "Optimal Reliability of a Complex System," IEEE Transactions on Reliability, R-19 (August 1970), p. 95.

4. C. W. Carroll, "An Operations Research Approach to the Economic Optimization of a Draft Pulping Process" (unpublished Ph.D. thesis, Institute of Paper Chemistry, Appleton, Wis., 1959); A. V. Fiacco and G. P. McCormick, "The Sequential Unconstrained Minimization Technique for Nonlinear Programming: a Primal-Dual Method," Management Science 10 (January 1964), 360; A. V. Fiacco and G. P. McCormick, Nonlinear Programming: Sequential Unconstrand Minimization Technique (New York: John Wiley, 1968).

5. K. C. Lai, "Optimization of Industrial Management Systems by Sequential Unconstrained Minimization Technique" (unpublished masters thesis, Department of Industrial Engineering, Kansas State University, 1970).

6. R. Hooke and T. A. Jeeves, "Direct Search Solution of Numerical and Statistical Problems," Journal of the Association of Computer Mechanics, 8 (1961), 212.

7. D. A. Paviani and D. M. Himmelblau, "Constrained Nonlinear Optimization by Heuristic Programming," Operations Research, Vol. 17 (1969), 872-82.

8. Ibid.

9. The time and costs for safeguards measures are given in Tables III and IV of Avenhaus and Gupta, "Effective Application." We have approximately translated DM to dollars by 4DM equals one dollar.

10. We do not fully understand this large difference in system reliability between our method and that of Avenhaus and Gupta at the same cost of $260,000. We attempted to calculate the cost of the Avenhaus and Gupta model with $P_i = 95\%$ at each point i, and were unable to duplicate their overall cost of 1.03×10^6 DM/year quoted in ibid., Table X.

11. Possible diversion points are defined as only those points with a probability of detection less than unity. Avenhaus and Gupta assume that only 10 percent of the unit measurement amount can be diverted at the inputs of the Reprocessor and Conversion II. As can be seen from Table 25, the Reprocessor U stream input and Conversion

II input are completely safeguarded by only one measurement each per year since under the above assumption all measurements at these two points must be falsified to accumulate the hazard quantity. At the remaining points in the fuel cycle, any fraction of the unit measure is assumed divertable.

12. The enrichments of UF_6, UO_2, and uranyl nitrate given in the Rappoport-Pettinelli study are 5 percent. We realize that the fuel cycle in our work contains enrichments of natural, 1 percent and 3 percent. However, since 5 percent is in the "low enrichment" class, we feel it acceptable to employ the survey results in our work, treating all low enrichments equally.

13. With the SUMT procedure used here, the equality constraints tend to zero with successive search operations of the program. However, inasmuch as the criteria for "optimum" is that the difference between two successive computed values of the Q function is less than some predetermined ϵ, "optimum" may be reached without the equality constraint being satisfied identically. A multiplicative factor such as the factor 10^2 in equation (13) may be used to give added weight to a given N_i such that the constraint to be satisfied—in the case of equation (13), $P_s - P_s^*$—will approach zero quickly and thus be of the order of "smallness" desired upon reaching "optimum."

14. F. Morgan, "The Usefulness of System Analysis," in Safe-guards Techniques, Vol. II (Vienna: IAEA, 1970), p. 265.

APPENDIX

In this appendix we derive and discuss equation (2) which relates the probability, π, of detecting a diversion at point i to the number, n_i, of measurements made at the facility i, the number of measurements checked by the inspector, k_i, and the number of measurements that must be falsified to accumulate the hazard amount of nuclear material r_i.

If we assume that the operator of the facility has falsified r of the n measurements at point i (omitting subscripts) then the inspector has the probability $P^*(1) = r/n$ of checking one of the r bogus measurements on the first of the k inspections. The probability that the second inspection would reveal a diversion (none detected on the first), $P^*(2)$, is the product of the probability of choosing one of the r bogus measurements from the remaining n-1 measurements and the probability that the first check was of a legitimate measurement. Thus,

$$P^*(2) = \frac{r}{n-1}[1-P^*(1)],$$

$$P^*(2) = \frac{r}{n-1}(1 - \frac{r}{n}). \tag{A1}$$

The probability that either the first or second check (but not both) was of a bogus measurement we write as $P(2)$:

$$P(2) = P^*(1) + P^*(2), \tag{A2}$$

which is

$$P(2) = \frac{r}{n} + \frac{r}{n-1}(1-\frac{r}{n}) = 1 - (1 - \frac{r}{n})(1 - \frac{r}{n-1}). \tag{A3}$$

We may continue in this manner, computing the probability of detection of each successive inspection and summing; however, we find that considering probabilities from the diverter's point of view affords an easier method of computing the probability of detection of k inspections.

The probability that the diversion will go undetected by the first inspection, $\overline{P}^*(1)$, is the probability that the measurement checked by the inspector is one of the n-r legitimate measurements. Thus we write

$$\overline{P}^*(1) = \frac{n-r}{n}. \tag{A4}$$

The probability that the second inspection will not detect the diversion is then

$$\overline{P}^*(2) = \frac{n-1-r}{n-1}. \tag{A5}$$

The probability that the diversion will be undetected by both the first and second inspections, $\overline{P}(2)$, is the product of $\overline{P}^*(1)$ and $\overline{P^*(2)}$:

$$\overline{P}(2) = \frac{n-r}{n}\frac{n-1-r}{n-1}. \tag{A6}$$

We therefore conclude that the diversion will be undetected by all of the k inspections with a probability

$$\overline{P}(k) = \prod_{i=1}^{k} (1 - \frac{r}{n+1-i}). \tag{A7}$$

One minus the value of $\overline{P}(k)$ in equation (A7) is the probability that at least one of the k inspections will be a check of one of their falsified measurements, and therefore the probability of detection, $P(k)$, is:

$$P(k) = 1 - \overline{P}(k),$$

$$P(k) = 1 - \prod_{i=1}^{k} (1 - \frac{r}{n+1-i}). \tag{A8}$$

We observe that the product term in equation (A8) can be written as

$$\prod_{i=1}^{k} (1 - \frac{r}{n+1-i}) = \frac{(n-k)!}{n} \cdot \frac{(n-r)!}{(n-r-k)!}, \tag{A9}$$

and we note that

$$n^r > n(n-1) \ldots (n-r+1) > (n-r+1)^r. \tag{A10}$$

We deduce that

$$\frac{(n-k)^r}{(n-r+1)^r} \geq \prod_{i=1}^{k} (1 - \frac{r}{n+1-i}) \geq \frac{(n-k-r+1)^r}{n^r}. \tag{A11}$$

However,

$$\left(\frac{n-k}{n-r+1}\right)^r \geq \left(\frac{n-k}{n}\right)^r \geq \left(\frac{n-k-r+1}{n}\right)^r. \tag{A12}$$

Thus, we may suppose that if the difference between the two extremum in equation (A11) is small we may approximate

$$\prod_{i=1}^{k} (1 - \frac{r}{n+1-i}) \approx (1 - \frac{k}{n})^r, \tag{A13}$$

and

$$P(k) \approx 1 - (1 - \frac{k}{n})^r, \tag{A14}$$

which is equation (2).

The question remains: By what criterion can we justify the approximation above, i.e., when is the difference between the extremum

of equation (A11) "small"? Clearly, if $r + 1 > k$, the difference is
large since $(n-k/(n-r+1)) > 1$ and $(n-k-r+1)/n < 1$.

We can define the difference between the extremum as δ, and
from equation (A11) we have

$$\delta = (1 - \frac{k}{n})^r [(1 - \frac{r-1}{n})^{-r} - (1 - \frac{r-1}{n-k})^r]. \qquad (A15)$$

We rewrite equation (A13) as

$$P(k) = 1 - (1 - \frac{k}{n})^r \pm \delta, \qquad (A16)$$

and $\Delta = \delta/P(k)$ becomes the criterion of "small." Typically, we found
values of Δ less than 10^{-3} in our study. The largest and smallest
values of Δ were found to be 1.9×10^{-2} and 10^{-7} respectively. The
ranges of n, k, and r for this work were all such that $n > k >> r$ for
each point i.

The assumption that each measurement the inspector makes is definitive was examined by Carl Bennett (Battelle Seattle). This assumption of definitive measurements was involved in the preceding analysis by Frank Costanzi, where each measurement by the inspector was assumed to determine conclusively whether or not the plant measurement was valid. Bennett pointed to the existence of false positives due to errors in measurement and to the consequent high probability of "detecting" diversion when in fact it had not occurred. Although admitting this potential difficulty, Costanzi said that the effects of false positives could readily be incorporated into extensions of their model. The value of their optimization calculations, Costanzi believed, was in demonstrating the ability of the method to optimize complex problems in safeguards.

Such limitations on the assurance of inspection measurements also were discussed by Rudolf Avenhaus (Kernforschungszentrum), but he argued that these should not discourage making safeguards measurements. Falsifications might be attempted, but only with measurements, fallible as they might be, can these falsifications be detected.

The limitation of safeguards when certain types of measurements are made was considered in a comment by James Lovett (Nuclear Materials and Equipment Corporation). The type of measurements of concern were those where the inspector must involve the cooperation of the operator for each specific measurement. Obviously, a diverter would not divert at the time and location of inspection, but he simply needs to wait, even at that same location, for a time when a check measurement is not being made by the inspector.

A different constraint in such system analysis as made by Costanzi and by Avenhaus was proposed by Frank Morgan (United Kingdom Atomic Energy Authority). This constraint was the total number of inspector man-hours possible under the actual conditions of personnel availability being encountered. Again, Costanzi said that this desirable feature could be incorporated into a revised model. Costanzi suggested that other quantities of interest, such as minimization of intrusiveness, could be incorporated.

John Jaech (Jersey Nuclear Company) asked for clarification on the large difference in reliability for $260,000 expenditure, which was 94 percent for the Costanzi optimization and 46 percent for the

Avenhaus analysis. Costanzi replied that much of the difference
reflects the basically different goals of the two analyses, his being
designed specifically to minimize overall costs. Other factors, such
as calculation inaccuracy, also could account for part of the difference.

24

Frank Morgan

Meetings such as this symposium leave one with the sense of déjà vu. Some of the concepts involved have been batted around now for several years and yet there still exists considerable semantic confusion. For example, there is a good deal of woolliness in the words "deter," detect," and "prevent". The arguments are not yet crystal clear. Even the rationale of inspection and control is not too well understood. I suggest that it would be a public service if two investigations could be carried out: (1) a survey and impartial summary of arguments that already exist by a competent lawyer, since he is obviously qualified to deal with similar situations in the fields of criminal or commercial litigation and (2) a clear statement, possibly by the International Atomic Energy Agency (IAEA) of the statistical and other considerations that underlie Document INFCIRC 153.

We had a number of challenging questions raised by Craig Hosmer which I hoped to hear discussed, but these must now await another occasion. Current safeguards are largely based on the concept of material balance, but there is general recognition that the state of the art is not as good as it should be. Even if a twofold improvement, were possible, material balances alone can never be entirely adequate since the projected amounts of material are just too big. There will have to be increased emphasis on the allocation of responsibility in all aspects of manipulation and transportation. Management must be seen to manage. Opinions on transportation safeguards vary widely even within the U.S. participants in this group. There is a clear need for activating cooperation by police forces in the recovery of stolen

material on both a national and an international basis: This is not
new. It is generally agreed that there is a clear disparity between
the value of plutonium, the treatment it is accorded, and the incremental
cost of improvement. A subsidiary argument that we have not resolved
is what incremental cost on power is acceptable. It was pointed out
that one terrorist bomb or material dissemination in a large city
would have a tremendous cost in social and monetary terms. In fact,
it was suggested that fissile material is not currently treated as
securely as other hazardous or valuable materials.

It is easy to have "imaginative thinking" and to invent situation
that in might practice never arise. For example, no one has yet
suggested the use of dynamite in a reprocessing or fuel fabrication
plant. We do need not more bogeymen but a sober assessment of
hazards and their relative importance and the creation of an appropriate policy that will need to be modified from time to time. A
consequential is a system of rewards and penalties for promoting
"deterrence" and information and detection; these are dependent on the
particular country.

Arguments on the dissemination of diffusion plant technology are
not yet resolved, and it would be wholly improper for me to comment
on this—a current U.S. domestic matter. An associated problem is
the degree of concern to be attached to low-enrichment uranium and
a possible capacity for clandestine enrichment. In this context, it
was noted that multinational plants and the growth of multinational
corporations would help reduce such problems and indeed this is
explicitly reflected in Article 8ld of INFCIRC 153.

Experience of safeguards was discussed, and we heard the view
from an industrialist that the impact of international safeguards thus
far has not proved burdensome; this is hopeful but we must not confuse
acceptability in a plant with a continuing degree of international
effectiveness, which may be expected to create a continued pressure
for improvement. The interfaces between IAEA, government, and
industry need to be clarified. We heard the suggestion that there
may be inequality of misery between government and industrial
organizations. The amount, scale, and timing of inspection of U. S.
industry by an international body under the terms of the Presidential
offer do not yet appear to have been clearly resolved.

We have had a group of studies dealing with statistical material—
for example, game theory and political surveys. These prompt me
to suggest a restatement of Parkinson's Law: "statistics expands to
fill the uncertainty available." Other studies dealt with wholly

technical matters and gave a sober and comprehensive view of the state of the art. Much as I appreciate these studies, they need little more discussion in an interdisciplinary symposium although clearly there is a requirement for rigorous analysis of the appropriate means of application: for example, the frequency of physical inventories or the comparative tolerances required at various stages in a manufacturing process.

Many have stressed that this is an interdisciplinary symposium: we obviously have made a great start and the Diversion Safeguards Program at Kansas State University is much to be congratulated on this bold and successful attempt. But clearly there is much yet to be done. I suggest that one of the first things is to define the questions to which we want answers; to have analytical thinking, not imaginative thinking; to test this analysis against political realities; to consider the weight to be given to the views of plant operators; and, to the extent that it would provide an informed view on possible policy, to examine the utility of political market-type surveys compared with public education.

LIST OF PARTICIPANTS

Name	Professional Affiliation
Allen, B.	Kaman Nuclear Corporation
Althoff, P.	Political Science Department, Kansas State University
Avenhaus, Rudolf	Kernforschungszentrum
Bennett, C. A.	Battelle Seattle Research Center
Berkowitz, Benjamin J.	ADCON Corporation
Billy, Gerard	Commissariat à l'Energie Atomique
Bowie, Thomas B.	Combustion Engineering Corporation
Brady, David	Political Science Department, Kansas State University
Brenner, Leonard	U.S. Atomic Energy Commission
Butler, Richard	Australian Mission to the United Nations
Chambers, William	Los Alamos Scientific Laboratory
Chanda, Richard	Dow Chemical Corporation
Cornella, Alexander	Diversion Safeguards Program, Kansas State University
Costanzi, F. A.	Diversion Safeguards Program, Kansas State University
Crooks, Peter	Australian Embassy in Washington
Crowson, Delmar	U.S. Atomic Energy Commission
Colvin, Curtis	Atlantic Richfield Hanford Company
DeMerschman, A. W.	WADCO
Devine, B. D.	Argonne National Laboratory
Doher, Louis	Dow Chemical Corporation
Edlow, Samuel	Edlow International
Elster, Marvin	Westinghouse Electric Corporation
Empson, F. M.	Oak Ridge National Laboratory
Faw, Richard	Nuclear Engineering Department, Kansas State University
Forscher, Frederick	Consulting Engineer
Garcia, Louis	University of Michigan
Gilbert, William	Argonne National Laboratory
Hajda, Joseph	Political Science Department, Kansas State University
Hall, David	Los Alamos Scientific Laboratory

Name	Professional Affiliation
Hathaway, Charles	Physics Department, Kansas State University
Haymon, D. J.	Westinghouse Electric Corporation
Hazelton, L. D.	Dow Chemical Corporation
Heinisch, Ray	Nuclear Assurance Corporation
Higinbotham, W. A.	Brookhaven National Laboratory
Hoffman, J.	Kaman Nuclear Corporation
Hosmer, Craig	U.S. House of Representatives, Joint Committee on Atomic Energy
Jacchia, Enrico	Euratom Safeguards
Jackson, Raymond L.	Battelle-Columbus Laboratories
Jaech, John L.	Jersey Nuclear Corporation
Jennekens, Jon	Canadian Atomic Energy Control Branch
Jones, Ralph J.	Nuclear Fuel Service, Incorporated
Kanter, Manuel A.	Argonne National Laboratory
Kinderman, E. M.	Stanford Research Institute
Kops, Sheldon	U.S. Atomic Energy Commission
Kramer, Mark	University of Michigan
Kull, Lorenz	Science Applications Corporation
Kuramochi, Tetsushi	Japanese Embassy in Washington
Lawroski, Stephen	Argonne National Laboratory
Leachman, Robert	Physics Department, Kansas State University
Loeding, John W.	Argonne National Laboratory
Lovett, James E.	Nuclear Material and Equipment Corporation
Lumb, Ralph	Nuclear Surveillance and Auditing Corporation
Menzel, Joerg	Los Alamos Scientific Laboratory
Miskel, John	Lawrence Radiation Laboratory
Molen, G. F.	Allied Gulf Corporation
Morgan, F.	U.K. Atomic Energy Authority
Nelson, George W.	University of Arizona
Nutter, James D.	Monsanto Research Corporation
Osborn, K. R.	Allied Chemical Corporation
Page, Ralph G.	U.S. Atomic Energy Commission
Pearce, Jack	Advanced Research Project Agency
Perella, Fred J.	National Bureau of Standards
Pickles, William	Lawrence Radiation Laboratory
Pittman, F. K.	U.S. Atomic Energy Commission
Rappoport, L. H.	Psychology Department, Kansas State University

Name	Professional Affiliation
Rasmussen, Norman	Massachusetts Institute of Technology
Rosescue, Thedor	State Committee for Nuclear Energy, Romania
Roth, E. B.	Arms Control and Disarmament Agency
Rometsch, Rudolf	International Atomic Energy Agency
Ross, Mark	University of Michigan
Rudy, Clifford	Diversion Safeguards Program, Kansas State University
Rutenkroger, Earl O.	Tristate Motor Transport
Scheinman, Lawrence	University of Michigan
Schubert, A. E.	General Electric Company
Scoville, H.	Carnegie Endowment for International Peace
Seaman, Gregory	Physics Department, Kansas State University
Seefeldt, Waldemar B.	Argonne National Laboratory
Sewell, R. B.	Consumers Power
Shapley, Deborah	Science magazine
Shore, Bruce	Physics Department, Kansas State University
Shultis, J.	Nuclear Engineering Department, Kansas State University
Sohngen, James	Atomic Industrial Forum
Solem, Erik	Political Science Department, Kansas State University
Starrett, John P.	Department of Defense
Stumpf, John	Atomic Industrial Forum
Suda, S. C.	Brookhaven National Laboratory
Taylor, Theodore	International Research and Technology
Thornton, C. D. W.	U.S. Atomic Energy Commission
Thorpe, Munson M.	Los Alamos Scientific Laboratory
Van Doren, Charles	Arms Control and Disarmament Agency
VanHoomissen, John E.	General Electric Company
Williams, Alden	Political Science Department, Kansas State University
Williams, Robert	University of Michigan
Wilson, D. W.	General Electric Company
Wittenbrock, N. G.	Battelle Northwest Corporation
Zollman, D. A.	Physics Department, Kansas State University